HOUGHTON BOOKS IN LITERATURE

KENNETH S. LYNN · ADVISORY EDITOR

DESIGNS FOR READING

- ○ Plays
- ○ Poems
- ○ Short Stories
- ○ Nonfiction Prose

THE RANGE OF LITERATURE

- ● Drama
- ○ Poetry
- ○ Fiction
- ○ Nonfiction Prose

HOUGHTON
BOOKS IN
LITERATURE

THE RANGE OF LITERATURE

Drama

ROBERT LAMBERT

HOUGHTON MIFFLIN COMPANY· BOSTON

NEW YORK   ATLANTA   GENEVA, ILLINOIS   DALLAS   PALO ALTO

ABOUT THE AUTHOR AND EDITOR

Robert Lambert is the author of many provocative articles on the teaching of drama and composition. His writing draws on a varied teaching experience in both high school (Watchung Hills Regional High School in Warren, New Jersey) and in college (Carnegie Tech, Western Michigan University, and Chicago State College). In each college where he has taught, Dr. Lambert has given courses in the teaching of English.

Kenneth S. Lynn, advisory editor for the Houghton Books in Literature, is an authority in American literature. The author of *Mark Twain and Southwestern Humor* and *The Dream of Success: A Study of the Modern American Imagination,* he is also preëminent for his editing of classic American writers. Dr. Lynn is now Chairman of American Studies at Federal City College in Washington, D.C.

ACKNOWLEDGMENTS

Grateful acknowledgment is made to publishers and agents for permission to reprint the following plays:

An Enemy of the People, from *Six Plays by Henrik Ibsen*, translated by Eva Le Gallienne, © copyright 1957 by Eva Le Gallienne. Reprinted by permission of Random House, Inc. CAUTION: This translation of *An Enemy of the People* is fully protected by copyright. It may not be acted by professionals or amateurs without formal permission and the payment of a royalty. All rights, including professional, amateur, stock, radio and television broadcasting, motion picture, recitation, lecturing, and public reading, are reserved. All inquiries should be addressed to the Author's agent, Brandt & Brandt, 101 Park Avenue, New York, New York.

Cyrano de Bergerac by Edmond Rostand, translated by Harold Whitehall, from *World's Great Plays*, edited by George Jean Nathan, copyright 1944 by The World Publishing Company. All rights reserved; no part of this play may be reproduced in any form without the express permission of the copyright owners.

You Can't Take It With You by Moss Hart and George S. Kaufman, copyright © 1937 by Moss Hart and George S. Kaufman, renewed in 1964. Reprinted by permission of Virginia Rice.

Our Town by Thornton Wilder, copyright © 1938, 1957 by Thornton Wilder. Reprinted by permission of Harper & Row, Publishers. CAUTION: *Our Town* is the sole property of the author and is fully protected by copyright. It may not be acted by professionals or amateurs without formal permission and the payment of a royalty. All rights, including professional, amateur, stock, radio and television, broadcasting, motion picture, recitation, lecturing, public reading, and the rights of translation into foreign languages, are reserved. All professional inquiries should be addressed to the author's agent: Harold Freedman, Brandt & Brandt Dramatic Department, Inc., 101 Park Avenue, New York, New York 10017. All requests for amateur rights should be addressed to Samuel French, 25 West 45th Street, New York, New York 10019.

In White America by Martin B. Duberman, copyright © 1964 by Martin B. Duberman. Reprinted by permission of The Sterling Lord Agency.

CONTENTS

FIRST PERFORMANCE

The Reader's Role

To read a play is one of the easiest — and most difficult — of performances. It is easy because a good play sweeps its audience into a moving conflict, the intense clash of human wills and desires that we call drama. Since a play must grip its audience — or die — there is no room in it for the padding or lengthy descriptions of scenery that sometimes bore readers of novels. There, thumbing and skipping may be appropriate, but never in reading a play. For the play is already condensed, compressed into a three hour playing time, or ninety minute reading time. Unlike a novel, it can and should be first read at a single sitting.

But to fully grasp a play, it must be read at least twice. For reading literature involves a special kind of "knowing": a play is emotional rather than factual information. The first reading of a play shows us what happened, carries us into the whirlpool of conflict and clashing wills; the second reading charts the currents towards that whirlpool, shows us *how* we were carried so far so fast. Since we are less involved with what is going to happen in the second reading, we can start to see the structure of the play, to get a clearer sense of what motivates the characters, and to identify the irony and symbolism that make the play more than just a re-enactment of what happened to a set of characters in one place at one time. Indeed, only through a second reading can we begin in any real sense to "know" a play. A good second reading is less repetition than re-creation.

Actually, all worthwhile literature deserves a second reading, but this is especially true of a drama, because it was never designed to be read in the first place: it was meant to be played, perceived through the voices and gestures of the actors, and through the vision of a director employing costumes, lights, and stage settings designed for the most intensely dramatic effect possible.

As a reader of cold type on a white page, you must supply
all that would otherwise be given in a stage production. For
if the play is to come to life, all the color, movement, design,
and emotion must be orchestrated in the imagination of the
reader. Ideally, of course, each play should be seen in live
production, but failing that, a skillful reading can approach
the stimulating experience provided in live theater. Fortunately, there are specific and learnable techniques that will
help you to fully realize, or experience, a play you are reading.
Most of these suggestions also apply to reading poems and
stories: all literature must be visualized and is meant to be
heard through the medium of a human voice. It's up to you
to "hear" the appropriate voice in your head.

Avoid the monotone of the mind's ear — When reading a
newspaper or the Yellow Pages, we are seldom aware of a
human voice behind the words: they run on in our minds as
flat and uninflected, much as you are reading this now, tone-
lessly. While this may be appropriate for textbook material,
it is *destructive* to read drama that way. Its words are meant to
be spoken with passion. When Cyrano expresses his dis-
guised love for Roxane — "Your name is like a bell within
my heart, and all the time I'm quivering, my Roxane, and all
the time the bell shakes with my heart, and all the time it's
pealing out your name" — the actor's voice itself must sing,
soaring and tolling to echo the sense of the words in the depth
of his emotion. Often, in drama, voices clash in a staccato
interchange of accusation and denial. During *In White
America*, President Wilson discusses Post Office segregation
practices with Monroe Trotter, a Negro spokesman:

> TROTTER: We cannot control the minds of the colored
> people and would not if we could on the segregation
> question. Two years ago you were regarded as a second
> Abraham Lincoln.
> WILSON: I want no personal reference.
> TROTTER: Sir, if you will allow me to continue you will
> see my intent.
> WILSON: I am the one to do the interrupting, Mr. Trotter.
> TROTTER: We colored leaders are denounced in the
> colored churches as traitors to our race.

WILSON: What do you mean by traitors?

TROTTER: Because we supported the Democratic ticket in 1912.

WILSON: Gentlemen, the interview is at an end.

The interplay of voices sets up an intensity of rhythm that, like the hit and return, hit and return, hit and return of a closely contested tennis match, achieves an almost hypnotic intensity. Then the rhythm of different voices is sometimes snapped, creating a startling effect because the response is not immediate. In *An Enemy of the People,* Dr. Stockmann is about to print an article in the local newspaper exposing the fact that the town's health baths, the prime source of income for the village, are dangerously polluted. A local political leader tells him the editor of the town newspaper will not print his disclosure:

ASLAKSEN: Mr. Hovstad's no fool; he's not likely to ruin both himself and the paper for the sake of a delusion.

DR. STOCKMANN: (*Looks from one to the other*): What does this mean?

Both the stage directions and the shocked tone of Stockmann's question clearly indicate a pause, almost a freeze, in the speech and activity of the play as the news sinks in. The reader too must pause to imagine the impact of this message on Stockmann: the town will attempt to conceal the truth about the poisoned springs.

Envision the gestures described in the text — More than just a pause occurs, of course, in the Stockmann scene quoted above. Were you to see an actor perform the scene, his jaw might go slack, his eyes widen, and he would turn mechanically from one antagonist to the other on stage as the shock of what they have just said hits him. In *Cyrano,* to take another example, one of the most famous gestures in stage history occurs at the opening of the play-within-a-play in Act One. The actor Montfleury has been forbidden to go onstage by Cyrano. Foolishly, Montfleury disobeys the command.

MONTFLEURY (*in a trembling voice*): "Can list the breath of Zephyr in the wood —"

THE VOICE (CYRANO'S): Must I plant the wood on your shoulders, you monarch of rascals?

*(An arm furnished with a cane leaps out above the heads
of the audience.)*

This gesture defines Cyrano even before he appears on
stage: forceful, arrogant, threatening, commanding, even
witty — above the mass of men. And at the close of the drama,
Cyrano — now mortally wounded by a log dropped on his
head by enemies — gestures futilely in a pathetic dance of
death against the flaws that have plagued his grandeur: "I
know you now — my ancient adversaries. Falsehood! (*Striking the empty air with his sword.*) And Cowardice! And
Prejudice! Compromise too? (*Striking hard.*)" All the slipping and staggering of this grotesque ballet — in contrast to
the grace and adroitness of Cyrano's earlier swordplay — must
be imagined, or the impact is lost.

Build the sets in your head — And of course these gestures
take place on a stage designed to enhance them, and to give
the play dramatic impact by mirroring its mood, its theme,
its world. The stage setting for Ibsen is meticulous in its
detail and realism — with actual chairs, lamps, and books —
for Ibsen tries to tell his audience: "It's your blind and com-
placent middle-class world I'm writing about and against."
Our Town, on the other hand, is acted on virtually a bare
stage, for this play is concerned with internal events, eternal
feelings, universal longings. The usual clutter of the stage
set would only distract the audience from the play's time-
lessness. In contrast, the set of *You Can't Take It With You*
is nothing *but* clutter — snake cages, xylophones, and Erector
Sets, suggesting the improbable interests of the non-con-
formist Vanderhofs. Try to design and keep in mind the stage
— whether the lush, romantic set of *Cyrano* or the stripped
boards of *Our Town*. For the stage set is metaphor as well
as platform.

See the costumes and changes in lighting — Costumes and
lighting, as well as stage design, need to be imagined in reading. As Cyrano's life ebbs, so do the stage lights, bringing a
darkness far deeper than night's to the convent park. In *You
Can't Take It With You*, Grandpa Vanderhof's final prayer of
thanks to God takes place at the supper table. While he
speaks, the table and the gathered family begin to glow as

more and more light illumines the scene. The tableau takes on an almost holy radiance. As you read, lights must be clicked on, switches thrown in your head so that the play may live before your eyes as well as within your brain. At the same time, Cyrano's plume must dart and glow in decisive, triumphant motion; the Stage Manager in *Our Town* must be as drably dressed as anyone in the audience, for he's just the plainest man around; the millionaire in *You Can't Take It With You* must be garbed in an impeccable tuxedo to offer maximum contrast to Grandpa's homespun or Penny's rakish artist's costume. Your imagination must sew costumes and dress actors as well as read words.

Interpret the play — Although the words of the play appear on the page before you, they are not frozen to one meaning. They do not speak for themselves, but change in the playing. They need to be interpreted through the consciousness of the director, who suggests to the actors how the words on the page are to be spoken, played, felt. We know from personal experience that it's more the feeling behind the word than the word itself that's important. Even a simple "Hi" or "Hello" can range from a sparkling greeting to a glum recognition depending on *your* mood at the time and *your* feelings towards the person you're speaking to. Yet if you were merely to write that "Hi" on a piece of paper — as the playwright must — there would be no way of knowing how you said it, no way of interpreting your mood and response. In essence, the job of the play's director is to do just that: to instruct each actor about how the character in the play is supposed to feel about himself and about those he is talking to. Again, as a silent reader of the play, you must take on the director's role of interpreter, instructing each actor's "voice" in your head how to read and feel the lines.

But no director agrees fully with another on the interpretation of character: should the silliness and clowning of Dr. Stockmann be stressed so that half the time he appears a fool? Or should this trait in him be muted, so that his personal courage in the face of an outraged community be stressed? Is Cyrano's Roxane a vain and shallow girl capable of responding only to words that praise her — and not to the feelings that lie behind these words? Or is she a woman of grace and wit who encourages her lovers to speak poetry so they both may share deeper moments of communion? There are no final answers to these questions. How does it "play"? Does the interpretation seem credible to the audience? Does the interpretation divert the overall thrust of the drama as a whole? These seem the kinds of questions that can be asked about a director's — or your own — interpretation of a character.

And beyond the realm of character interpretation lies the key to reading imaginative literature: recognizing, understanding, and responding to the symbols in a play. A good play is both very specific — taking place in a certain time at a stated place with believable characters — and very general. A great play talks about the facts and emotions that constantly confront us as human beings — death, love, happiness, betrayal, hatred, hypocrisy. As a play is performed before our eyes in a theater, or inside our heads as we read, certain objects in the play become charged with symbolic meaning: they spill out of the play and into our awarenesses. At the start of *An Enemy of the People*, for example, the polluted water of the health spa is just that: mineral spring water carrying the bacteria that produce diphtheria, typhoid, and cholera. As the play continues, however, and the town refuses to recognize there really is filth in the water, we begin to see that the water reflects the town: seemingly clear and healthy, but actually seething with moral and spiritual corruption. Similarly, in *Cyrano*, the shining white feather — the plume — that tops his hat is at first only a decoration. But as we come to understand the mixture of chivalry, courtesy, arrogance, pride, wit, and love that make up Cyrano, his plume — which he takes off to no man — stands for that strange combination of qualities that *is* Cyrano. In his dying moment, Cyrano knows that this plume, erect and unspotted, is his greatest offering to God. It is his best self.

For symbolism to function with full power, it is often fused to irony — that essential recognition of the distance between what things appear to be, and what they really are. How deeply ironic in *Enemy*, for instance, that it is a health spa which is polluted. Waters meant to soothe and heal actually inflame and destroy. It is ironic in *Our Town* that Emily can only see how rich life could have been once she is dead and beyond changing the life she so desperately wants to relive. In *You Can't Take It With You*, the central irony is that the poor are spiritually rich, while the rich are spiritually poor. In the documentary drama *In White America*, the historical irony is that the passage of time does not bring a change in basic social attitudes towards race. They are as they always were.

Props, objects that actually appear on-stage, can also take on ironic as well as symbolic overtones. The first object we see associated with Cyrano is a cane raised imperiously above the mob by his vigorous, skillful arm. In the final act, a maimed, weakened, mortally wounded Cyrano hobbles on stage, supported by that same cane, and the object suddenly becomes ironic: a reminder of Cyrano's past vigor and present frailty. Similarly, the mayor's cap and scepter are ironic stage props: Dr. Stockmann pretends that he is the mayor. Ironically, he is the hated, unacknowledged spiritual leader of the community, and fully deserves the symbols of power he so childishly toys with.

Sensing symbolism and irony is central to a rich reading of imaginative literature. Indeed, a good reader might very well be defined as one who recognizes and responds to those symbolic and ironic elements that make literature so deeply relevant to — and revealing of — human life.

Why These Plays?

To encourage this kind of reading and response, the editor of this book has chosen five plays. Two considerations went into selecting each play: first, is the play genuinely exciting and relevant to today's reader; second, do the plays represent the types of drama you are likely to read or see in the future? For plays, like other forms of literature, tend to fall into different traditions, or genres, which follow certain conventions and aim at established effects.

The genres represented in this book are:

Social Realism: *An Enemy of the People*
Romanticism: *Cyrano de Bergerac*
Comedy: *You Can't Take It With You*
Tragedy: *Our Town*
Documentary Drama: *In White America*

An Enemy of the People is the sort of play you may already be most familiar with. A doctor finds himself in conflict with his community after he discovers that health baths that are the economic lifeblood of the town are polluted. A social problem is posed. The sets are realistic, and the language ordinary, everyday speech. Realism has been the dominant mode of twentieth-century theater, and realistic plays are widely produced on television.

Cyrano de Bergerac represents Romantic theater at its highest level. Ideals such as heroism, chivalry, and chaste devotion to women are glorified. The sets are lush and grand. The language is poetry. The human impulses that led to Romantic theater have largely been transferred to films — mainly the Western — and have usually been debased to a display of heroics rather than heroism. However, Alan Ladd's Shane and Gary Cooper's Marshal Will Kane in *High Noon* might be considered modern reincarnations of Cyrano. But even though they share his ideals, they lack the verbal wit and poetry of his tongue.

You Can't Take It With You represents American comedy at one of its highest peaks. Chronicling the encounter between the rich Kirbys and the poor Vanderhofs, *You Can't Take It With You* points out the absurdity of measuring happiness by wealth and demonstrates that love for life — doing the things that make you the happiest rather than what society expects you to do — leads to riches beyond the value of gold.

Our Town is tragedy brought down from its traditional setting — the courts of kings — to the homes of everyman. Its characters are ordinary, undistinguished but easily recognizable human beings who simply look for the happiness most of us seek: a good job, someone to love, children to raise. Yet Emily, through no fault of her own, dies in childbirth and is denied all she has striven for and earned. As if this denial were not enough, she also comes to see — after death — that her past life was shallow, unexplored. Emily is denied fulfillment during her life, denied because of her death, and denied after her death.

In White America is frankly an experimental play in a totally new form of playwriting, documentary drama. The documentary films of Robert Flaherty or the TV documentaries of

Edward R. Murrow possess the vitality and excitement of art. Belatedly, the theater is now looking at these forms, and trying to adapt them to stage performance by having the human voice recount history — and create drama — simultaneously. Only a few docudramas have been written, but the idea is attracting playwrights and historians who wish to make the past known and relevant to the present. Will the form succeed or die out? As yet, no one knows. Audience response, as it always has, will determine whether this kind of play will live or die, resonate in a theater or gather dust on a library shelf. And all of you are part of that audience.

An Enemy of the People

BEFORE THE CURTAIN

Although not all critics have praised *An Enemy of the People,* its many productions prove the play's power to intrigue and hold an audience. In the early 1950's Arthur Miller, one of America's greatest living playwrights, "adapted" the Ibsen play for the New York stage at a time when he felt a tremendous weight of political oppression in American life. In his preface to this "adaptation" Miller writes:

> And I believed this play could be alive for us because its central theme is . . . the central theme of our social life today. Simply, it is the question of whether one's vision of the truth ought to be a source of guilt at a time when the mass of men condemn it as a dangerous and devilish lie. It is an enduring theme . . . because there never was, nor will there ever be, an organized society able to countenance calmly the individual who insists that he is right while the vast majority is absolutely wrong.

Yet the theme of this play — the need for an individual who possesses the truth to stand against the pressures of a majority who would pervert this truth to their own interests — would be flat, even obvious, were it not for Ibsen's skill and artistry in creating conflict on the stage and suspense in the audience. For people go to plays to become deeply involved in the struggles and decisions of the characters on the stage, not to be morally uplifted by a play's "message," however important that may be. Indeed, only to the degree that it feels involved

3

in the action and able to identify with the characters of a play is the audience likely to take the play's theme seriously.

Ibsen succeeds in involving his audience in this play by making its hero a sometimes foolish, sometimes brave human being faced with an urgent moral dilemma. Dr. Stockmann, who knows with scientific certainty that the water of the town where he lives is polluted, would publish this information to prevent an epidemic. But he is opposed by the financial and political interests of the town, who fear that spreading this knowledge would destroy the town by driving tourists away and by raising taxes to a ruinous level. With his good name and livelihood in the balance, Stockmann must decide whether to fight or run.

Each of the five acts of the play serves to introduce and develop a chapter in this mounting struggle, to advance the action toward its inevitable crisis. At the same time it provides new revelations of character. These revelations come with each individual's response to the indisputable fact of the bath's pollution, the standard against which all the characters in the play are to be measured: how they react to it determines who they are morally. Of particular interest here is the way in which a character like Aslaksen disguises his real motives, even from himself, and only gradually reveals his true colors — and thus his essential hypocrisy. To appreciate the importance of dramatic structure, consider the way in which each act is designed so as to ring down the curtain on a high point of suspense or action. With every curtain until the last, a question or problem is posed which forces the theater audience to return from its between-the-acts cigars and chatter to find out what will happen next. In reading the play ask yourself, at the end of each act, "What questions now demand to be answered? what problems resolved?"

But not every problem *is* resolved — certainly not how we are to take Dr. Stockmann himself, and therefore how we are to understand the very tone and intention of the play. On this point Ibsen himself, it would seem, was undecided. "I am not yet sure whether I shall call it a comedy or a drama," he confided in a letter. "It partakes of the nature of either, or lies half-way between...." Ibsen's statement remains true. What are we to make of Dr. Stockmann, a man of genuine bravery who clowns up and down the stage playing at being mayor; a man so out of touch with human nature that he thinks his home town will reward him for discovering that its principal source of income, a health bath, is really a filthy sewer? Is Dr. Stockmann a fool or a saint? Does his ridiculous side make him a more human, a more sympathetic figure, or does it belittle the moral courage he displays? Only a careful and sensitive reading of the play can help you answer that question.

The stage on which *An Enemy of the People* was first played would look little different from the one in a normal high school auditorium: a raised platform built against the rear wall and faced by rows of chairs. The play was written with the "picture frame" or "fourth wall" convention in mind. We, the audience, are sitting where the fourth wall of Stockmann's rented house would be had it not been removed so we may hear and see the actors, who are unaware of our presence.

Since Ibsen intends the play to be realistic, he carefully sets the scene: Stockmann's living room is neatly decorated and furnished with "a lighted lamp with a shade" and "a sofa above which hangs a mirror." To see an early production of Ibsen would be disappointing: technically, the theater of 1882 was not up to his demands for realism. Candles or gas lamps provided erratic illumination, and the walls of Stockmann's home would obviously be "unreal" painted canvas. Yet the emphasis on realism was important at the time: the stage and the set and the actors had to look real to remind and convince the audience that the theater was no longer a place mainly for diversion and entertainment — for vaudeville, tumblers, and magicians with an occasional performance of Shakespeare thrown in. Instead, for Ibsen and the other realists, the theater also dealt seriously with the problems of the real world, and their dramas are not "just plays," but serious assertions about what life is and how it should be lived. With its real lamps and real bookcases, the stage for the first time mirrored and talked about the actual world the audience lived in. Surprisingly, it had never done this before.

An Enemy of the People

HENRIK IBSEN

Translated by Eva LeGallienne

Characters

DR. TOMAS STOCKMANN, physician at the Baths.

MRS. KATRINE STOCKMANN, his wife.

PETRA, their daughter, a schoolteacher.

EJLIF
MORTEN } their sons, aged thirteen and ten.

PETER STOCKMANN, the doctor's elder brother; Mayor and Chief of Police; Chairman of the Board at the Baths.

MORTEN KIIL, owner of a tannery; Mrs. Stockmann's foster father.

HOVSTAD, editor of *The People's Monitor*.

BILLING, his colleague on the paper.

CAPTAIN HORSTER.

ASLAKSEN, a printer.

Citizens of various types and standing; some women and a number of schoolboys.

The action takes place in a town on the South Coast of Norway.

ACT ONE

SCENE: *Evening. Doctor Stockmann's living room.
It is decorated and furnished simply but neatly. In the
side wall right are two doors, the upstage door leading
to the hall and the one downstage to the doctor's study.
In the opposite wall, facing the hall door, a door leading
to the other rooms of the house. Against this wall, in
the center of it, stands the stove: further downstage a
sofa above which hangs a mirror, and in front of it an
oval table: on this table is a lighted lamp with a shade.
In the back wall, an open door leads to the dining room.
The table is laid for supper and a lighted lamp stands
on it.*

*Billing is seated at the supper table; he has a napkin
tucked under his chin. Mrs. Stockmann stands by the
table and places a dish of cold roast beef before him.
The other seats round the table are empty; the table is in
disorder, as though a meal had recently been finished.*

MRS. STOCKMANN. I'm afraid you'll have to put up with a cold
meal, Mr. Billing; you were an hour late, you know.

BILLING (*eating*). Never mind. It's delicious — absolutely delicious.

MRS. STOCKMANN. Stockmann is very strict about having his
meals on time.

BILLING. It doesn't matter a bit. In fact I think food tastes
even better when one's alone and undisturbed.

MRS. STOCKMANN. Well — as long as you enjoy it — (*Turns
toward the hall door, listening.*) That may be Mr. Hovstad
— perhaps he's come to join you.

BILLING. Very likely.

[*The Mayor, Peter Stockmann, enters. He wears an over-
coat and the gold-braided cap of his office. He carries a
cane.*]

THE MAYOR. Good evening, Sister-in-law.

MRS. STOCKMANN. Well! Good evening. (*She comes forward
into the living room.*) So, it's you! How nice of you to look
in.

THE MAYOR. I happened to be passing by, and so — (*With a glance toward the dining room*) Oh — you have company, I see.

MRS. STOCKMANN (*slightly embarrassed*). No, no — not really. Mr. Billing just happened to drop in. Won't you join him for a bite to eat?

THE MAYOR. No, thank you — nothing for me! I never eat hot food at night — not with my digestion.

MRS. STOCKMANN. Oh, just for once! It surely couldn't hurt you.

THE MAYOR. I'm much obliged — but, no! I stick to my tea and bread and butter; it's much better for you — and it's more economical too.

MRS. STOCKMANN (*smiling*). I hope you don't think Tomas and I are extravagant!

THE MAYOR. I know *you're* not, my dear; far be it from me to think that of *you*. (*Points to the doctor's study.*) Is he home?

MRS. STOCKMANN. No. He went for a little walk after supper — with the boys.

THE MAYOR. Is that good for one's health, I wonder? (*Listens.*) Here he comes now.

MRS. STOCKMANN. No, I don't think it can be he. (*A knock at the door*) Come in! (*Hovstad comes in from the hall.*) Oh, it's Mr. Hovstad.

HOVSTAD. You must excuse me; I was held up at the printer's. Good evening, Mr. Mayor.

THE MAYOR (*bowing rather stiffly*). Good evening. You're here on business, I presume?

HOVSTAD. Yes, partly. It's about an article for the paper.

THE MAYOR. I thought as much. I hear my brother has become quite a prolific contributor to *The People's Monitor*.

HOVSTAD. He's kind enough to write a piece for us now and then; whenever he has anything particular on his mind.

MRS. STOCKMANN (*to Hovstad*). But don't you want to —? (*She points toward the dining room.*)

THE MAYOR. It's natural, I suppose, that he should want to reach the kind of people who understand his point of view. Not that I have any personal objection to your paper, Mr. Hovstad — you may rest assured of that.

HOVSTAD. No — of course not.

THE MAYOR. We have a fine spirit of mutual tolerance here in our town, I'm glad to say; a truly cooperative spirit; it comes, of course, from the great common interest we all share — an interest that naturally concerns all right-thinking citizens.

HOVSTAD. The Baths, of course.

THE MAYOR. Precisely. Those splendid Mineral Baths of ours! You mark my words, Mr. Hovstad; the whole life of our community will center more and more around the Baths — there can be no doubt of that!

MRS. STOCKMANN. That's just what Tomas says.

THE MAYOR. The way the town has grown in these past two years is quite extraordinary. People are prosperous; housing developments are springing up; the value of property is soaring; there's life and activity everywhere!

HOVSTAD. And far less unemployment too.

THE MAYOR. That's true, of course; and that's a great load off the upper classes; taxes for home-relief have already been reduced — and they will be reduced still further if we have a really prosperous summer; a good rush of visitors — plenty of invalids to give the Baths a reputation —

HOVSTAD. I hear there's a good chance of that.

THE MAYOR. Every day inquiries about living quarters — apartments and so forth — keep pouring in. Things look highly promising.

HOVSTAD. Then the doctor's article will be most timely.

THE MAYOR. So he's been writing again, has he?

HOVSTAD. This is something he wrote during the winter. It's an article about the Baths — strongly recommending them, and laying particular stress on the excellence of sanitary conditions here. But I didn't use it at the time — I held it over.

THE MAYOR. Why? Was he indiscreet, as usual?

HOVSTAD. No, nothing like that; I only thought it would be better to hold it over till the spring, when people start thinking about summer plans.

THE MAYOR. Very sensible; highly sensible, Mr. Hovstad.

MRS. STOCKMANN. Tomas never spares himself where the Baths are concerned.

THE MAYOR. As one of the staff that's no more than his duty.

HOVSTAD. And, after all, it was his idea in the first place.

THE MAYOR. His idea? Was it indeed? I know some people
are of that opinion. But it seems to me I too had at least a
modest share in the enterprise.

MRS. STOCKMANN. That's what Tomas always says.

HOVSTAD. Of course, Mr. Mayor, that's undeniable; you put
it all on a practical basis — you made the whole thing possible; we all know that. I simply meant that the initial idea
was Dr. Stockmann's.

THE MAYOR. My brother has had plenty of ideas in his time —
unfortunately; but it takes a very different type of man to
work them out. I should have thought the members of this
household would be among the first to —

MRS. STOCKMANN. My dear Peter —

HOVSTAD. You surely don't — ?

MRS. STOCKMANN. Do go in and have some supper, Mr. Hovstad; my husband is sure to be home directly.

HOVSTAD. Thank you; I think I will have just a bite. (*He goes
into the dining room.*)

THE MAYOR (*lowering his voice*). It's amazing! These people
who come from peasant stock never seem to lose their want
of tact.

MRS. STOCKMANN. Now, why should you be upset? You and
Tomas are brothers — isn't it natural that you should share
the honor?

THE MAYOR. One would think so, yes; but a share is not
enough for some people, it seems.

MRS. STOCKMANN. What nonsense! You and Tomas get on so
well together. (*Listening*) I think I hear him now. (*She goes
and opens the hall door.*)

DR. STOCKMANN (*is heard laughing; he shouts in a loud voice,
from the hall*). Here's another visitor for you, Katrine.
Isn't this splendid, eh? Hang your coat up there on the peg,
Captain Horster. But, I forgot — you don't wear an over-
coat, do you? What do you think of this, Katrine? I met him
on the street — I had a hard time persuading him; at first
he wouldn't hear of coming up! (*Captain Horster enters and
bows to Mrs. Stockmann.*) In with you, boys! They're starving again, Katrine! Come along, Captain Horster; you must
try a piece of our roast beef — (*He forces Captain Horster
into the dining room; Ejlif and Morten follow them.*)

MRS. STOCKMANN. But, Tomas, don't you see — !

DR. STOCKMANN (*turns in the doorway*). Oh, it's you, Peter! (*Goes to him and holds out his hand.*) Well, now this is really splendid!

THE MAYOR. I can only stay a minute —

DR. STOCKMANN. Nonsense! We'll have some hot toddy in a moment. You haven't forgotten the toddy, have you, Katrine?

MRS. STOCKMANN. Of course not! I've got the water boiling. (*She goes into the dining room.*)

THE MAYOR. Toddy, too — !

DR. STOCKMANN. Yes; let's sit down and be comfortable.

THE MAYOR. Thank you; I don't care for drinking parties.

DR. STOCKMANN. But this isn't a party!

THE MAYOR. It seems to me — (*He glances towards the dining room.*) It's incredible the amount of food they can get through!

DR. STOCKMANN (*rubs his hands*). Yes — it does one good to see young people eat! They're always hungry! That's the way it should be — they must keep up their strength. They've got things to stir up — they have to build the future!

THE MAYOR. May I ask what there is that requires "stirring up" — as you call it?

DR. STOCKMANN. You'll have to ask the young people about that — when the time comes. Of course we shan't live to see it. A couple of old fogies like you and me —

THE MAYOR. A fine way to talk, I must say!

DR. STOCKMANN. You mustn't mind my nonsense, Peter. I'm in such high spirits today. It makes me so happy to be a part of all this fertile, teeming life. What a wonderful age we live in! A whole new world is springing up around us!

THE MAYOR. Do you really think so?

DR. STOCKMANN. Of course you can't appreciate it as well as I do. You've spent your whole life surrounded by all this — you take it all for granted. But after being stuck away for years in that dreadful little hole up North — never seeing a soul — never exchanging a stimulating word with anyone — I feel as though I'd suddenly been transported into the heart of some great metropolis!

THE MAYOR. I should hardly call it a metropolis —

DR. STOCKMANN. Oh, I know it may seem small compared to lots of other places; but there's life here — there's a future — there are innumerable things to work and strive for; that's what's important, after all. (*Calls out.*) Katrine! Did the postman bring anything for me?

MRS. STOCKMANN (*from the dining room*). No — he didn't come today.

DR. STOCKMANN. And to be getting a good salary. Peter! That's something you appreciate when you've lived on starvation wages as long as we have —

THE MAYOR. Oh, come now —

DR. STOCKMANN. Things were often very hard for us up there, let me tell you; but now we can live like princes! Today, for instance, we had roast beef for dinner; and then we had it for supper too. Don't you want to taste it? At least let me show it to you — do come and see it!

THE MAYOR. Certainly not!

DR. STOCKMANN. Well — come over here then. Look! Isn't our new table cover handsome?

THE MAYOR. Yes — I noticed it.

DR. STOCKMANN. And we have a lampshade too; Katrine has been saving up for then. It makes the room look much more cozy. Don't you think so? Stand over here — no, no; not over there — here! That's right! You see how it concentrates the light? I think it's quite magnificent! What do you think?

THE MAYOR. Of course, if one can afford such luxuries —

DR. STOCKMANN. Oh, we can afford them now. Katrine says I earn almost as much as we spend.

THE MAYOR. Almost — !

DR. STOCKMANN. Besides, a man of science should live in a certain amount of style. I'll bet you a mere county commissioner spends more money a year than I do.

THE MAYOR. Well — I should hope so! A high-ranking government official — !

DR. STOCKMANN. Take an ordinary businessman, then. I'll bet you a man like that spends ever so much more —

THE MAYOR. Such things are purely relative —

DR. STOCKMANN. As a matter of fact I don't squander money, Peter. But I do so enjoy inviting people to my home — I

can't resist it; I was an exile for so long, you see. I feel the
need of company — buoyant, active people — liberal-
minded people — like those young fellows enjoying their
food in there. To me, that makes life worth while. I wish
you'd make a point of getting to know Hovstad —

THE MAYOR. That reminds me — Hovstad was telling me just
now he plans to publish another article of yours.

DR. STOCKMANN. Of mine?

THE MAYOR. Yes — about the Baths. An article you wrote last
winter.

DR. STOCKMANN. Oh, that one! I'd rather that didn't appear
just now.

THE MAYOR. Why not? This seems to me to be the ideal time
for it.

DR. STOCKMANN. Yes — under ordinary circumstances —
(*Paces across the room.*)

THE MAYOR (*follows him with his eyes*). What is there so
unusual about circumstances now?

DR. STOCKMANN (*stands still*). I'm afraid I can't tell you about
it just now, Peter — not this evening, at any rate. The circumstances may turn out to be in the highest degree unusual, you see. On the other hand it may all amount to
nothing — just an illusion on my part.

THE MAYOR. You sound very mysterious. Are you keeping
something from me? Is anything the matter? As chairman
of the Bath Committee I demand the right to — !

DR. STOCKMANN. And I demand the right to — ! Oh, don't let's
fly off the handle, Peter.

THE MAYOR. I am not in the habit of "flying off the handle,"
as you express it. But I must emphatically insist that all
matters concerning the Baths be handled in a businesslike
manner, and through the proper channels. I shall not
tolerate devious or underhanded methods.

DR. STOCKMANN. When have I ever used devious or underhanded methods?

THE MAYOR. You have an incorrigible tendency to take things
into your own hands; in a well-ordered community that is
equally reprehensible. The individual must subordinate
himself to Society as a whole; or, more precisely, to those
authorities responsible for the well-being of that Society.

DR. STOCKMANN. That may be so; but I can't see how the devil it concerns me!

THE MAYOR. That is where you are wrong, my dear Tomas; I can't seem to get that into your head! But be careful; sooner or later you'll have to pay for it. Now I've warned you. Good-bye.

DR. STOCKMANN. You're out of your mind, I tell you! You're on the wrong track entirely —!

THE MAYOR. I am seldom on the wrong track. Moreover — I take strong exception to —! (*Bows in the direction of the dining room.*) Good-bye, Katrine. Good-day, gentlemen. (*He goes.*)

MRS. STOCKMANN (*coming into the sitting room*). Has he gone?

DR. STOCKMANN. Yes — and in a towering rage too!

MRS. STOCKMANN. Tomas, dear! What did you do to him this time?

DR. STOCKMANN. Nothing at all! He can't very well expect me to give him an account of things — before they happen.

MRS. STOCKMANN. An account of what things?

DR. STOCKMANN. Never mind about that now, Katrine — It's very odd that the postman didn't come.

[*Hovstad, Billing, and Horster have risen from table and come into the sitting room; Ejlif and Morten follow presently.*]

BILLING (*stretching himself*). What a meal! Strike me dead if I don't feel like a new man!

HOVSTAD. His Honor didn't seem in a very sunny mood this evening.

DR. STOCKMANN. It's his stomach; his digestion's bad, you know.

HOVSTAD. I think he found it hard to digest us! He has no great love for *The People's Monitor*, I gather.

MRS. STOCKMANN. I thought you seemed to get on very well.

HOVSTAD. Only a temporary truce, I fear me!

BILLING. A truce, yes. That's the word for it.

DR. STOCKMANN. We mustn't forget poor Peter is a lonely bachelor. He has no home to be happy in. Business — nothing but business! And then that damned tea he's always filling himself up with. Now then, boys! Draw your chairs up to the table! Katrine — what about that toddy!

MRS. STOCKMANN (*going towards the dining room*). I'm just getting it.

DR. STOCKMANN. You sit here on the sofa with me, Captain Horster. We don't often have the chance of seeing you! — Go on, boys! Sit down!

[*They sit down at the table. Mrs. Stockmann brings in a tray with kettle, glasses, decanters, etc.*]

MRS. STOCKMANN. There you are! Now help yourselves. There's Arrak[1], rum, and this is cognac.

DR. STOCKMANN (*taking a glass*). We're ready for it! (*While the toddy is being mixed*) Now — the cigars. Ejlif, you know where the box is. And Morten can get my pipe. (*The boys go into the room, right.*) I have a suspicion Ejlif sneaks a cigar now and then — but I pretend not to notice. (*Calls.*) And my smoking-cap, Morten! Do you know where I left it, Katrine? Oh, he's found it. (*The boys bring in the various things.*) Now, my friends, help yourselves! I stick to my pipe, you know; many's the long cold trip, up there in the North, that *this* has kept me company. (*They clink glasses.*) Your health! It's a damn sight pleasanter to be sitting here in this warm comfortable room!

MRS. STOCKMANN (*sits and starts to knit*). Are you sailing soon, Captain Horster?

HORSTER. I hope to be ready next week.

MRS. STOCKMANN. And you're going to America?

HORSTER. That's the intention.

BILLING. Then you won't be able to vote in the town election.

HORSTER. Oh, there's to be an election, is there?

BILLING. Didn't you know?

HORSTER. No — I don't bother about such things.

BILLING. You mean you have no interest in public affairs?

HORSTER. I don't know anything about them.

BILLING. Still — one ought at least to vote.

HORSTER. Even if you understand nothing about it?

BILLING. Not understand? How do you mean? Society is like a ship; it's up to every man to put his hand to the helm.

[1] **Arrak:** a liquor similar to rum, made in the Far East from coconut-palm juice or molasses.

HORSTER. That may be all right on shore; but it would never do at sea.

HOVSTAD. Sailors rarely take an interest in public matters.

BILLING. Yes — it's amazing!

DR. STOCKMANN. Sailors are like birds of passage; North or South — every place is home to them! All the more reason for us to redouble our activities. Will there be anything of public interest in tomorrow's paper, Mr. Hovstad?

HOVSTAD. Nothing of local interest — no. But the day after tomorrow I thought I'd use your article.

DR. STOCKMANN. Oh, blast it, the article — of course! I'm afraid you'll have to hold it for a while.

HOVSTAD. Really? But we happen to have lots of space — and it seemed to me so timely.

DR. STOCKMANN. I daresay you're right — but you'll have to hold it all the same. I'll explain about it later —

[*Petra, wearing a hat and cloak, enters from the hall; she carries a number of exercise books under her arm.*]

PETRA. Good evening.

DR. STOCKMANN. Oh, it's you, Petra. Good evening.

[*General greetings. Petra takes off her hat and cloak and puts them, with the exercise books, on a chair by the door.*]

PETRA. So while I slave away at school — you sit here enjoying yourselves!

DR. STOCKMANN. Now you must come and enjoy yourself too.

BILLING. May I mix you a little drink?

PETRA (*goes to the table*). Thanks, I'll do it myself; you always make it too strong. Oh — by the way, Father, I have a letter for you. (*Goes to the chair where she left her things.*)

DR. STOCKMANN. A letter! From whom?

PETRA (*looking in the pocket of her cloak*). I met the postman on my way out —

DR. STOCKMANN (*rises and goes towards her*). You might have given it to me before!

PETRA. I really didn't have time to run upstairs again. Here it is.

DR. STOCKMANN (*seizing the letter*). Let me see — let me see, child. (*He reads the address.*) Yes! This is it!

MRS. STOCKMANN. Is it the one you've been expecting, Tomas?

DR. STOCKMANN. Yes. I must go in and read it at once. What about a light, Katrine? I suppose there's no lamp in my study again!

MRS. STOCKMANN. Oh, yes there is! It's already lighted on the desk.

DR. STOCKMANN. Good. Excuse me a moment — (*He goes into his study, right.*)

PETRA. What's all that about, Mother?

MRS. STOCKMANN. I don't know; these last few days he's done nothing but ask for the postman.

BILLING. Perhaps it's from one of his patients out of town —

PETRA. Poor father! He's getting to be frightfully busy. (*Mixes her toddy.*) Ah! This will be most welcome!

HOVSTAD. Have you been teaching at night school again this evening?

PETRA (*sipping her drink*). Two hours, yes.

BILLING. And four hours this morning at the girls' school —?

PETRA (*sitting down at the table*). Five.

MRS. STOCKMANN. And you have some exercises to correct this evening as well, I see.

PETRA. Quite a lot.

HORSTER. You seem to keep busy too!

PETRA. Yes — but I like it. It's good to feel thoroughly exhausted!

BILLING. Do you enjoy that?

PETRA. It makes one sleep so well.

MORTEN. You must be a great sinner, Petra.

PETRA. A sinner?

MORTEN. Yes — or you wouldn't have to work so hard. Work is a punishment for our sins — that's what Mr. Rörlund always says.

EJLIF. How can you be such a fool! Believing all that nonsense!

MRS. STOCKMANN. Now, now — Ejlif!

BILLING (*laughing*). That's a good one!

HOVSTAD. Shouldn't you like to work hard, Morten?

MORTEN. No, I shouldn't.

HOVSTAD. What do you want to do when you grow up?

MORTEN. I want to be a Viking.

EJLIF. You'd have to be a heathen, then.

MORTEN. Well — so I'd *be* a heathen!

BILLING. Good for you, Morten! That's the spirit!

MRS. STOCKMANN (*makes a sign to him*). I'm sure you don't really mean that, Mr. Billing!

BILLING. Strike me dead if I don't! I'm a heathen and I'm proud of it. You'll see — we'll all be heathens before long.

MORTEN. Then we could do anything we liked, couldn't we?

BILLING. Well — I don't know about that, Morten —

MRS. STOCKMANN. You'd better run along, boys; you must have homework to do.

EJLIF. Couldn't I stay a little bit longer —?

MRS. STOCKMANN. No — you couldn't. Now, run along — both of you.

[*The boys say good night and go into the room, left.*]

HOVSTAD. Do you think it's bad for them to hear that sort of talk?

MRS. STOCKMANN. I don't know; but I know I don't like it.

PETRA. Don't be so stuffy, Mother!

MRS. STOCKMANN. That's all very well — but I don't. Not in one's own home at any rate.

PETRA. All this hypocrisy! At home we're taught to hold our tongues; and at school we have to teach the children lies!

HORSTER. Teach them lies?

PETRA. Yes, of course — We have to teach all kinds of things we don't believe a word of!

BILLING. That's true enough.

PETRA. If I had enough money, I'd start a school myself — then I'd run things quite differently.

BILLING. Well — as far as the money goes —

HORSTER. If you're really serious about that, Miss Stockmann, I'd be glad to provide the necessary space; my father's old house is practically empty, and there's a huge dining room on the ground floor that would —

PETRA. Oh, I don't suppose anything will come of it — but, thanks, all the same!

HOVSTAD. I've a feeling Miss Petra is more likely to take up journalism. And, that reminds me — have you had a chance to read that English story you promised to translate for us?

PETRA. No, not yet. But I'll get it done for you in time — don't worry.

[*Dr. Stockmann comes in from his study with the letter open in his hand.*]

DR. STOCKMANN (*flourishing the letter*). Well! Here's some news that will make the town sit up and take notice!

BILLING. News?

MRS. STOCKMANN. What sort of news, Tomas?

DR. STOCKMANN. A great discovery, Katrine!

HOVSTAD. Really?

MRS. STOCKMANN. A discovery of yours, you mean?

DR. STOCKMANN. Of mine — yes! (*Paces up and down.*) And I defy them this time to call me a crackpot and laugh it off as nonsense. They won't dare! They simply won't dare!

PETRA. What is it, Father? Tell us!

DR. STOCKMANN. Just give me time, and I'll tell you all about it. I do wish Peter were here! It only goes to show how blind we are — just like a lot of moles!

HOVSTAD. What do you mean, Doctor?

DR. STOCKMANN. It's the general opinion that this town of ours is an exceedingly healthy place — isn't that true?

HOVSTAD. Of course.

DR. STOCKMANN. A quite exceptionally healthy place, as a matter of fact; a place to be highly recommended, not only to ordinary inhabitants, but to invalids as well —

MRS. STOCKMANN. My dear Tomas —

DR. STOCKMANN. And, as such, we have duly praised and recommended it; I myself have sung its praises innumerable times — not only in *The People's Monitor,* but in many pamphlets too —

HOVSTAD. Well — what then?

DR. STOCKMANN. And these Mineral Baths that have been called "the pulse of the town" — its "nerve center" — and the devil only knows what else besides —

BILLING. "The throbbing heart of our city" I remember I once called them — in a somewhat convivial mood —

DR. STOCKMANN. Yes — that too. Well — do you know what these Baths are? These precious, magnificent Baths that have been established at such great expense — can you guess what they really are?

HOVSTAD. No — what?

MRS. STOCKMANN. Tell us, Tomas!

DR. STOCKMANN. They're nothing but a pesthole!

PETRA. The Baths, Father?

MRS. STOCKMANN (*at the same time*). Our Baths!

HOVSTAD (*simultaneously*). But, Doctor —!

BILLING. This is incredible!

DR. STOCKMANN. I tell you the whole institution is a whited sepulcher, spreading poison; it's a menace to the Public Health! All that filth from the tanneries up at Milldale — and you know what a stench there is around there! — seeps into the feed pipes of the pump room; and, not only that, but this same poisonous offal seeps out onto the beach as well.

HOVSTAD. In the saltwater baths, you mean?

DR. STOCKMANN. Precisely.

HOVSTAD. How can you be sure of all this, Doctor?

DR. STOCKMANN. I've made the most painstaking investigations. I'd suspected something of the sort for quite some time, you see. I was struck by the curious amount of illness among the visitors at the Baths last year — there were several cases of typhoid and gastric fever —

MRS. STOCKMANN. Yes, I remember.

DR. STOCKMANN. At first we took it for granted that the visitors brought the infection with them; but later — this past winter — I began to think differently. I set to work to analyze the water, as best I could —

MRS. STOCKMANN. So that's what you've been working at!

DR. STOCKMANN. Yes — I've worked very hard at it, Katrine, but I didn't have the necessary equipment here; so I finally sent samples of the drinking water and the seawater by the beach to the laboratories at the university and asked them to give me a full analysis.

HOVSTAD. And is that what you just received?

DR. STOCKMANN (*showing the letter*). Yes — here it is! It proves beyond the shadow of a doubt the presence of decayed animal matter in the water — millions of infusoria.[2]

---

[2] **infusoria:** In Ibsen's time, the term referred to a variety of minute organisms found in the liquid in which decaying organic matter had been soaked. Now infusoria is the name used for a specific class of organisms.

The use of this water, both internally and externally, is in the highest degree dangerous to health.

MRS. STOCKMANN. What a blessing you found it out in time!

DR. STOCKMANN. It is indeed, Katrine!

HOVSTAD. What do you propose to do about it, Doctor?

DR. STOCKMANN. Set things straight, of course.

HOVSTAD. You think that can be done?

DR. STOCKMANN. It *must* be done. Otherwise the Baths are entirely useless — ruined! But there's no need for that to happen; I'm quite clear as to how we should proceed.

MRS. STOCKMANN. To think of your keeping all this secret, Tomas, dear!

DR. STOCKMANN. You wouldn't have had me rushing all over town gabbing about it before I was absolutely certain, would you? I'm not as mad as all that, you know!

PETRA. But, surely, to us —

DR. STOCKMANN. I couldn't say a word to a living soul! But tomorrow you can run and tell that badger of yours all about it —

MRS. STOCKMANN. Oh, Tomas!

DR. STOCKMANN. Well — your grandfather, then. That'll give the old man something to gape at! He thinks I'm cracked in the head — and a lot of other people think so too, I've noticed. But I'll show them! Yes — this time I'll show them! (*Walks up and down rubbing his hands.*) What a commotion there'll be in the town, Katrine! Think of it; they'll have to re-lay all the water pipes.

HOVSTAD (*rising*). All the water pipes — ?

DR. STOCKMANN. Well — naturally. The intake must be moved much higher up; I always said it was down too low.

PETRA. You were right after all, Father.

DR. STOCKMANN. Yes — you remember, Petra? I sent in a protest before they even started on the work; but, of course, at that time, no one listened to me. Well — I'll let them have it now! I've prepared a report for the Board of Directors; it's been ready for a week — I was only waiting for this. (*Points to the letter.*) I'll send it off at once. (*Goes into his study and returns with a manuscript.*) Look! Four closely written pages! And I'll enclose this letter too. A paper, Katrine! Something to wrap this up in. Good. And now give this to

— to — what the devil is that girl's name! To the maid — *you* know! Tell her to deliver it to the Mayor immediately!

[*Mrs. Stockmann takes the package and goes out through the dining room.*]

PETRA. What do you think Uncle Peter will say, Father?

DR. STOCKMANN. What *can* he say? He can't fail to be pleased that such an important fact has come to light.

HOVSTAD. May we announce this in *The People's Monitor?*

DR. STOCKMANN. I'd be most grateful if you would.

HOVSTAD. It's important that the public should know of this without delay.

DR. STOCKMANN. It is indeed!

MRS. STOCKMANN (*returning*). She's gone with it.

BILLING. Strike me dead if you're not hailed as the leading citizen of our community, Dr. Stockmann!

DR. STOCKMANN (*walks up and down in high glee*). Oh, nonsense! I only did my duty. I simply was lucky enough to spot it — that's all. But still —

BILLING. Hovstad, don't you think the town should get up some sort of a demonstration in Dr. Stockmann's honor?

HOVSTAD. I shall certainly propose it.

BILLING. I'll talk it over with Aslaksen.

DR. STOCKMANN. No, no — my dear friends! You mustn't bother with such nonsense; I won't hear of it! And, I warn you, Katrine — if the Board of Directors should think of offering me a raise in salary — I shall refuse it. I simply won't accept!

MRS. STOCKMANN. You're quite right, Tomas, dear.

PETRA (*raising her glass*). Your health, Father!

HOVSTAD *and* BILLING. Your good health, Doctor!

HORSTER (*clinks glasses with him*). I hope this brings you joy.

DR. STOCKMANN. Thank you, thank you — my dear, dear friends! I can't tell you how happy I am — ! It's a wonderful thing to feel you've deserved well of your own hometown, and of your fellow citizens. Hurrah, Katrine!

[*He puts his arms round her and whirls her round the room. Mrs. Stockmann screams and struggles to free herself. Laughter, applause and cheers for the doctor. The two boys poke their heads in the door to see what is going on.*]

CURTAIN

QUESTIONS

1. What had happened to Dr. Stockmann before he moved to the town? In which possessions and comforts does he take a special delight?

2. For what reason does the mayor, Dr. Stockmann's brother, value the baths? What is the basis of the rivalry between the two men?

3. Are Dr. Stockmann's motives in exposing the polluted waterworks wholly unselfish? What had he said before the pipes were laid?

4. Dr. Stockmann is certain that the town will welcome his revelations about the baths. Is there anything to suggest that some people may not respond as he expects? What is the importance of Petra's remarks about the school?

5. What questions have been raised by Act One? What conflicts are likely to arise in Act Two?

ACT TWO

SCENE: *The doctor's living room. The door to the dining room is closed. Morning. Mrs. Stockmann, carrying a sealed letter in her hand, comes in from the dining room, goes to the door of the doctor's study and peeps in.*

MRS. STOCKMANN. Are you in there, Tomas?

DR. STOCKMANN (*from the study*). Yes, I just got back. (*Enters.*) Do you want me?

MRS. STOCKMANN. Here's a letter from your brother. (*Hands it to him.*)

DR. STOCKMANN. Now — let's see. (*Opens the envelope and reads.*) "The manuscript forwarded to me is returned herewith —" (*He reads on, mumbling to himself.*) Hm.

MRS. STOCKMANN. Well? What does he say?

DR. STOCKMANN. Just that he'll be up to see me around noon.

MRS. STOCKMANN. You must be sure and be home, then.

DR. STOCKMANN. I can easily manage that; I've made all my morning calls.

MRS. STOCKMANN. I can't help wondering how he'll take it.

DR. STOCKMANN. He's sure to be annoyed that it was I, and not he, who discovered the whole business.

MRS. STOCKMANN. That's what I'm afraid of.

DR. STOCKMANN. He'll be glad at heart, of course. But still —; Peter's always so damnably resentful when anyone else does anything for the good of the town.

MRS. STOCKMANN. I know. I think it would be nice if you made a point of letting him share the honor; you might even imply that it was he who put you on the track —

DR. STOCKMANN. That's all right as far as I'm concerned. All I care about is getting the thing cleared up.

[*Old Morten Kiil sticks his head in at the hall door.*]

MORTEN KIIL (*slyly*). Is — is all this true?

MRS. STOCKMANN (*goes toward him*). Well! Here's Father.

DR. STOCKMANN. So it is! Good morning, Father-in-law!

MRS. STOCKMANN. Do come in.

MORTEN KIIL. If it's true, I will; otherwise I'll be off again.

DR. STOCKMANN. If what's true?

MORTEN KIIL. All this nonsense about the waterworks. Well? Is it?

DR. STOCKMANN. Of course it's true. But how did *you* find out about it?

MORTEN KIIL. From Petra. She ran in to see me on her way to school —

DR. STOCKMANN. Oh, did she?

MORTEN KIIL. Yes, indeed; and she told me — at first I thought she must be joking! But that's not like Petra, come to think of it.

DR. STOCKMANN. Of course not! She'd never joke about a thing like that.

MORTEN KIIL. You never know; and I don't like to be made a fool of. So it really is true, is it?

DR. STOCKMANN. Unquestionably. Do sit down, Father. (*Forces him down on the sofa.*) Well — what do you think? It's a lucky thing for the town, isn't it?

MORTEN KIIL (*with suppressed laughter*). A lucky thing for the town?

DR. STOCKMANN. Yes, that I made this discovery in time —

MORTEN KIIL (*as before*). Oh, of course! Of course! — I must say I never thought you'd try your monkey-tricks on your own brother!

DR. STOCKMANN. Monkey-tricks —!

MRS. STOCKMANN. Father, dear —!

MORTEN KIIL (*rests his hands and chin on the top of his cane and blinks slyly at the doctor*). Let me see — what was it now? Oh! yes — the water pipes are full of little animals — isn't that it?

DR. STOCKMANN. Infusoria, yes.

MORTEN KIIL. And Petra said there were a lot of them — whole swarms of them.

DR. STOCKMANN. Certainly; hundreds of thousands of them.

MORTEN KIIL. And yet no one can see them — isn't that the story?

DR. STOCKMANN. Of course no one can see them.

MORTEN KIIL (*with quiet chuckling laughter*). I'll be damned if this isn't the best thing you've hit on yet!

DR. STOCKMANN. What do you mean?

MORTEN KIIL. You'll never get the Mayor to believe this nonsense!

DR. STOCKMANN. We shall see.

MORTEN KIIL. You think he's as crazy as all that?

DR. STOCKMANN. I'm confident that the whole town will be as crazy as all that.

MORTEN KIIL. The whole town! Yes — I wouldn't put it past them. And it'll serve them right, too — teach them a lesson. We old-timers aren't good enough for them — oh, no! They think themselves so clever! They hounded me out of the Town Council — hounded me out like a dog, that's what they did! But they'll get paid back now! Just you go on playing your monkey-tricks with them, Stockmann —

DR. STOCKMANN. But, Father — listen —!

MORTEN KIIL (*rising*). Give 'em all the monkey-tricks you can think of, say I! If you can put this over on the Mayor and his cronies — so help me, I'll give a hundred crowns to charity!

DR. STOCKMANN. Very handsome of you.

MORTEN KIIL. Mind you, I've little enough to spare! But just you put this over, and next Christmas I'll give fifty crowns to charity!

[*Hovstad enters from the hall.*]

HOVSTAD. Good morning! (*Pausing*) Oh, excuse me —

DR. STOCKMANN. No — come in; come in.

MORTEN KIIL (*chuckling again*). Is *he* in on this?

HOVSTAD. What do you mean?

DR. STOCKMANN. Yes, of course he is.

MORTEN KIIL. I might have known it! He's to put it in his paper. Ah! You're a good one, Stockmann! Well — I'm off. I'll leave you two together.

DR. STOCKMANN. No, Father; don't go yet.

MORTEN KIIL. Yes — I'll be off. Just you think up all the monkey-tricks you can. You can be damn sure you won't lose by it!

[*He goes; Mrs. Stockmann goes with him.*]

DR. STOCKMANN (*laughing*). What do you think — ? The old man doesn't believe a word about the waterworks!

HOVSTAD. Oh, was that what you were talking about?

DR. STOCKMANN. Yes. I suppose you've come about that, too?

HOVSTAD. Yes, I have. Have you a few moments, Doctor?

DR. STOCKMANN. As many as you like.

HOVSTAD. Have you heard anything from the Mayor yet?

DR. STOCKMANN. No, not yet. But he's to be here presently.

HOVSTAD. Since I left here last night I've thought a great deal about this matter.

DR. STOCKMANN. You have?

HOVSTAD. Yes. As a doctor and a man of science you naturally think of this business of the waterworks as a thing apart. I mean by that — you probably haven't stopped to realize how many other things it may involve.

DR. STOCKMANN. In what way — ? Let's sit down, my dear fellow. No — here on the sofa. (*Hovstad sits down on the sofa and Stockmann in an armchair on the other side of the table.*) So — you think — ?

HOVSTAD. You said last night that the water was polluted by decayed matter in the soil.

DR. STOCKMANN. The trouble comes from that poisonous swamp by the tanneries at Milldale. I'm convinced of that.

HOVSTAD. Forgive me, Doctor — but I think the trouble comes from poison of quite another sort.

DR. STOCKMANN. What poison do you mean?

HOVSTAD. I mean the poison that is polluting and contaminating our whole community.

DR. STOCKMANN. What the devil do you mean by that?

HOVSTAD. Little by little the whole town has come under the control of a pack of bureaucrats.[3]

DR. STOCKMANN. Oh, come now — they're not all bureaucrats.

HOVSTAD. Perhaps not — but those of them who are not bureaucrats are the friends and hangers-on of those who are. We are under the thumb of a small clique of powerful men; it's the old established families, the men of wealth and position, who rule the town.

DR. STOCKMANN. But, remember — they are also men of ability and insight.

HOVSTAD. I suppose it was their ability and insight that controlled the installation of the water system?

DR. STOCKMANN. That was a colossal piece of stupidity, I grant you. But it will be corrected now.

HOVSTAD. Do you think that will be such a simple matter?

DR. STOCKMANN. Simple or not, it must be done.

HOVSTAD. Yes; especially if the press exerts its influence.

DR. STOCKMANN. That won't be necessary, I assure you; I'm certain that my brother —

HOVSTAD. Excuse me, Doctor, but I want you to know that I intend to publicize the matter.

DR. STOCKMANN. In the newspaper?

HOVSTAD. Yes. When I took over *The People's Monitor*, it was with the thought of breaking up this ring of obstinate old reactionaries[4] who now have full control.

DR. STOCKMANN. With the result that you nearly wrecked the paper — you told me that yourself.

HOVSTAD. We were obliged to draw in our horns for a while — that's true enough; if these particular men had been put out

---

[3] **bureaucrats:** government officials who follow a rigid routine rather than using their own judgment.

[4] **reactionaries:** people who support outdated political policies.

of office at that time, the Bath scheme might have fallen through entirely. But now that danger's over; the Baths are an accomplished fact — and we can afford to do without these high and mighty gentlemen.

DR. STOCKMANN. Do without them, yes; but still, we have a lot to thank them for.

HOVSTAD. Oh, we shall make a point of acknowledging the debt! But a journalist of my liberal turn of mind cannot be expected to let an opportunity like this go by. This myth of official infallibility must be exploded. That kind of superstition must be rooted out.

DR. STOCKMANN. There I agree with you entirely, Mr. Hovstad; if it's a superstition, we must get rid of it!

HOVSTAD. I hesitate to attack the Mayor — since he's your brother; on the other hand, I'm sure you feel as I do, that truth comes first.

DR. STOCKMANN. Undoubtedly — of course. (*Vehemently*) But, all the same!

HOVSTAD. I don't want you to think ill of me. I'm no more egotistical — no more ambitious — than the majority of men.

DR. STOCKMANN. My dear fellow — ! No one says you are.

HOVSTAD. I come of a very humble family, Dr. Stockmann; and my knowledge of the common people has been gained through personal experience. I know their needs — I understand their aims. It's because they wish to develop their own ability, knowledge and self-respect, that they claim the right to share in the responsibilities of government —

DR. STOCKMANN. That's very understandable —

HOVSTAD. Yes. And it seems to me a journalist would incur a heavy responsibility by failing to seize the slightest chance of furthering the emancipation of the downtrodden masses. Oh! I know the powers that be will call this anarchy. But, let them! I shall at least have done my duty.

DR. STOCKMANN. Quite so — quite so, dear Mr. Hovstad. Still — damn it all — you must remember — ! (*A knock at the door*) Come in!

[*Aslaksen, the printer, appears at the hall door. He is shabbily but respectably dressed in a black suit with a slightly crumpled white necktie. He carries a silk hat and gloves.*]

ASLAKSEN (*bowing*). Excuse me, Doctor, if I intrude —

DR. STOCKMANN (*rising*). Well — well! It's Mr. Aslaksen!

ASLAKSEN. Yes, it's me, Doctor —

HOVSTAD (*gets up*). Do you want me, Aslaksen?

ASLAKSEN. No; I didn't even know you were here. It's the doctor I —

DR. STOCKMANN. What can I do for you?

ASLAKSEN. Is it true, what Mr. Billing tells me, that you're planning to improve our water system?

DR. STOCKMANN. For the Baths, yes.

ASLAKSEN. Just as I thought; then I'd like you to know, Doctor, that I shall support this plan with all my might.

HOVSTAD (*to the doctor*). You see!

DR. STOCKMANN. I'm most grateful to you, I'm sure; but —

ASLAKSEN. You never know — we small middle-class men might be very useful to you. We form what you might call a solid majority in the town; if we really make up our minds to it, that is. And it's always a good thing to have the support of the majority, Dr. Stockmann.

DR. STOCKMANN. That's unquestionably true; but I can't conceive that any special measures will be necessary in this case. The matter is so simple — so straightforward —

ASLAKSEN. It might be helpful all the same. I know the local authorities very well. Suggestions from people outside their immediate circle are not looked upon too favorably by the powers that be. So I thought it might be a good idea if we arranged a demonstration of some sort.

HOVSTAD. I quite agree.

DR. STOCKMANN. A demonstration? But what form would this demonstration take?

ASLAKSEN. Oh, it would be conducted with the utmost moderation, Doctor; I strive for moderation in all things; moderation is a citizen's prime virtue — at least in my opinion.

DR. STOCKMANN. Your moderation is well-known, dear Mr. Aslaksen.

ASLAKSEN. I think I may safely say it is. And to us small middle-class men, this business of the waterworks is of very great importance. Our Baths bid fair to become a small gold mine, as it were. Many of us count on them to provide us with a means of livelihood — the homeowners especially; so we naturally wish to support the Baths in every possible way. Now, since I happen to be chairman of the Homeowners Association —

DR. STOCKMANN. Yes — ?

ASLAKSEN. — and also an active worker in the Temperance Society[5] — you know of course, Doctor, that I'm a temperance man — ?

DR. STOCKMANN. That goes without saying —

ASLAKSEN. Then I need hardly tell you that I am in constant touch with a great number of my fellow citizens. And since my reputation is that of a prudent, law-abiding man — as you yourself remarked — I have a certain influence in the town; a kind of modest authority — though I do say so myself.

DR. STOCKMANN. I'm well aware of that.

ASLAKSEN. So — should it be advisable — it would be a comparatively simple matter for me to get up some sort of a petition.

DR. STOCKMANN. A petition?

ASLAKSEN. Yes — a petition of thanks; of thanks to you, on behalf of the townspeople, for having taken up this all-important matter. It goes without saying that it must be worded with suitable moderation; it would never do to offend the authorities, or any of the men in power. But, if we keep this in mind, I see no reason for any possible objection.

HOVSTAD. Well — even if they did object — !

ASLAKSEN. No, no! There must be nothing in it to offend the powers that be, Mr. Hovstad. We can't afford to antagonize the men who control our destinies. I've seen plenty of that in my time — no good ever comes of it. But no one could object to a citizen expressing his opinion freely — provided it is couched in temperate terms.

DR. STOCKMANN. I am delighted, my dear Mr. Aslaksen, to know I can count on the support of my fellow townsmen;

---

[5] **Temperance Society:** a society opposed to drinking. The Norwegian word for temperance also means moderation, adding to Aslaksen's "moderate" virtues.

I can't tell you how happy this makes me! And now — how about a glass of sherry?

ASLAKSEN. No — many thanks; I never indulge in spirits.

DR. STOCKMANN. Well — you surely won't refuse a glass of beer?

ASLAKSEN. Thank you — but I never touch anything so early in the day. Now I'll be on my way; I must talk to some of the homeowners, and set about preparing public opinion.

DR. STOCKMANN. It's extremely kind of you, Mr. Aslaksen; but I can't conceive that all this preparation should be necessary. The issue is clear — I can't see any room for disagreement.

ASLAKSEN. The authorities have a way of functioning very slowly, Dr. Stockmann. Oh, far be it from me to blame them — !

HOVSTAD. We'll give them a good stirring up in the paper tomorrow —

ASLAKSEN. But I beg you, Mr. Hovstad — no violence! If you wish to get results, you must use moderation. Take my advice; I speak from experience. Well — now I'll say good-bye. Remember, Doctor, we — of the middle class — stand behind you to a man. The solid majority is on your side.

DR. STOCKMANN. I'm most grateful to you, Mr. Aslaksen. (*Holds out his hand.*) Good-bye, good-bye!

ASLAKSEN. Are you coming to the office, Mr. Hovstad?

HOVSTAD. I'll be there presently. There are still a couple of things I'd like to discuss.

ASLAKSEN. Very well. (*He bows and goes out; Dr. Stockmann shows him into the hall.*)

HOVSTAD (*as the doctor re-enters*). Well — now what do you say, Doctor? Don't you agree it's high time we put a stop to all this halfhearted, cowardly shilly-shallying?

DR. STOCKMANN. Are you referring to Aslaksen?

HOVSTAD. Yes, I am. He's been infected by the poison too, you see — though he's not a bad sort, in his way. He's typical of most people around here; always wavering, always on the fence. They never dare take a definite stand — they're too full of doubts, and scruples, and caution.

DR. STOCKMANN. He seems like a thoroughly well-intentioned man.

HOVSTAD. Intentions may be all very well — but give me a man with some self-confidence, some self-assurance.

DR. STOCKMANN. Yes — I agree with you there.

HOVSTAD. I'm going to use this opportunity to inject a little backbone into their good intentions. This servile worship of the "Powers that be" must be wiped out. The inexcusable bungling about the waterworks must be fully exposed. Every single voter must be made aware of it.

DR. STOCKMANN. Very well; as long as you think it's for the good of the Community. But I must speak to my brother first.

HOVSTAD. Meanwhile — I'll be writing my editorial. And if the Mayor refuses to take action —

DR. STOCKMANN. That's inconceivable.

HOVSTAD. Perhaps not so inconceivable as you might think. But suppose he does —

DR. STOCKMANN. Then, my dear Mr. Hovstad — if that should happen — you may print my full report, word for word — just as it is.

HOVSTAD. Is that a promise?

DR. STOCKMANN (*hands him the manuscript*). Look — here it is; take it with you. There's no harm in your reading it; you can return it to me later on.

HOVSTAD. Very good; I shall do so. Good-bye for now, dear Doctor.

DR. STOCKMANN. Good-bye. But, you'll see, this whole thing will be cleared up quite simply, Mr. Hovstad; I'm confident of that.

HOVSTAD. Well — we shall see. (*He bows and goes out through the hall.*)

DR. STOCKMANN (*goes to the dining room and looks in*). Katrine — ! Oh! Are you back, Petra?

PETRA (*enters the sitting room*). Yes; I just got back from school.

MRS. STOCKMANN (*enters*). Hasn't he been here yet?

DR. STOCKMANN. Peter? No. But I had a long talk with Hovstad. He's quite excited about my discovery. He feels its implications are even more important than I thought. He's placed his newspaper at my disposal — in case I should require it.

MRS. STOCKMANN. But do you think you will?

DR. STOCKMANN. No! I'm sure I shan't. Still — it's very flattering to have the support of an enlightened, independent
paper, such as his. I had a visit from the chairman of the
Homeowners Association, too.

MRS. STOCKMANN. Really? What did he want?

DR. STOCKMANN. He, too, wanted to assure me of his support.
They're all ready to stand by me, in case of need. Do you
know what I have on my side, Katrine?

MRS. STOCKMANN. On your side? No — what?

DR. STOCKMANN. The solid majority.

MRS. STOCKMANN. And is that a good thing for you, Tomas,
dear?

DR. STOCKMANN. A good thing! Well — I should hope so!
(*He rubs his hands and paces up and down.*) What a wonderful thing it is to feel in such close harmony with one's
fellow men!

PETRA. And to know one's doing good and valuable work!

DR. STOCKMANN. Especially when it's for your own hometown, Petra.

MRS. STOCKMANN. There's the bell.

DR. STOCKMANN. That must be he. (*A knock at the door*)
Come in!

THE MAYOR (*enters from the hall*). Good morning.

DR. STOCKMANN. I'm glad to see you, Peter.

MRS. STOCKMANN. Good morning, Brother-in-law. And how
are you today?

THE MAYOR. Thank you — only so-so. (*To the doctor*) Last
night, after office hours, I received a long dissertation from
you on the subject of the Baths.

DR. STOCKMANN. Have you read it?

THE MAYOR. Yes — I have.

DR. STOCKMANN. Well — what do you think of it?

THE MAYOR (*with a side glance*). Hm —

MRS. STOCKMANN. Come along, Petra. (*She and Petra go
into the room, left.*)

THE MAYOR. Why did you find it necessary to carry on these
investigations behind my back?

DR. STOCKMANN. As long as I wasn't absolutely sure, I —

THE MAYOR. Then you think you're absolutely sure now?

DR. STOCKMANN. Didn't my report convince you of that?

THE MAYOR. Is it your intention to submit this report to the Board of Directors as an official document?

DR. STOCKMANN. Of course. Something must be done about it; and at once.

THE MAYOR. In your customary manner, you make use of some very strong expressions. You say, among other things, that what we offer our visitors is nothing short of poison.

DR. STOCKMANN. But, Peter — what else can you call it? I tell you — whether you drink it or bathe in it — the water is poison! We can't do this to poor sick people who come here in good faith expecting to be cured!

THE MAYOR. You conclude your report by stating that a sewer must be built to carry off the alleged impurities at Mill-dale, and that the entire water system must be redesigned and reinstalled.

DR. STOCKMANN. Can you think of any other solution?

THE MAYOR. I found a pretext for calling on the town engineer this morning and brought the matter up — in a joking way, of course — as something we should perhaps consider sometime in the future.

DR. STOCKMANN. In the future!

THE MAYOR. He laughed at the extravagance of the suggestion — I naturally let him think it was my own idea. Have you taken the trouble to find out the cost of these proposed alterations? I gathered from the engineer it would amount to several hundred thousand crowns.

DR. STOCKMANN. As much as that?

THE MAYOR. Yes. But that's not the worst of it. The work would take at least two years.

DR. STOCKMANN. Two years? Two whole years?

THE MAYOR. At least. And what's to happen to the Baths in the meantime? Are we to close them? We'd have no alternative. You don't imagine people would go on coming here if it were rumored that the waters were injurious to the health?

DR. STOCKMANN. But, Peter — that's just what they are.

THE MAYOR. And that this should happen now — just when the Baths are beginning to gain a reputation. Other towns in this vicinity might qualify equally well as health resorts.

They'd bend every effort to divert this stream of visitors from us to them; why shouldn't they? And we should be left stranded. All the money that has been invested in this costly undertaking would be wasted; most likely the whole scheme would have to be abandoned. The town would be completely ruined — thanks to you!

DR. STOCKMANN. Ruined — !

THE MAYOR. The only future the town has is through the Baths — the only future worth mentioning, that is! You know that as well as I do.

DR. STOCKMANN. Well? What do you think should be done?

THE MAYOR. I find myself unconvinced by your report. I cannot fully persuade myself that conditions are as critical as your statement represents.

DR. STOCKMANN. If anything they're worse! At least they will be, during the summer, when the hot weather sets in.

THE MAYOR. I repeat that in my opinion you greatly exaggerate the situation. I am certain that a competent physician would find adequate steps to take — would be able to counteract any harmful agents, should their presence be definitely established.

DR. STOCKMANN. I see. And then — ?

THE MAYOR. The present water system is an established fact and must, of course, be treated as such. At some future time the Directors might see their way clear — provided the cost was not too exorbitant — to inaugurate certain improvements.

DR. STOCKMANN. You don't imagine I could ever be party to such a swindle?

THE MAYOR. Swindle?

DR. STOCKMANN. Swindle, yes! It would be the worst kind of trickery — an out-and-out crime against Society!

THE MAYOR. I've already told you, I've not been able to persuade myself of the existence of any imminent danger.

DR. STOCKMANN. Yes, you have! You couldn't possibly have done otherwise. My report is so obviously clear and convincing. You understand the situation perfectly, Peter, but you simply refuse to face it. You were responsible for the placement of the Baths and the waterworks — it was you who insisted on putting them where they are. It was a damnable mistake and now you refuse to admit it. Do you think I don't see through you?

THE MAYOR. And what if it were so? If I am concerned with protecting my reputation, it's only for the good of the town. I cannot possibly direct affairs in a manner conducive to the general welfare as I see it, unless my integrity and authority are unassailable. For this reason — among others — I consider it imperative that your report should not be brought to the notice of the Board of Directors. It must be withheld for the sake of the community. Later on I will bring the matter up for discussion and we will go to work quietly and see what can be done. Meanwhile not a word — not a breath — about this unfortunate business must be allowed to leak out.

DR. STOCKMANN. I'm afraid that can hardly be prevented, my dear Peter.

THE MAYOR. It must and shall be prevented.

DR. STOCKMANN. It's no use, I tell you; too many people know of it already.

THE MAYOR. Know of it! Whom? Surely not those fellows from *The People's Monitor* — ?

DR. STOCKMANN. Yes — they know about it too. The free press will certainly see to it that you're made to do your duty.

THE MAYOR. You're an incredibly rash man, Tomas. Hasn't it occurred to you that all this might have serious consequences for you?

DR. STOCKMANN. Consequences — for me?

THE MAYOR. For you — and those dear to you, yes.

DR. STOCKMANN. What the devil do you mean by that?

THE MAYOR. As your brother, I've always been ready and willing to help you — I think I may say that?

DR. STOCKMANN. You have indeed — and I thank you for it.

THE MAYOR. I don't ask for thanks. In a way I was forced into it — for my own sake. By helping you to greater financial security I had hoped to keep you in check, to some extent.

DR. STOCKMANN. Do you mean to tell me you only did it for your own sake?

THE MAYOR. In a way, I said. It's extremely awkward for an official, when his closest relative is continuously compromising himself.

DR. STOCKMANN. You think I do that, do you?

THE MAYOR. Yes, you do — unfortunately; I daresay you're not even aware of it. You have a restless, violent, rebellious nature, and you can't resist going into print indiscriminately on any and all subjects. No sooner does a thought strike you than you dash off an article to the newspaper — or you write a whole pamphlet on the subject.

DR. STOCKMANN. Surely if one has new ideas, it's one's duty to share them with the public!

THE MAYOR. Believe me, the public has no need of new ideas; it's better off without them. The best way to serve the public is to give it what it's used to.

DR. STOCKMANN. That's a very bald statement!

THE MAYOR. For once I must be frank with you. I've tried to avoid it hitherto, because I know how irritable you are; but it's time I told you the truth, Tomas. You don't realize how you antagonize people by this intolerant attitude of yours. You criticize the authorities — you even criticize the Government; you do nothing but find fault. And then you complain of being slighted — of being persecuted. With your difficult nature, what can you expect?

DR. STOCKMANN. Oh — so I'm difficult too, am I?

THE MAYOR. Yes, Tomas; you are an extremely difficult man to get along with. I speak from experience. You seem to forget that you have me to thank for your present position as medical adviser to the Baths —

DR. STOCKMANN. I was entitled to that position — it belonged to me by right! It was I who first saw the possibility of creating a health resort here, and I was the only one at that time who believed in it. I fought for the idea single-handed for many years. I wrote about it — publicized it —

THE MAYOR. That is undeniable. But at that time the scheme was premature. Living as you did then, in that out-of-the-way corner of the world, you naturally couldn't be a judge of that. But later, when circumstances seemed more favorable, I — and the others — took the matter in hand —

DR. STOCKMANN. Yes. And a fine mess you made of it! You took my splendid plan and ruined it. And now the results of your cleverness and shrewdness are all too obvious.

THE MAYOR. Only one thing is obvious, in my opinion: you feel the need to be belligerent — to strike out at your superiors; that's an old habit of yours. You refuse to submit to the slightest authority; you regard anyone above you as a personal enemy and are prepared to use every conceivable weapon against him. I have now pointed out to you what is at stake for the town as a whole — and consequently for me personally. I warn you, Tomas, I shall be completely ruthless unless you accept certain conditions.

DR. STOCKMANN. What conditions?

THE MAYOR. Since you have seen fit to go round gossiping about a subject which should, of course, have been treated with the utmost discretion as an official secret, it is too late to hush the matter up. There are bound to be all sorts of rumors, and malicious-minded people will of course elaborate them. It will therefore be necessary for you publicly to refute them.

DR. STOCKMANN. I? But how? I don't understand.

THE MAYOR. We shall expect you, on further investigation, to come to the conclusion that the situation is not nearly as pressing or as dangerous as you had at first imagined.

DR. STOCKMANN. Oh! You expect that of me, do you?

THE MAYOR. Furthermore we will expect you to make a public statement expressing your faith in the management's integrity and in their intention to take thorough and conscientious steps to remedy any possible defects.

DR. STOCKMANN. But that's out of the question, Peter. No amount of patching or tinkering can put this matter right; I tell you I *know!* It is my firm and unalterable conviction —

THE MAYOR. As a member of the staff you have no right to personal convictions.

DR. STOCKMANN (*with a start*). No right to — ?

THE MAYOR. Not as a member of the staff — no! As a private individual — that's of course another matter. But as a subordinate in the employ of the Baths you have no right openly to express convictions opposed to those of your superiors.

DR. STOCKMANN. This is too much! Do you mean to tell me that as a doctor — a scientific man — I have no right to — !

THE MAYOR. But this is not purely a scientific matter; there are other questions involved — technical and economic questions.

DR. STOCKMANN. To hell with all that! I insist that I am free to speak my mind on any and all questions!

THE MAYOR. You are free to do anything you please — as long as it doesn't concern the Baths. But we forbid you to touch on that subject.

DR. STOCKMANN (*shouts*). Forbid it — you! A bunch of — !

THE MAYOR. *I* forbid it. I personally — your superior in chief. And when I give an order I expect to be obeyed.

DR. STOCKMANN (*controlling himself*). By God! If you weren't my brother, Peter — !

PETRA (*flings open the door*). Don't put up with this, Father!

MRS. STOCKMANN (*following her*). Petra! Petra!

THE MAYOR. So! We've been listening at doors, have we?

MRS. STOCKMANN. You talked so loud — we couldn't very well help hearing —

PETRA. That's not true. I was listening on purpose.

THE MAYOR. Well — I can't say I'm sorry —

DR. STOCKMANN (*a step toward him*). You talked to me in terms of forbidding — of forcing me to obedience —

THE MAYOR. I had to; you gave me no choice.

DR. STOCKMANN. So you expect me to recant in public.

THE MAYOR. We consider it imperative that you issue a statement along the lines indicated.

DR. STOCKMANN. And what if I refuse?

THE MAYOR. Then — in order to reassure the public — we shall have to issue a statement ourselves.

DR. STOCKMANN. Very well. I shall attack you in the newspapers; I shall use every means to prove that I am right and that you are wrong. What do you say to that?

THE MAYOR. In that case I shall not be able to prevent your dismissal.

DR. STOCKMANN. What — !

PETRA. Dismissal! Father!

MRS. STOCKMANN. Dismissal!

THE MAYOR. I shall be obliged to advise the Board to give you

your notice and to see that you have no further connection
with the Baths.

DR. STOCKMANN. You would dare do that!

THE MAYOR. It is you who force me to it.

PETRA. Uncle! This is a disgraceful way to treat a man like
Father!

MRS. STOCKMANN. Do be quiet, Petra!

THE MAYOR (*looking at Petra*). So! We already presume to
have opinions, do we? I suppose it's only natural. (*To Mrs.
Stockmann*) Sister-in-law, you seem to be the only sensible
member of this household. I advise you to use what
influence you have on your husband; try and make him
realize what this will mean both for his family —

DR. STOCKMANN. My family is my own concern!

THE MAYOR. I repeat — both for his family, and for the town
he lives in.

DR. STOCKMANN. I'm the one who has the good of the town at
heart — you know that perfectly well! This my hometown
and I love it. That's why I want to expose this dangerous
situation that, sooner or later, must come to light.

THE MAYOR. And in order to prove your love for it you insist
on destroying the town's one hope of prosperity?

DR. STOCKMANN. But it's a *false* hope, man! Are you mad? Do
you want the town to grow rich by selling filth and poison?
Must its prosperity be founded on a lie?

THE MAYOR. That's worse than nonsense — it's downright
libelous! Only an enemy of Society could insinuate such
things against his native town.

DR. STOCKMANN (*steps towards him*). You dare to — !

MRS. STOCKMANN (*throws herself between them*). Tomas!

PETRA (*seizes her father's arm*). Steady, Father!

THE MAYOR. I refuse to expose myself to violence. You've
been warned. I advise you to remember what you owe to
yourself and to your family. Good-bye. (*He goes.*)

DR. STOCKMANN. They expect me to put up with that kind of
treatment, do they? And in my own house too! What do you
say to that, Katrine?

MRS. STOCKMANN. It's disgraceful, Tomas, I know — it's
shameful —

PETRA. I wish I could have a talk with Uncle — !

DR. STOCKMANN. I suppose it's my own fault; I should have stood up to them long ago — held my own — defied them! An enemy of Society, am I? I'm damned if I'll put up with that!

MRS. STOCKMANN. Remember, Tomas — your brother has the power on his side —

DR. STOCKMANN. But I have the right on mine!

MRS. STOCKMANN. The right — yes, I daresay; but what good is right against might?

PETRA. Mother! How can you talk like that!

DR. STOCKMANN. Might, might! Don't talk nonsense, Katrine. In a free society to be *right* is what counts! I have the free press behind me, and the solid majority on my side — you heard what Aslaksen said. Isn't that might enough for you?

MRS. STOCKMANN. But, Tomas — you're surely not thinking of — ?

DR. STOCKMANN. Of what?

MRS. STOCKMANN. Of going against your brother's wishes?

DR. STOCKMANN. What the devil do you expect me to do? What else *can* I do if I'm to stick up for what's honest and right?

PETRA. That's what I'd like to know!

MRS. STOCKMANN. But you know it won't be of any use! If they won't do it — they won't!

DR. STOCKMANN. Just give me time, Katrine. I'll succeed in the end — you'll see.

MRS. STOCKMANN. You'll succeed in getting dismissed — that's what it'll end with.

DR. STOCKMANN. In any case I shall have done my duty to Society — even though I am supposed to be its enemy!

MRS. STOCKMANN. But what about your family, Tomas? What about those dependent on you? Would you be doing your duty to us?

PETRA. Oh, do stop putting us first, Mother!

MRS. STOCKMANN. It's all very well for you to talk — you can manage alone, if need be. But what about the boys, Tomas? And yourself? And me?

DR. STOCKMANN. You must be stark, raving mad, Katrine! If

I were such a coward as to kowtow to Peter and his blasted
crew — do you think I'd ever again have a moment's
happiness?

MRS. STOCKMANN. I don't know about that; but God preserve
us from the sort of happiness we'll have if you persist in
defying them! We'll have nothing to live on; you'll be job-
less, penniless — just as you were in the old days. We can't
go through that again! Be sensible, Tomas; think of the
consequences!

DR. STOCKMANN (*struggling with himself and clenching his
hands*). It's disgraceful that these damned bureaucrats
should be able to do this to a free, honorable man! Don't
you agree, Katrine?

MRS. STOCKMANN. They've treated you abominably — there's
no doubt about that. But there's so much injustice in the
world — one must just put up with it. Think of the boys,
Tomas! Look at them! What's to become of them? You
surely wouldn't have the heart to —

[*Ejlif and Morten have entered while she speaks; they
carry their schoolbooks.*]

DR. STOCKMANN. The boys — ! (*Firmly and decisively*) I don't
care if the whole world crumbles, I refuse to be a slave to
any man! (*He goes towards his study.*)

MRS. STOCKMANN (*follows him*). Tomas! What are you going
to do?

DR. STOCKMANN (*at the door*). When my boys grow up to be
free men, I want to be able to look them in the face! (*He
goes into his study.*)

MRS. STOCKMANN (*bursting into tears*). God help us all!

PETRA. Father's wonderful, Mother! He'll never give in!

CURTAIN

QUESTIONS

1. What is Morten Kiil's motive for supporting Stockmann's fight?
How do Kiil's motives differ from editor Hovstad's? Is the difference
significant?

2. With what single word does Aslaksen seek to identify himself? What impression does Aslaksen make on you? Is there any hint that he does not live in accordance with his professions of alcoholic abstinence?

3. How do Mrs. Stockmann and Petra differ in their feelings about Dr. Stockmann's campaign against the baths? What concerns are most important to Mrs. Stockmann? Are they appropriate for her role in the family?

4. Why is Dr. Stockmann so confident that his cause will prevail? Why is he willing to sacrifice his sons' future, if that is necessary?

5. Is the ending of Act Two dramatically effective? Explain. With what new questions will you approach Act Three?

ACT THREE

SCENE: *The editorial office of* The People's Monitor. *The entrance door is in the background to the left; in the same wall to the right another door with glass panes, through which can be seen the composing room.[6] A door in the wall right. A large table stands in the middle of the room covered with papers, newspapers and books. Down left a window and by it a desk with a high stool. A couple of armchairs by the table; other chairs along the walls. The room is dingy and cheerless, the furniture old and the armchairs dirty and torn. In the composing room some printers can be seen at work; further back a hand press is in operation.*

Hovstad is seated at the desk writing. In a few moments Billing enters from the door right, with the doctor's manuscript in his hand.

BILLING. Well, I must say — !

HOVSTAD (*still writing*). Have you read it?

BILLING (*laying the ms.[7] on the desk*). I have indeed!

HOVSTAD. The doctor has courage, hasn't he? It's a strong statement!

BILLING. Strong! Strike me dead — it's positively crushing! Every word has the impact of a sledgehammer.

[6]*composing room:* room in a printing establishment where type is set.
[7] *ms:* manuscript.

HOVSTAD. It'll take more than one blow to knock those fellows out.

BILLING. That's true enough; but we'll keep on pounding at them and one of these days they'll come crashing down. As I sat there reading that article, I could almost hear the revolution thundering in the distance.

HOVSTAD (*turning round*). Careful! Don't let Aslaksen hear that.

BILLING. Aslaksen is a chickenhearted milksop — he hasn't an ounce of manly feeling in him! But you'll insist on having your own way this time, won't you? You'll definitely use the doctor's statement?

HOVSTAD. If the Mayor doesn't give in — yes.

BILLING. It'd be a damn nuisance if he did!

HOVSTAD. Well — fortunately we're bound to gain by the situation in any case. If the Mayor doesn't agree to the doctor's proposition, he'll have all the little people on his neck — the Homeowners Association, and all the rest of them. And if he does agree to it, all the rich people will be up in arms; all the people who've hitherto been his chief supporters — including of course those who have the biggest investment in the Baths —

BILLING. Yes; I suppose it would cost them a pretty penny to make the alterations —

HOVSTAD. There's no doubt of that! And once the reactionary part is split up, we can continue to expose the Mayor's total inefficiency and convince the public that the Liberals must be brought to power, for the general good of the community.

BILLING. Strike me dead if that isn't the truth! I feel it — I feel it — the revolution is approaching!

[*A knock at the door.*]

HOVSTAD. Hush! (*Calls out.*) Come in!

[*Dr. Stockmann enters from the door upper left.*]

HOVSTAD (*going to meet him*). Ah, here's the doctor now. Well?

DR. STOCKMANN. You may go ahead and print it, Mr. Hovstad.

HOVSTAD. So it's really come to that, has it?

BILLING. Hurrah!

DR. STOCKMANN. Yes — it's come to that; so print away, I say! They've asked for war, now let them have it.

BILLING. War to the death, I hope; war to the death!

DR. STOCKMANN. This first article is only the beginning; I have four or five others in mind — my head's bursting with ideas. Where's Aslaksen?

BILLING (*calling into the printing room*). Oh, Aslaksen! Come here a minute, will you!

HOVSTAD. Four or five others, you say? On the same subject?

DR. STOCKMANN. Oh, by no means; they'll deal with quite different matters. They all stem from the waterworks and the sewerage system, of course — one thing leads to another. It's exactly like trying to patch up an old building.

BILLING. Strike me dead — that's the truth! You do a bit here and a bit there, but the whole thing's so rotten, you end by tearing it down!

ASLAKSEN (*enters from the printing room*). Tearing down! Surely, Doctor, you're not thinking of tearing down the Baths!

HOVSTAD. No, of course not; you needn't be alarmed.

DR. STOCKMANN. We were talking about something quite different. Well — what do you think of my article, Mr. Hovstad?

HOVSTAD. I think it's an absolute masterpiece —

DR. STOCKMANN. Yes, isn't it — ? I'm so glad you agree!

HOVSTAD. It's clear and to the point — anyone could follow it; there's no need to be a specialist. You'll have every intelligent man on your side.

ASLAKSEN. And the prudent ones as well, I hope.

BILLING. Prudent — and imprudent too! Pretty nearly the whole town in fact —

ASLAKSEN. In that case, I think we might safely venture to print it.

DR. STOCKMANN. Well — I should hope so!

HOVSTAD. It'll be in tomorrow morning.

DR. STOCKMANN. Splendid! There's no time to lose, you know. By the way, Mr. Aslaksen, there's one thing I'd like to ask you; you'll supervise the printing of the article yourself, won't you?

ASLAKSEN. Indeed I will.

DR. STOCKMANN. It's very precious, remember. We don't want any errors; every word is important. I'll drop in again presently — you might let me see a proof.[8] I can't wait to have the thing in print — to get it launched.

BILLING. It'll be a bombshell!

DR. STOCKMANN. I want every enlightened citizen to read it and judge for himself. You've no idea what I've been through today. I've been exposed to every kind of pressure; my rights as an individual have been threatened —

BILLING. Your rights — !

DR. STOCKMANN. Yes! I was expected to crawl and humble myself. My deepest — my most sacred convictions were to be sacrificed for purely personal ends —

BILLING. Strike me dead! This is an outrage!

DR. STOCKMANN. But this time they've gone too far — and they shall be told so in no uncertain terms! I shall set up my headquarters here at *The People's Monitor* and continue to attack them daily —

ASLAKSEN. But, just a minute —

BILLING. Hurrah! It's war — war!

DR. STOCKMANN. I'll run them into the ground; smash them to pieces — wipe them out! I'll show the public what they really are — that's what I'll do!

ASLAKSEN. But you will use moderation, my dear Doctor; attack — but prudently.

BILLING. No! Don't spare the dynamite!

DR. STOCKMANN. It's no longer merely a question of sewers and waterworks, you see; it's a question of cleaning up the whole community —

BILLING. That's the way to talk!

DR. STOCKMANN. All those old fogies must be kicked out of office, no matter what position they may hold. I have such a clear perspective on everything today; I don't see all the details yet, but I'll soon work them out. What we need, my friends, is young and vital leaders — new captains at the outposts.

BILLING. Hear, hear!

DR. STOCKMANN. If we stand together, we're bound to win. This whole revolution will be launched quite smoothly —

[8] **proof:** trial set of printed pages, used for checking accuracy.

like a new ship gliding down the ways. Don't you believe
that?

HOVSTAD. I believe we have every hope of putting the right
people into power at last.

ASLAKSEN. And if we proceed with caution, I see no reason
why we should run into any danger.

DR. STOCKMANN. Who the hell cares about danger! This is a
matter of truth and conscience!

HOVSTAD. You deserve every support, Doctor.

ASLAKSEN. Dr. Stockmann is a true friend of the town; a
friend of Society — that's what he is.

BILLING. Strike me dead! He's a friend of the People, Aslaksen!

ASLAKSEN. I'm sure the Homeowners Association will use
that as a slogan.

DR. STOCKMANN. My dear friends — I can't thank you enough
for all your loyalty; it does me good to hear you. My sainted
brother called me something very different; but he'll be
repaid — with interest! I'll be off now — I have to see a poor
devil of a patient — but I'll be back. Take good care of my
article, won't you, Mr. Aslaksen? And don't cut out any
exclamation marks! You can even add a few if you like!
Well — good-bye for now; I'll be back shortly. Good-bye.

[*General good-byes as they accompany him to the door;
he goes.*]

HOVSTAD. He can be exceedingly useful to us.

ASLAKSEN. Yes, providing he sticks to this matter of the Baths;
if he goes beyond that, it might be unwise to follow him.

HOVSTAD. Hm; it all depends on —

BILLING. You're always so damned frightened, Aslaksen.

ASLAKSEN. Frightened? Yes, when it comes to attacking the
local authorities, I am frightened, Mr. Billing. I've learned
in a hard school, you see. National politics, however, are
another matter; in such things you wouldn't find me frightened, I assure you — even if you were to pit me against the
Government itself.

BILLING. I daresay not; that's where you're so inconsistent.

ASLAKSEN. Where the good of the town is concerned, I am
very conscientious. There's no harm in attacking the Gov-

ernment — what does the Government care? Those men at the top are unassailable. But the local authorities are different — they can be dismissed; and should their power fall into the hands of inexperienced men, not only the Homeowners but the entire community would suffer.

HOVSTAD. If the People are never allowed self-government, how can they ever gain experience? Haven't you thought of that?

ASLAKSEN. When one has vested interests, Mr. Hovstad, one must protect them. A man can't think of everything.

HOVSTAD. Vested interests! Then I hope I never have any!

BILLING. Hear, hear!

ASLAKSEN (*with a smile*). Hm. (*Points to the desk.*) There was a time when Commissioner Stensgaard sat in that editor's chair, if you remember.

BILLING (*spitting*). Pooh! That turncoat!

HOVSTAD. Well — I'm no weathercock,[9] and never will be!

ASLAKSEN. A politician should never say "never" about anything, Mr. Hovstad. And as for you, Mr. Billing — I understand you've applied for the post of secretary to the Town Council; hadn't you better use a little caution?

BILLING. I — !

HOVSTAD. Billing — is this true?

BILLING. As a matter of fact, it is. I'm only doing it to spite the Bigwigs, mind you!

ASLAKSEN. Well — it's no business of mine. I may be accused of cowardice and inconsistency, but my political record is an open book. I've never changed in any way — except, possibly, to become more moderate. My heart is, and always has been, with the People; I must admit, however, that my common sense inclines me towards the side of the authorities, to some extent; the local authorities, I mean. (*He goes into the printing office.*)

BILLING. Shouldn't we try and get rid of him, Hovstad?

HOVSTAD. Do you know of anybody else who'd be willing to pay our expenses?

BILLING. It's damnable to have no capital!

---

[9] **I'm no weathercock:** Hovstad is saying he doesn't turn, like a weathervane, with every political wind that blows.

HOVSTAD (*sits down at the desk*). Yes; we'd be all right if we had that!

BILLING. Why don't you talk to Dr. Stockmann?

HOVSTAD (*looking through some papers*). What good would that do? He hasn't a penny.

BILLING. No — but he has connections; old Morten Kiil — "the badger" as they call him.

HOVSTAD (*writing*). You really think he has money?

BILLING. Strike me dead — of course he has! And Stockmann's family is bound to get part of it. The old man's sure to provide for — for the children, at any rate.

HOVSTAD (*half turning*). Are you counting on that?

BILLING. What do you mean — "counting?" You know I never count on anything.

HOVSTAD. You're wise. And you'd better not count on that job as secretary either; I assure you, you won't get it.

BILLING. Do you suppose I don't know that? That's the very reason I've applied for it. A slight of that sort fires the spirit of rebellion in one — gives one a fresh supply of vitriol,[10] as it were; and that's a very necessary thing in a god-forsaken hole like this where nothing really stimulating ever seems to happen.

HOVSTAD (*still writing*). Yes, yes; I know, I know.

BILLING. But — one of these days they'll hear from me, I promise you! — Well — I'd better go in and write that appeal to the Homeowners Association. (*He goes into the room on the right.*)

HOVSTAD (*at the desk: he bites the end of his penholder and says slowly*). Hm. — I see. — So that's it. (*A knock at the door*). Come in!

[*Petra enters from the back, left.*]

HOVSTAD (*rising*). Well! It's you, is it? What are you doing here?

PETRA. You must excuse me for —

HOVSTAD (*pushes an armchair forward*). Do sit down.

PETRA. No thanks; I can only stay a minute.

HOVSTAD. Is it a message from your father — ?

[10] **vitriol:** hostility.

PETRA. No, I've come on my own account. (*Takes a book out of her coat pocket.*) I've brought back that English story.

HOVSTAD. Brought it back — why?

PETRA. Because I don't want to translate it after all.

HOVSTAD. But you gave me a definite promise —

PETRA. I know; but I hadn't read it then. You haven't read it, have you?

HOVSTAD. No — I don't read English; but —

PETRA. That's what I thought; so I felt I should advise you to look around for something else. (*Putting the book on the table*) This would never do for *The People's Monitor*.

HOVSTAD. Why not?

PETRA. Because it's against everything you stand for.

HOVSTAD. Well, as far as that goes —

PETRA. No — you don't see my point; this story claims that there's a supernatural power looking after all the so-called good people in the world, so that everything turns out well for them in the end — whereas all the so-called bad people get punished.

HOVSTAD. Splendid! Just what the public wants.

PETRA. Yes; but you surely wouldn't want to be the one to give them such nonsense. You don't believe a word of it yourself; you know perfectly well that's not the way things really happen.

HOVSTAD. You're right, of course; but, you see, a publisher can't always do as he pleases — he often has to cater to the public in minor matters. Politics, after all, are the main thing — to a newspaper at any rate; if I want to steer people towards a more liberal way of thinking, I can't afford to scare them off. If they come across a nice moral tale like that tucked away somewhere in the back pages of the paper they feel safer, and they're more willing to accept what we give them on the front page.

PETRA. But that's disgusting! I'm sure you'd never play a trick like that. You're not a hypocrite!

HOVSTAD (*smiling*). I'm glad you think so well of me. As a matter of fact it's Billing's idea, not mine.

PETRA. Billing's!

HOVSTAD. Yes; at least he was talking along those lines only

the other day. It was Billing who wanted to print the story;
I don't know anything about it.

PETRA. Mr. Billing! But that seems impossible; he has such a
modern point of view!

HOVSTAD. Well, you see — Billing is a man of many parts.
He's now decided he wants to become secretary to the
Town Council — or so I hear.

PETRA. I don't believe that for a moment, Mr. Hovstad. He
could never lower himself to that!

HOVSTAD. You'd better ask him about it.

PETRA. I never would have thought such a thing of Mr.
Billing.

HOVSTAD (*looks at her intently*). No? Is it really such a surprise to you?

PETRA. Yes, indeed it is. And yet — perhaps it isn't really. I
don't know what to think —

HOVSTAD. We newspapermen are worthless fellows, Miss
Petra.

PETRA. Do you really mean that?

HOVSTAD. Yes; at least, I sometimes think so.

PETRA. That may be true as far as ordinary petty everyday
matters are concerned. But now that you're involved in a
great cause —

HOVSTAD. You mean this business about your father?

PETRA. Yes, of course. It must give you a proud feeling; a
sense of being worth more than just ordinary people.

HOVSTAD. You're right; I do feel a bit like that today.

PETRA. I'm sure you must. What a wonderful career you've
chosen! To be a pioneer; to promote the truth; to fight for
bold ideas — new ways of thinking! The mere fact of
coming to the defense of someone who's been wronged —

HOVSTAD. Especially when that someone is — I don't quite
know how to put it —

PETRA. When he's so true and honorable, you mean?

HOVSTAD (*in a low voice*). Yes; and especially when he
happens to be your father.

PETRA (*suddenly taken aback*). You mean — ? Oh, no!

HOVSTAD. Yes, Petra — Miss Petra.

PETRA. Is that your reason — ? Is that what matters most to
you? Then, it isn't the thing itself; the truth means nothing

to you — and my father's generosity of soul means nothing either!

HOVSTAD. Yes, of course it does, but —

PETRA. Thank you, Mr. Hovstad. You've said more than enough. I shall never trust you again in anything.

HOVSTAD. Come now — you mustn't be too hard on me! Even if it is mainly for your sake —

PETRA. What makes me angry is that you haven't been honest with my father. You let him think you were concerned with the truth, with the good of the community, when all the time — ! You've made fools of us both, Mr. Hovstad. You're not at all the sort of man you pretended to be. I shall never forgive you for it — never!

HOVSTAD. I wouldn't be too caustic, Miss Petra; this is not the time for that.

PETRA. Not the time? Why not?

HOVSTAD. Because your father can't very well get on without my help.

PETRA. I see. So you're that sort of a person too.

HOVSTAD. No, no — really I'm not! I didn't think what I was saying; you must believe me!

PETRA. I know what to believe, I assure you. Good-bye.

ASLAKSEN (*enters hurriedly and mysteriously from the printing office*). Hell and damnation, Mr. Hovstad — ! (*Sees Petra.*) Oh, I beg your pardon —

PETRA. There's the book. Get someone else to do it for you. (*Goes towards the main entrance.*)

HOVSTAD (*following her*). But, Miss Petra —

PETRA. Good-bye. (*She goes.*)

ASLAKSEN. Mr. Hovstad, listen!

HOVSTAD. Well — what is it? What's the matter?

ASLAKSEN. It's the Mayor! He's out in the printing office.

HOVSTAD. The Mayor?

ASLAKSEN. Yes; he says he wants to talk to you. He came in the back way — didn't want to be seen, I suppose.

HOVSTAD. What does this mean, I wonder? Wait a minute — I'll go myself — (*He goes toward the printing office, opens the door, bows and invites the Mayor to come in.*)

HOVSTAD. Be on the lookout, Aslaksen, and see that no one —

ASLAKSEN. I understand — (*He goes into the printing office.*)

THE MAYOR. I don't suppose you expected to see me here, Mr. Hovstad.

HOVSTAD. No, I can't say I did.

THE MAYOR (*looking round*). A nice place you have here; most comfortable.

HOVSTAD. Well —

THE MAYOR. You must forgive me for dropping in like this, and taking up your time.

HOVSTAD. I'm only too delighted, Mr. Mayor; always at your service. Let me take your things — (*Takes the Mayor's hat and cane and puts them on a chair.*) And now — won't you sit down?

THE MAYOR (*sits by the table*). Thanks. (*Hovstad sits down at the table also.*) I've been faced with — with a very troubling matter today, Mr. Hovstad.

HOVSTAD. Really? But, of course, you must have so many duties —

THE MAYOR. It concerns my brother, Mr. Hovstad.

HOVSTAD. Dr. Stockmann?

THE MAYOR. Yes. He's written a sort of memorandum to the directors of the Baths, alleging that there are certain defects in the establishment.

HOVSTAD. Really? Has he?

THE MAYOR. Hasn't he told you? I thought he said —

HOVSTAD. Now I come to think of it, I believe he did mention —

ASLAKSEN (*enters from the printing office*). I'd better have that manuscript —

HOVSTAD (*with annoyance*). It's over on the desk.

ASLAKSEN. Ah, yes — here it is.

THE MAYOR. But surely — Isn't that — ?

ALAKSEN. It's Dr. Stockmann's article.

HOVSTAD. Oh — was that what you were referring to?

THE MAYOR. Precisely — What do you think of it?

HOVSTAD. I've only just glanced at it — and, of course, I'm not an expert —

THE MAYOR. And yet you intend to print it?

HOVSTAD. I can't very well refuse anything signed by —

ASLAKSEN. I've nothing to do with editing the paper, Mr. Mayor.

THE MAYOR. No, of course not.

ASLAKSEN. I just do the printing.

THE MAYOR. I understand.

ASLAKSEN. So — if you'll excuse me — (*Goes towards the pressroom.*)

THE MAYOR. Just one moment, Mr. Aslaksen. With your permission, Mr. Hovstad — ?

HOVSTAD. Of course.

THE MAYOR. Mr. Aslaksen — you seem to me to be a discreet and sensible man.

ASLAKSEN. It's very kind of you to say so —

THE MAYOR. And a man of widespread influence too.

ASLAKSEN. Only among the little people, Your Honor.

THE MAYOR. It's the small taxpayers who form the majority — here, as everywhere.

ASLAKSEN. That's true enough.

THE MAYOR. And I've no doubt you are familiar with the general trend of sentiment among them. Are you not?

ASLAKSEN. I think I may say I am, Your Honor.

THE MAYOR. Well — since there appears to be such a fine feeling of self-sacrifice among the poorer classes —

ASLAKSEN. How do you mean?

HOVSTAD. Self-sacrifice?

THE MAYOR. It indicates an admirable sense of public spirit. I find it a little surprising, I admit; but then I don't know the public sentiment as well as you do.

ASLAKSEN. But, Your Honor —

THE MAYOR. And it will entail no small sacrifice to the town, I can assure you.

HOVSTAD. To the town?

ASLAKSEN. I don't understand; surely, this concerns the Baths —

THE MAYOR. At a rough preliminary estimate, the alterations Dr. Stockmann has in mind will cost in the neighborhood of two hundred thousand crowns.

ASLAKSEN. That's a lot of money; but —

THE MAYOR. A municipal loan will naturally be necessary.

HOVSTAD (*rising*). You surely can't mean that the town — ?

ALAKSEN. You mean the townspeople would have to pay for it out of their own pockets?

THE MAYOR. My dear Mr. Aslaksen, where else should the money come from?

ASLAKSEN. I should think the owners of the Baths would be responsible.

THE MAYOR. The owners are not prepared to increase their investment at this time.

ASLAKSEN. Are you quite sure of that?

THE MAYOR. I have positive information to that effect. So if these alterations are to be made, the town itself will have to pay for them.

ASLAKSEN. But then, damn it all, Mr. Hovstad — excuse me, Your Honor — this puts the matter in quite a different light!

HOVSTAD. It does indeed.

THE MAYOR. The worst part of it is we shall be obliged to close down the Baths for a couple of years.

HOVSTAD. Close them? Completely close them?

ASLAKSEN. For two years!

THE MAYOR. Yes; it will take at least two years to do the work.

ASLAKSEN. But, damn it! We could never survive that, Your Honor; we homeowners depend on these visitors — what are we to live on in the meantime?

THE MAYOR. That is a difficult question to answer, Mr. Aslaksen. But what's to be done? Once people get this notion into their heads that the waters are tainted, that the whole place is a pesthole — we can hardly expect them to come here.

ASLAKSEN. Then you think it's no more than a notion?

THE MAYOR. Try as I will, I can't persuade myself to think otherwise.

ASLAKSEN. Then it's downright inexcusable of Dr. Stockmann — I beg pardon, Your Honor, but —

THE MAYOR. Unfortunately you're quite right, Mr. Aslaksen; my brother has always been an exceedingly rash man.

ASLAKSEN. And yet you are prepared to back him up in this, Mr. Hovstad!

HOVSTAD. But, who would ever have thought that — !

THE MAYOR. I've drawn up a short statement on the matter, interpreting the facts from a more rational point of view;

I've also indicated ways in which any small defects that might conceivably exist can be taken care of within the scope of the present financial budget.

HOVSTAD. Have you it with you?

THE MAYOR (*feeling in his pocket*). Yes; I thought I'd better bring it in case you —

ASLAKSEN (*quickly*). Damn it — there he is!

THE MAYOR. Who? My brother?

HOVSTAD. Where?

ASLAKSEN. Coming through the pressroom.

THE MAYOR. This is unfortunate! I don't want to run into him here — yet there are several things I'd still like to talk to you about.

HOVSTAD (*pointing to the door on the right*). Wait in there for a moment.

THE MAYOR. But — ?

HOVSTAD. There's no one in there but Billing.

ASLAKSEN. Quick, Your Honor! Here he comes!

THE MAYOR. Very well; get rid of him as soon as you can, though. (*He goes out by the door right which Aslaksen opens, and closes after him.*)

HOVSTAD. Pretend to be busy, Aslaksen. (*He sits down and starts to write. Aslaksen goes through a pile of newspapers on a chair, right.*)

DR. STOCKMANN (*enters from the composing room*). Well — Here I am, back again. (*Puts down his hat and stick.*)

HOVSTAD (*writing*). Already, Doctor? Get on with what we were just talking about, Aslaksen. We've no time to waste today.

DR. STOCKMANN (*to Aslaksen*). No proofs yet, I hear.

ASLAKSEN (*without turning round*). You could hardly expect them yet, Doctor.

DR. STOCKMANN. No, of course not. It's just that I'm impatient — you can understand that; I can't wait to see the thing in print.

HOVSTAD. It'll be another hour at least; wouldn't you say so, Aslaksen?

ASLAKSEN. I'm afraid so, yes.

DR. STOCKMANN. Never mind; I'll come back. I don't mind

coming back twice if need be. What's a little inconvenience compared to the welfare of the town — ! (*Starts to go but stops and comes back.*) By the way, there's something I must discuss with you.

HOVSTAD. I'm afraid, just now, you must excuse me, Doctor —

DR. STOCKMANN. It'll only take a moment. I was just thinking: when people read this article of mine tomorrow morning, and realize I devoted my whole winter to working for the good of the town —

HOVSTAD. But, after all, Doctor —

DR. STOCKMANN. Oh, I know what you're going to say — it was no more than my duty as a citizen — I know that as well as you do. But my fellow townsmen — well, bless their hearts, they're so fond of me, you see —

ASLAKSEN. Yes — they've thought very highly of you up to now —

DR. STOCKMANN. I know; that's why I'm so afraid they might — what I mean is this: the people, especially the poorer classes, are bound to take this article of mine as a rousing call to action — as a summons to run things for themselves from now on —

HOVSTAD (*rising*). As a matter of fact, Doctor, I think I ought to tell you —

DR. STOCKMANN. I knew it! I was sure they'd be up to something. But I won't hear of it, I tell you! So if they're planning anything like that —

HOVSTAD. Like what?

DR. STOCKMANN. Oh, I don't know — a parade, or a banquet, or a testimonial dinner of some sort — I count on you to put a stop to it. You, too, Mr. Aslaksen — remember now!

HOVSTAD. Excuse me, Doctor, I think you'd better know the truth once and for all —

[*Mrs. Stockmann enters from the rear door, left.*]

MRS. STOCKMANN (*seeing the doctor*). Just as I thought!

HOVSTAD (*goes towards her*). You here too, Mrs. Stockmann?

DR. STOCKMANN. What the devil do you want here, Katrine?

MRS. STOCKMANN. You know very well what I want.

HOVSTAD. Won't you sit down? Or perhaps you'd rather —

MRS. STOCKMANN. Thanks — but please don't bother about me; and forgive my coming here to fetch my husband. I'm the mother of three children, let me tell you.

DR. STOCKMANN. Don't talk nonsense! As if we didn't all know that!

MRS. STOCKMANN. You don't seem to be giving much thought to it — otherwise you wouldn't be so anxious to ruin us all!

DR. STOCKMANN. You must be stark raving mad, Katrine! Just because he has a wife and children, can't a man stand up for the truth? Be a useful citizen? Serve the town he lives in?

MRS. STOCKMANN. If you'd only use a little moderation, Tomas!

ASLAKSEN. That's what I always say: everything in moderation!

MRS. STOCKMANN. It's very wrong of you, Mr. Hovstad, to lure my husband away from house and home; persuading him to get mixed up in all this — making a fool of him!

HOVSTAD. I don't make a fool of anyone —

DR. STOCKMANN. A fool! You think I let people make a fool of me!

MRS. STOCKMANN. Yes, Tomas — you do! Oh, I know you're the cleverest man in town, but you're easily fooled all the same. (*To Hovstad*) Don't you realize he'll lose his position if you print that article of his —

ASLAKSEN. What!

HOVSTAD. As a matter of fact, Dr. Stockmann —

DR. STOCKMANN (*laughing*). They can't do a thing to me — they'd never dare! Don't forget, my dear, the solid majority is with me.

MRS. STOCKMANN. More's the pity. You'd be better off without it!

DR. STOCKMANN. Don't talk nonsense, Katrine; go home and tend to your housework and leave Society to me. What is there to be afraid of? Can't you see how happy and confident I am? (*Rubs his hands and walks up and down.*) The truth will conquer — I'm convinced of it. The people will band together in the cause of truth and freedom, and nothing can stop them — ! (*Stops suddenly by a chair.*) Why — what the devil's this doing here?

ASLAKSEN (*realizing*). Oh, Lord.

HOVSTAD (*the same*). Hm —

DR. STOCKMANN (*he picks up the Mayor's cap and holds it gingerly aloft*). The crown of authority, is it not?

MRS. STOCKMANN. It's the Mayor's cap!

DR. STOCKMANN. And the staff of office, too! But what the devil are they doing here?

HOVSTAD. You might as well know —

DR. STOCKMANN. Ah, I see! He came to try and win you over. Well — he chose the wrong customer for once! I suppose he caught sight of me in the office and — (*Bursts out laughing.*) Did he turn tail, Mr. Aslaksen?

ASLAKSEN (*hurriedly*). Yes, Doctor, he — he turned tail.

DR. STOCKMANN. Ran off and left his stick and — But, wait a minute — that's not a bit like Peter. What have you done with him? Oh, of course — he's hiding in there. Now you're going to see something, Katrine!

MRS. STOCKMANN. Please, Tomas — !

ASLAKSEN. Be careful, Doctor!

[*Dr. Stockmann has put on the Mayor's cap and seized his stick; he goes to the door, flings it open and makes a military salute. The Mayor enters, flushed with anger, followed by Billing.*]

THE MAYOR. What is the meaning of these antics?

DR. STOCKMANN. Show some respect, Peter, if you please. (*Struts up and down.*) I'm in authority now!

MRS. STOCKMANN (*almost in tears*). Tomas — for heaven's sake!

THE MAYOR (*following him*). Give me my cap and stick!

DR. STOCKMANN (*as before*). You may be chief of police, but I'm the Mayor — I'm king of the whole town!

THE MAYOR. Take off that cap, I tell you. Don't you realize it's a badge of office!

DR. STOCKMANN. Listen to him! We've roused the spirit of democracy — do you think a bit of gold braid can frighten me? Tomorrow the revolution starts, I'd have you know. You threatened to dismiss me, did you? Well, now it's my turn to dismiss you — I'm going to kick you out of office! And if you don't think I can do it, you'll soon find out! The power is on my side — the power of an aroused public! Hovstad and Billing here will thunder away at you in the *Monitor,* and Aslaksen will lead the entire Homeowners Association into battle — !

ASLAKSEN. No, Doctor; I'll do nothing of the sort.

DR. STOCKMANN. Nonsense! Of course you will —

THE MAYOR. I see; so perhaps Mr. Hovstad will decide to join the rebels after all?

HOVSTAD. No, Your Honor.

ASLAKSEN. Mr. Hovstad's no fool; he's not likely to ruin both himself and the paper for the sake of a delusion.

DR. STOCKMANN (*looks from one to the other*). What does this mean?

HOVSTAD. You've presented this whole matter in a false light, Doctor; that is why I cannot possibly give you my support.

BILLING. After what the Mayor so kindly explained to me just now —

DR. STOCKMANN. A false light, eh? Leave that part of it to me — you just print my article; I'll prove the truth of every word of it.

HOVSTAD. I shall not print it. I neither can, nor will, nor dare.

DR. STOCKMANN. Not *dare?* But that's absurd. You're the editor, aren't you? Don't you control your own paper?

ASLAKSEN. No — the subscribers do.

THE MAYOR. Fortunately — yes.

ASLAKSEN. Public opinion, majority interests, the Homeowners Association and other similar groups — they control the paper.

DR. STOCKMANN (*calmly*). And they would all be against me, you think?

ASLAKSEN. Unquestionably. If your article were printed, it would mean the ruin of the town.

DR. STOCKMANN. I see.

THE MAYOR. And now, my cap and stick!

[*Dr. Stockmann takes off the cap and lays it on the table; he places the stick beside it.*]

THE MAYOR (*picking them up*). Your term of office came to rather an abrupt end, didn't it?

DR. STOCKMANN. This is not the end, Peter — believe me. (*To Hovstad*) So you find it impossible to print my article in the *Monitor?*

HOVSTAD. Quite impossible; apart from anything else, consideration for your family would —

DR. STOCKMANN. Kindly leave my family to me, Mr. Hovstad.

THE MAYOR (*takes a manuscript from his breast pocket*). This will put the necessary facts before the public. It is an official statement; I trust you to deal with it accordingly.

HOVSTAD (*taking the manuscript*). Very good. We shall take care of it; it will appear without delay.

DR. STOCKMANN. But mine will be suppressed. Do you think you can suppress the truth? You'll find it's not so easy! Mr. Aslaksen, please take my manuscript and print it as a pamphlet — at my own expense — I'll publish it myself. I want four hundred copies; no, five — better make it six.

ASLAKSEN. I can't possibly use my printing press for such a purpose, Doctor — not if you were to pay me its weight in gold. I dare not offend public opinion. No one in town will print it, I assure you.

DR. STOCKMANN. Then give it back to me.

HOVSTAD (*hands it to him*). Gladly.

DR. STOCKMANN (*takes up his hat and stick*). But you won't be able to suppress it all the same! I'll call a public meeting — I'll read it to the people myself; my fellow townsmen are going to hear the truth!

THE MAYOR. It won't be any good; not a single hall will be available to you.

ASLAKSEN. Not one — I'll vouch for that.

BILLING. That's true — strike me dead if it isn't!

MRS. STOCKMANN. But this is disgraceful, Tomas! Why are they suddenly all against you?

DR. STOCKMANN. I'll tell you why. It's because all the men in this town are a lot of old women — just like you! They think of nothing but themselves; they don't care a damn about the general good!

MRS. STOCKMANN. Then I'll show them here's at least one old woman who knows how to be a man. I'll stand by you, Tomas!

DR. STOCKMANN. Well said, Katrine! Nothing can stop me;

if I can't rent a hall, I'll hire a drum and march through the town with it. I'll read my statement at the corner of every street, of every square — the people are going to know the truth!

THE MAYOR. You can't do that! Are you a raving lunatic?

DR. STOCKMANN. Yes, I am!

ASLAKSEN. No one will go with you, Doctor Stockmann.

BILLING. Strike me dead — I'm sure of that!

MRS. STOCKMANN. Don't give in now, Tomas. I'll ask the boys — they'll go with you.

DR. STOCKMANN. That's a splendid thought!

MRS. STOCKMANN. Morten would be delighted — and I'm certain Ejlif would go too.

DR. STOCKMANN. Yes — and then there's Petra! And you, Katrine!

MRS. STOCKMANN. Oh, no; it wouldn't do for me to go. But I tell you what I'll do — I'll watch you from the window.

DR. STOCKMANN (*throws his arms round her*). Thanks! Well — the fight is on, gentlemen! We'll see if you and your chicanery[11] can prevent an honest citizen from cleaning up the town he lives in! Come, Katrine!

[*He and Mrs. Stockmann go out by the door upper left.*]

THE MAYOR (*shakes his head thoughtfully*). He's managed to turn her head at last! Now she's as mad as he is.

CURTAIN

QUESTIONS

1. How does Hovstad show hypocrisy as an editor? as a lover? What has been his real purpose in planning to expose the mismanagement of the baths? In what ways had he planned to use both Dr. Stockmann and Aslaksen?

2. The mayor finds the weak spot in each of Dr. Stockmann's supporters. What is it in the case of Aslaksen? Hovstad? What connection do you see between the characters of these men and the kind of schools Petra describes in Act One?

3. At what point in this act does Dr. Stockmann behave like a clown? How good a judge is he of men? How realistic is he in expecting to have

[11] **chicanery:** trickery.

the town's gratitude for his actions? Do you think Dr. Stockmann is motivated solely by unselfish principles, or may pride or a self-destructive impulse be driving him into the role of martyr? Is he a brave man? an egoist? some combination?

4. Why does Mrs. Stockmann come to the newspaper office? How does her outlook change once her husband is attacked by the others? Is this sudden change in attitude convincing?

ACT FOUR

SCENE: *A large, old-fashioned room in Captain Horster's house. Open double doors in the back wall lead to an anteroom. In the wall left are three windows; in the center of the opposite wall is a platform on which stands a small table with two candles, a carafe of water, a glass and a bell placed on it. Sconces*[12] *between the windows provide the general lighting. Down left a small table with a candle, and a chair beside it. Down right a door and near it a couple of chairs.*

There is a large gathering of townspeople of various types. Among the crowd are seen a few women and schoolboys. People continue to stream in from the anteroom until the main room is quite full.

FIRST MAN (*as he bumps into another one*). You're here too, are you, Lamstad?

SECOND MAN. I never miss a public meeting.

ANOTHER MAN. I see you've brought your whistle.

SECOND MAN. Of course; haven't you?

THIRD MAN. I should hope so! Skipper Evensen said he was going to bring his big horn!

SECOND MAN. That Evensen's a good one, he is!

[*Laughter in the group.*]

FOURTH MAN (*joining them*). Tell me — what's going on here this evening?

SECOND MAN. Doctor Stockmann and the Mayor are holding a debate.

FOURTH MAN. But the Mayor's his brother, isn't he?

[12] *Sconces:* wall brackets holding lights.

FIRST MAN. That makes no difference; Doctor Stockmann's not afraid of anyone.

THIRD MAN. But he's all wrong; it says so in the *Monitor*.

SECOND MAN. He must be wrong this time; no one would let him have a hall — not the Homeowners Association, nor the Citizens' Club either.

FIRST MAN. Even the Baths refused him.

SECOND MAN. That's not surprising.

A MAN (*in another group*). Whom do we support in this business?

ANOTHER MAN (*in the same group*). Just keep an eye on Aslaksen and do as he does.

BILLING (*with a portfolio under his arm pushes his way through the crowd*). Excuse me, gentlemen. May I get by please? I'm reporting for *The People's Monitor*. Thanks — thank you! (*He sits at the table left.*)

A WORKMAN. Who's he?

ANOTHER WORKMAN. Don't you know him? That's Billing — he writes for Aslaksen's paper.

[*Captain Horster ushers in Mrs. Stockmann and Petra through the door down right. Ejlif and Morten follow them.*]

CAPTAIN HORSTER. I thought this would be a good place for you to sit; it'll be easy for you to slip away if anything should happen.

MRS. STOCKMANN. Will there be any disturbance, do you think?

HORSTER. It's hard to say — with all these people. But don't be anxious — just sit here quietly.

MRS. STOCKMANN (*sitting down*). It was so kind of you to let Stockmann have the room.

HORSTER. Since nobody else would, I thought I —

PETRA (*who has also seated herself*). And it was brave of you too, Captain Horster.

HORSTER. I don't see anything specially brave about it.

[*Hovstad and Aslaksen enter at the same time, but separately, and make their way through the crowd.*]

ASLAKSEN (*going up to Horster*). Isn't Doctor Stockmann here yet?

HORSTER. He's waiting in there.

[*A movement in the crowd by the door at the back of the room.*]

HOVSTAD (*to Billing*). Here comes the Mayor! Look!

BILLING. Yes — strike me dead! So he's put in an appearance after all!

[*Mayor Stockmann advances graciously through the crowd, bowing to right and left. He takes his stand near the wall on the left. A moment later Dr. Stockmann enters from the door down right. He wears a black frock coat and a white tie. There is scattered applause countered by subdued hissing. Then, silence.*]

DR. STOCKMANN (*in a low tone*). How do you feel, Katrine?

MRS. STOCKMANN. I'm all right, thank you, dear. (*Whispers to him*) Don't lose your temper, Tomas!

DR. STOCKMANN. Don't worry — I'll keep myself in hand. (*Looks at his watch, mounts the platform and bows.*) It's a quarter past; I'm going to begin — (*Takes out his manuscript.*)

ASLAKSEN. Wait! We·must elect a chairman first.

DR. STOCKMANN. That won't be necessary.

SEVERAL GENTLEMEN (*shouting*). Yes! Yes!

THE MAYOR. By all means; of course we must have a chairman.

DR. STOCKMANN. But I've called this meeting to read a paper, Peter.

THE MAYOR. All the same — your paper is likely to cause discussion.

SEVERAL VOICES IN THE CROWD. A chairman! We want a chairman!

HOVSTAD. The general voice seems to be in favor of a chairman.

DR. STOCKMANN (*controlling himself*). Oh, very well — Let the "general voice" have its way.

ASLAKSEN. Perhaps the Mayor will honor us?

THREE GENTLEMEN (*clapping*). Bravo! Bravo!

THE MAYOR. Many thanks. But for various obvious reasons, I must decline. However, we are fortunate in having in our midst a man who, I am certain, will be acceptable to all.

I refer, of course, to the chairman of the Homeowners Association — Mr. Aslaksen.

MANY VOICES. Yes! Yes! Long live Aslaksen! Hurrah for Aslaksen!

[*Dr. Stockmann takes his manuscript and leaves the platform.*]

ASLAKSEN. Since my fellow citizens are pleased to show me this signal mark of confidence — who am I to refuse?

[*Applause and cheers. Aslaksen ascends the platform.*]

BILLING (*making notes*). Mr. Aslaksen elected by acclamation —

ASLAKSEN. And now — since I stand here as your chairman — allow me to say a few brief words to you. I am a quiet, peace-loving man, gentlemen; a man in favor of discreet moderation, and of — and of — moderate discretion. All those who know me are aware of that.

SEVERAL VOICES. Yes, yes! To be sure, Aslaksen!

ASLAKSEN. I have learned in the great common school of life and of experience that moderation is the citizen's prime virtue — a virtue from which he reaps the highest benefits —

THE MAYOR. Hear! Hear!

ASLAKSEN. — and that discretion and moderation are also the best servants of Society. Allow me therefore to suggest to our respected fellow citizen who has seen fit to call this meeting, that he take note; let us hope he will bend every effort to keep within the bounds of moderation.

A MAN (*by the door*). I propose a toast to the Temperance Society! Hurrah!

A VOICE. Shame! Shame!

VOICE. Sh! Quiet!

ASLAKSEN. No interruptions if you please, gentlemen! — Does anyone wish to offer any observations?

THE MAYOR. Mr. Chairman!

ASLAKSEN. The Mayor has the floor!

THE MAYOR. Because of my close relationship to the present medical adviser to the Baths — a relationship of which most of you are undoubtedly aware — I should have preferred not to speak here this evening. But my position as Chairman of the Board, as well as my deep concern for the wel-

fare of the town, force me to make this motion. I think I
may venture to assume that not a single soul here present
would condone the spreading of exaggerated and irrespon-
sible statements concerning the sanitary conditions of our
Baths and of our town.

MANY VOICES. No, no! Never! Certainly not! We protest!

THE MAYOR. I therefore move that this meeting pass the following resolution: Dr. Stockmann cannot be allowed to
read his paper or to address this assembly on this particular
subject.

DR. STOCKMANN (*flaring up*). Cannot be allowed — ! What do
you mean?

MRS. STOCKMANN (*coughing*). Hm, hm!

DR. STOCKMANN (*controlling himself*). So, I'm not to be allowed; I see.

THE MAYOR. I have acquainted the Public with the relevant
facts through my statement in *The People's Monitor,* so
that all right-thinking citizens may have no difficulty in
forming their own judgment. It will be clearly seen that
the doctor's report on the situation — apart from being a
direct vote of censure against the leading men in the community — simply means saddling the taxpayers with a
totally unnecessary outlay of at least one hundred thousand
crowns.

[*Cries of protest and scattered whistles.*]

ASLAKSEN (*rings the bell*). Order, order, gentlemen! I beg
to second the Mayor's motion. I share the opinion that
there are other motives behind the doctor's agitation; he
may talk about the Baths, but his real aim is nothing short
of revolution — the complete overthrow of the parties now
in power. No one doubts the doctor's integrity of purpose —
there can be no two opinions about that. I too am in favor
of self-government by the People, provided it doesn't result
in too great a burden on the taxpayer; in this case that is
precisely what would occur. For this reason — well, damn
it — excuse me, gentlemen! — on this occasion I cannot
possibly side with Dr. Stockmann. You can pay too high a
price — even for gold. At all events, that's my opinion.

[*Loud applause from all sides.*]

HOVSTAD. I too should like to make my position clear in this matter. At first Dr. Stockmann's agitation met with considerable favor in many quarters, and I did my best to give it my impartial support. It soon appeared, however, that we had been misled; that the facts had been presented in a false light —

DR. STOCKMANN. False — !

HOVSTAD. — an ambiguous light, if you prefer. The Mayor's report leaves no doubt on that score. I trust no one here questions my liberal principles; on the great political issues of the day, the views of *The People's Monitor* are well-known to you all. But I have learned from men of judgment and experience that when it comes to purely local matters, a newspaper should proceed with a certain amount of caution.

ASLAKSEN. I wholeheartedly endorse the speaker's views.

HOVSTAD. In the matter now under discussion public opinion is quite obviously against Dr. Stockmann. Now — what is a publisher's first and foremost duty, gentlemen? Is it not to work in harmony with his readers? Is he not obligated — by a tacit mandate,[13] as it were — to serve indefatigably and tenaciously the interests of the majority? Or am I mistaken?

MANY VOICES. No, no! Hovstad is right!

HOVSTAD. It has not been easy, I assure you, to break with a man in whose home I have been a frequent guest of late. A man who up to this very day has enjoyed the unqualified goodwill of his fellow citizens. A man whose only, or perhaps one should say whose chief fault, consists in following his heart rather than his head.

A FEW SCATTERED VOICES. That's true! Hurrah for Dr. Stockman!

HOVSTAD. But my duty to Society has forced me, much against my will, to make this break. And there's another consideration that impels me to oppose him, and try, if I can, to stop him on the rash course on which he is embarked: consideration for his family, gentlemen —

DR. STOCKMANN. Stick to the sewers and waterworks!

---

[13] **tacit mandate:** command that is understood without being expressed in a written or spoken agreement.

HOVSTAD. — consideration for his wife, and for his helpless children.

MORTEN. Does he mean us, Mother?

MRS. STOCKMANN. Hush!

ASLAKSEN. I shall now put the Mayor's resolution to a vote.

DR. STOCKMANN. That won't be necessary! I don't intend to speak about the filth and corruption of the Baths this evening. No! You're going to hear about something very different.

THE MAYOR (*half to himself*). Now what's he up to?

A DRUNKEN MAN (*near the main entrance*). I'm entitled to pay taxes — so I suppose I'm entitled to an opinion too. And it is my irrefutable and incomprehensible opinion that —

SEVERAL VOICES. Silence over there!

OTHERS. He's drunk! Throw him out!

[*The drunken man is put out.*]

DR. STOCKMANN. May I speak?

ASLAKSEN (*ringing the bell*). Dr. Stockmann has the floor.

DR. STOCKMANN. I'd like to have seen anyone try — even a few days ago — to gag me as I've been gagged this evening. I should have fought like a lion for what I know to be my sacred rights. But that doesn't matter to me now. Now I have more important things to say.

[*The people crowd closer round him. Morten Kiil appears among the crowd.*]

DR. STOCKMANN (*continuing*). I've done a lot of thinking these past days — turning things over in my mind, till my brain seemed all muddled and confused —

THE MAYOR (*coughing*). Hm — !

DR. STOCKMANN. But gradually things straightened out, and I saw them in their true perspective. That's why I'm here this evening. I'm going to expose many things to you, my friends! The fact that our waterworks are poisoned and that our health resort is nothing but a pesthole is comparatively unimportant compared to the discovery I'm about to reveal now.

MANY VOICES. No mention of the Baths! We won't listen! Leave them out of it!

DR. STOCKMANN. I've just told you — I'm going to speak about a great discovery I've made in these past days — and this is it: The very sources of our spiritual life are poisoned, and our whole community is founded on a pestilential lie!

A MURMUR OF AMAZED VOICES. What's he saying?

THE MAYOR. How dare he — !

ASLAKSEN (*his hand on the bell*). I call upon the speaker to moderate his language!

DR. STOCKMANN. No man could love his native town more than I've loved mine! I was very young when I left here, and distance, memory, and homesickness combined to cast a kind of aura round the place and round its people. (*Scattered applause and expressions of approval*) I spent many years in the far North, in a godforsaken hole of a place. I used to visit the few starving wretches scattered about in that rocky wilderness, and I often thought a horse doctor would have served their purpose better than a man of science like myself.

[*Murmurs throughout the room.*]

BILLING (*laying down his pen*). Strike me dead! I've never heard such —

HOVSTAD. An insult to honest countryfolk!

DR. STOCKMANN. Just wait a minute! — All that time I don't think anyone could have accused me of forgetting my hometown. I sat there brooding over an idea — like an eider duck on her eggs — and what I finally hatched out was the plan for our Baths. (*Applause and protests*) And when at last fate was kind enough to make my return home possible — I felt as though my every wish had been fulfilled. I still had one wish, though; an ardent, unwavering, passionate desire to serve my hometown and my fellow citizens.

THE MAYOR (*gazing into space*). A strange way to show it — !

DR. STOCKMANN. I was supremely happy — basking in joyous illusions. Then, yesterday morning — no, the preceding evening to be exact — I received a mental jolt; my eyes were suddenly wide open and the first thing I saw was the colossal stupidity of our reigning authorities —

[*Noise, cries and laughter. Mrs. Stockmann coughs repeatedly.*]

The public meeting, from the Walter
Hampden production, 1927.

THE MAYOR. Mr. Chairman!

ALSAKSEN (*ringing his bell*). By virtue of my office — !

DR. STOCKMANN. Let the expression pass, Mr. Aslaksen —
there's no need to be petty! I simply mean that the whole
disgraceful situation at the Baths was suddenly revealed to
me — a mess for which the so-called leading men of the
town must take the blame. These leading men — I'm sick
of them and all their works! They're like a lot of goats let
loose in a young orchard — destroying everything; they
stand in the way of free men and hamper them at every turn.
For my part I'd like to see them exterminated together with
all other predatory creatures —

[*Uproar in the room.*]

THE MAYOR. Mr. Chairman — can such things be allowed?

ASLAKSEN (*his hand on the bell*). Dr. Stockmann — !

DR. STOCKMANN. I can't conceive why it should have taken

71

me so long to see through these gentlemen; every single day
I've had a prime example before my very eyes — my brother
Peter — empty of ideas and filled with prejudice —

[*Laughter, noise, and catcalls. Mrs. Stockmann coughs.
Aslaksen violently rings his bell.*]

THE DRUNKEN MAN (*who has returned*). Are you referring to
me? My name's Pettersen all right — but I'll be damned
if —

ANGRY VOICES. Throw him out! Throw that drunk out!

[*They throw him out again.*]

THE MAYOR. Who was that person?

A BYSTANDER. I don't know him, Your Honor.

ANOTHER MAN. He's not from around here.

A THIRD MAN. He must be that lumber dealer from — (*The
rest is inaudible.*)

ASLAKSEN. The man was unquestionably intoxicated. Proceed, Dr. Stockmann; but with moderation, if you please!

DR. STOCKMANN. Well, fellow citizens, I shall say no more
about our leading men. And if anyone imagines, after what
I have just said, that I'm here to attack these gentlemen this
evening, he is quite wrong, I assure you. You see, I cherish
the comfortable conviction that these reactionaries, these
relics of another age, are busily engaged in cutting their own
throats — they don't need a doctor to help them. And besides, they are not the worst menace to Society; it is not
primarily due to them that our spiritual well-being is en-
dangered, and that the very ground we stand on reeks with
corruption. They are not the most dangerous enemies to
truth and freedom!

CRIES FROM ALL SIDES. Who then? Who do you mean? Name
them! Name them!

DR. STOCKMANN. Oh, I shall name them — never fear! You
see, that is my great discovery; I made it yesterday. (*Raising
his voice*) In our Society, the worst enemy to truth and freedom is the majority. Yes! The damnable, solid, liberal
majority — that's the great menace! There's your answer!

[*Great commotion in the room. Most of the audience are
shouting, stamping, and whistling. A few old gentlemen*

exchange covert glances and seem to be enjoying the
situation. Mrs. Stockmann gets up anxiously; Ejlif and
Morten advance threateningly towards the schoolboys
who are making catcalls. Aslaksen rings his bell and
calls for order. Hovstad and Billing both try to speak but
are drowned out. At last quiet is restored.]

ASLAKSEN. The speaker is requested to withdraw this out-
rageous statement.

DR. STOCKMANN. Never, Mr. Aslaksen — never! This same
great majority robs me of my freedom and wishes to prevent me from stating the truth!

HOVSTAD. The majority is always right.

BILLING. Yes — but, strike me dead — truth is right too!

DR. STOCKMANN. The majority is never right — never, I tell
you! That's one of those social lies against which every free,
intelligent man ought to rebel. What does the majority con-
sist of — of wise men or of fools? I think we must all of us
agree that from one end of the world to the other the pro-
portion is overwhelmingly in favor of the fools. And are
wise men to be ruled by fools? What could be more senseless! (*Uproar and yells*) You can shout me down if you like,
but you can't deny it! The majority has the power, unfortunately — but right is on the side of people like me — of the
few — of the individual. It's the minority that's always right!

[*Renewed commotion.*]

HOVSTAD. Ha, ha! Dr. Stockmann has turned aristocrat!

DR. STOCKMANN. I've said I won't waste any words on that
little rear-guard of puny, narrow-chested, self-important
men — the stream of life has already left them far behind.
I'm thinking of the few — those rare spirits among us who
have had the vision to recognize the truth in new ideas,
new ways of thought — and have made those ways their
own. These men are in the vanguard — so far ahead that the
solid majority can't begin to reach them; and there they
fight for newborn truths — too new and too daring to be ac-
cepted by that sacred majority of yours.

HOVSTAD. Now he's a revolutionist!

DR. STOCKMANN. Yes, by Heavens, I am, Mr. Hovstad! I intend to revolt against the lie that truth belongs exclusively

to the majority. And what are these truths the majority worships? They're truths so old and worn — they're practically decrepit. And when a truth reaches that age, you can hardly tell it from a lie! (*Laughter and jeers*) You can believe me or not as you like; but truths are not such tough old Methuselahs[14] as most people imagine. A normal, ordinary truth is good for, say, seventeen or eighteen — at most twenty years; seldom more. And truths as venerable as that are nothing but skin and bones; yet it isn't until then that the great majority adopts them and prescribes them to Society as wholesome spiritual food. But there's not much nourishment in that kind of a diet, I assure you; as a doctor you can take my word for that. These tired old truths are as rancid and moldy as last year's bacon; they're the cause of all that moral scurvy that plagues Society.

ASLAKSEN. Our honored speaker appears to have strayed somewhat from his subject.

THE MAYOR. I heartily endorse the chairman's observation.

DR. STOCKMANN. You must be mad, Peter! I'm doing my best to stick to my subject; I'm saying that it's the masses — that damnable solid majority — that poison the sources of our spiritual life and corrupt the very ground we walk on.

HOVSTAD. I see; in other words you condemn the great majority of liberal-minded men for having sense enough to rely on truths that are fundamental and conclusive.

DR. STOCKMANN. My dear Mr. Hovstad, don't speak about fundamental truths! The truths endorsed by the great majority of men today were considered fundamental by the vanguard in our grandfather's time; they are no longer endorsed by the vanguard of today. There's only one fundamental truth, in my opinion — and that is that Society cannot live a healthy life based on truths that have become old and spineless.

HOVSTAD. Can't you be more explicit? Instead of this vague talk, give us some examples of these so-called spineless truths you say we base our lives on.

[*Approval from several parts of the room.*]

---

[14] **Methuselahs:** Methuselah was a biblical character who lived for 969 years. (See Genesis 5:27.)

DR. STOCKMANN. I could give you innumerable examples —
but one will serve: the fundamental truth which, though
basically a lie, you and your *People's Monitor* and its ad-
herents swear by all the same —

HOVSTAD. — which is?

DR. STOCKMANN. A doctrine inherited from your grandparents,
and that you thoughtlessly go on proclaiming far and wide;
the doctrine that the common herd, the crowd, the masses,
are the very flower of the people — in fact *are* the people —
and that the uncouth man, the vulgar man, the ignorant and
unevolved, have the same right to condemn and sanction,
to govern and counsel, as the intellectually and spiritually
distinguished few.

BILLING. Well — strike me dead! I've never — !

HOVSTAD (*shouting at the same time*). Take note of this,
citizens!

ANGRY VOICES. Aren't we the people? Are we to have no say?

A WORKMAN. A man who talks like that deserves to be kicked
out!

OTHERS. Throw him out!

A MAN (*shouting*). Now's the time to blow your horn, Evensen!

[*The deep notes of a horn are heard; whistles, catcalls
and uproar.*]

DR. STOCKMANN (*as the noise subsides*). Be reasonable! Can't
you endure the truth? I don't expect you all to agree with
me — but I certainly thought Mr. Hovstad would calm down
and back me up. Mr. Hovstad lays claim to being a freethinker[15] —

SEVERAL VOICES (*subdued and astonished*). A freethinker, did
he say? What? Hovstad a freethinker?

HOVSTAD. I dare you to prove it, Dr. Stockmann! Have I ever
said so in black and white?

DR. STOCKMANN. No, damn it — you've never had the courage!
Well, I don't want to get you into trouble; I'm the one who's
the freethinker, Mr. Hovstad. And now — let me prove to
you all, scientifically, that *The People's Monitor* makes fools

[15] **freethinker:** one whose opinions — especially concerning religion — are
not influenced by authority.

of you and leads you by the nose when it tells you that you, the masses, the crowd, are the flower of the people. That's just a journalistic lie! The masses are only the raw material from which a People can be made. (*Murmurs, laughter, and general disturbance*) It's the same thing in all other forms of life. Fine animals are created by breeding and selection. Take an ordinary common hen, for instance — she's not much good for eating, and her eggs are not much better than a crow's eggs — or a raven's; she can't be compared with a really fine strain of poultry. But now take a Japanese or Spanish hen — a pheasant or a turkey — and you'll soon see the difference! Or in the case of dogs — so closely related to mankind; think first of a common ordinary cur — one of those filthy, ragged, plebeian mongrels that haunt the gutters and dirty up the sidewalks; and compare that mongrel with a pedigreed poodle, bred for generations from the finest stock, used to good food and accustomed to well-modulated voices and the sound of music. Don't you suppose the poodle's brain shows a marked superiority? Of course it does! A trainer can take a poodle pup like that and teach it the most fantastic tricks — things a common mongrel could never dream of learning!

[*Noise and laughter.*]

A MAN (*shouting*). Are you comparing us with dogs?

ANOTHER. We're not animals, Doctor!

DR. STOCKMANN. Of course you are! We're all animals, my friend! What are we else? But there aren't many well-bred animals among us. There's a tremendous difference between poodle-men and mongrel-men. And it's so ridiculous — Mr. Hovstad agrees with me entirely as long as it's four-legged animals we're talking of —

HOVSTAD. An animal's an animal — and there's an end of it!

DR. STOCKMANN. Perhaps; but as soon as I apply the rule to two-legged animals, Mr. Hovstad rebels; he no longer has the courage of his convictions — he refuses to think things through to the end; so he turns the rule upside down and proclaims in the *Monitor* that the ordinary hen and the common cur are the prize specimens in the menagerie. And that's the way it'll always be, while we allow the cur in us to triumph, instead of working our way up to some sort of spiritual distinction.

HOVSTAD. I make no pretense of being distinguished in any way; I come from simple peasant stock and I'm proud of it. I'm proud to belong to those common people you're insulting!

SOME WORKMEN. Hurrah for Hovstad! Hurrah! Hurrah!

DR. STOCKMANN. The kind of common people I mean don't necessarily come from the lower classes; they're crawling and swarming all around us — you often find them in the very top ranks of Society. You've only to look at that smug, respectable Mayor of yours! He's about as low as any man that ever walked on two feet —

THE MAYOR. I must protest against these personal remarks!

DR. STOCKMANN. — and that has nothing to do with the fact that one of our ancestors was a disgusting old pirate from somewhere in Pomerania —

THE MAYOR. Pure invention! Utterly groundless!

DR. STOCKMANN. — no! It's because he thinks the thoughts of his superiors in office, and kowtows to their opinions. And people who do that are common in spirit; that's why, in spite of his magnificence, my brother Peter is so fundamentally lacking in distinction and is consequently so antiliberal.

THE MAYOR. Mr. Chairman — !

HOVSTAD. So it seems you have to be a liberal to be distinguished! That's a new point of view if you like!

[*Laughter.*]

DR. STOCKMANN. Yes, that's part of my new discovery too. And there's something else: I've discovered that morality and liberalism are almost precisely the same thing. That's why I consider it downright inexcusable of *The People's Monitor* to go on proclaiming day in and day out that morality and liberalism are the sole monopoly of the mob and the masses; and that culture automatically generates vice and spiritual depravity — just as the filth from the Milldale Tanneries generates the poison that pollutes our waterworks. (*Noise and interruptions*) And yet this same *People's Monitor* prates about raising the masses to a higher level! Why,

damn it — if the *Monitor's* premise were really sound, raising them to a higher level would be equivalent to hurling
them straight to perdition! Fortunately the theory that culture demoralizes is just another of those lies handed down
from the past. No! Stupidity, poverty, and ugliness are the
true evils — they're demoralizing if you like! And to live in
a house that is never aired, and where the floors are never
swept — my wife, incidentally, claims that floors should be
scrubbed every day, but that's a debatable point — that's
demoralizing too! Lack of oxygen weakens the moral fiber.
And there must be precious little oxygen in the houses
around here, if the moral fiber of our citizens is so feeble
that the great majority of them are anxious and willing to
build the future of our town on a foundation of hypocrisy
and lies!

ASLAKSEN. This is an insult to the entire community — we
shall not tolerate it!

A GENTLEMAN. I move that the speaker be called to order!

EAGER VOICES. Yes, yes! He's right! Sit down! Sit down!

DR. STOCKMANN (*flaring up*). Then I shall shout it from the
housetops! I'll write to all the newspapers! I'll let the whole
country know of the situation here!

HOVSTAD. Dr. Stockmann is evidently bent on ruining the
town.

DR. STOCKMANN. I love my native town so much that I'd rather
see it ruined than prosper on a lie!

ASLAKSEN. There's a statement for you!

[*Noise and catcalls. Mrs. Stockmann coughs in vain; the
doctor no longer hears her.*]

HOVSTAD (*shouting above the tumult*). You're an enemy to
this whole community, or you couldn't talk so lightly of the
ruin of the town!

DR. STOCKMANN (*with growing excitement*). A community
based on lies and corruption deserves to be destroyed! Men
who live on lies should be wiped out like a lot of vermin.
This poison will spread throughout the country, and eventually the whole country will deserve to be destroyed; and,
should it ever come to that, I'd say from the bottom of my
heart: let it be destroyed, and let all its people perish!

A MAN (*in the crowd*). He's the People's enemy — that's what
  he is!

BILLING. Strike me dead! Did you hear that? The Voice of the
  People!

THE WHOLE CROWD (*shouting*). Yes, yes, yes! He's an enemy
  of the People! He's a traitor to his country! He's against
  the People!

ASLAKSEN. As a citizen of this town, and as a human being, I
  am deeply shocked by what I have heard here tonight. I
  must regretfully concur with the sentiments expressed by
  so many of my fellow citizens, and I move that those sentiments be formulated in the following resolution: "This
  meeting hereby declares the former medical adviser to the
  Baths, Dr. Tomas Stockmann, to be an enemy of the People."

[*Thunders of applause and cheers. A number of people
crowd around Dr. Stockmann, jeering and booing. Mrs.
Stockmann and Petra have risen. Morten and Ejlif exchange blows with some of the schoolboys who have
joined in the jeering. Some grownups separate them.*]

DR. STOCKMANN (*to the jeering crowd*). Fools! You fools! I
  tell you that —

ASLAKSEN (*ringing his bell*). Doctor Stockmann is out of
  order! A formal vote must now be taken. However, out of
  consideration for personal feelings, it will be by secret
  ballot. Have you any sheets of blank paper, Mr. Billing?

BILLING. Yes — I have some here; both blue and white.

ASLAKSEN. Splendid. That will expedite matters. We'll just
  cut it into slips — There! (*To the meeting*) Blue stands for
  no, and white for yes. I shall collect the votes myself.

[*The Mayor leaves the room. Aslaksen and a couple of
others circulate about the room with the pieces of paper
in hats.*]

A GENTLEMAN (*to Hovstad*). What can be the matter with the
  doctor? I don't know what to make of it!

HOVSTAD. He's a dreadfully impetuous man, you know!

ANOTHER GENTLEMAN (*to Billing*). You've been a guest there;
  tell me — does the fellow drink?

BILLING. Strike me dead — I don't know how to answer that.

I know there's always plenty of hot toddy in the house!

A THIRD GENTLEMAN. He strikes me as unbalanced.

FIRST GENTLEMAN. Is there any insanity in the family, I wonder?

BILLING. I don't know — I shouldn't be surprised.

A FOURTH GENTLEMAN. It's pure malice, if you ask me. He's got a chip on his shoulder about something.

BILLING. I remember one day he mentioned wanting a raise in salary — but I know he didn't get it.

ALL THE GENTLEMEN (*together*). Then that must be it, of course!

THE DRUNKEN MAN (*in the crowd*). Give me a blue one! And I want a white one, too!

SEVERAL PEOPLE. There's that drunk again! Throw him out!

MORTEN KIIL (*comes up to Stockmann*). Well, Stockmann! Look where your monkey tricks have led to!

DR. STOCKMANN. I've simply done my duty.

MORTEN KIIL. What was that you said about the Milldale Tanneries?

DR. STOCKMANN. You heard; I said they generated filth.

MORTEN KIIL. You mean mine too?

DR. STOCKMANN. Yours is among the worst.

MORTEN KIIL. And are you going to print that in the papers?

DR. STOCKMANN. I shall keep nothing back.

MORTEN KIIL. It'll cost you dear — I warn you! (*He goes out.*)

A FAT GENTLEMAN (*goes up to Horster without bowing to the ladies*). I see you lend your house to enemies of the People, Captain.

HORSTER. I've a right to use my property as I see fit, sir.

THE GENTLEMAN. Very good. Then I shall follow your example.

HORSTER. What do you mean by that?

THE GENTLEMAN. You'll hear from me tomorrow. (*Turns away and goes out.*)

PETRA. Captain Horster — wasn't that the owner of your ship?

HORSTER. Mr. Vik, yes.

ASLAKSEN (*his hands full of slips of paper, mounts the platform and rings*). Allow me to announce the result of the vote, gentlemen. All the voters, with one exception —

A YOUNG GENTLEMAN. That must have been the drunk!

ASLAKSEN. With the exception of one intoxicated person this meeting unanimously declares Dr. Tomas Stockmann to be an enemy of the People. (*Cheers and applause*) Three cheers for our deeply loved and honorable community! (*Cheers*) And three cheers for our able and energetic Mayor who has so loyally set family prejudice aside! (*Cheers*) The meeting is adjourned. (*He steps down from the platform.*)

BILLING. Let's have three cheers for the chairman!

ALL. Three cheers for Aslaksen!

DR. STOCKMANN. Give me my hat and coat, Petra. Captain — have you room for any passengers on your trip to the New World?

HORSTER. There'll always be room for you and yours, Dr. Stockmann.

DR. STOCKMANN (*as Petra helps him with his coat*). Thanks. Come, Katrine! Come, boys! (*He gives his wife his arm.*)

MRS. STOCKMANN (*in a low voice*). Let's go out the back way, Tomas, dear.

DR. STOCKMANN. No back ways for us, Katrine. (*Raises his voice.*) You'll hear more from the enemy of the People before he finally shakes the dust off his feet! I'm not as forbearing as a certain person I could mention; I can't bring myself to say "I forgive you, for you know not what you do." [16]

ASLAKSEN. That comparison is blasphemous, Doctor Stockmann!

BILLING. Strike me — ! If that isn't too much for a decent man to stand!

A COARSE VOICE. And he actually threatens us, too!

ANGRY SHOUTS. Let's smash in his windows! Duck him in the fjord! [17]

A MAN (*in the crowd*). Blow your horn, Evensen! Go on, man! Blow!

[*Horn-blowing, whistles, and catcalls; wild shouts. Dr. Stockmann and his family go towards the door — Captain Horster clears the way for them.*]

[16] **I forgive . . . what you do:** Stockmann is echoing the words of Christ on the cross. (See Luke 23:24.)

[17] **fjord** (fyòrd): narrow inlet of the sea bounded by cliffs.

ALL (*yelling after them as they go out*). Enemy of the People!
Enemy of the People! Enemy of the People!
BILLING. Strike me dead! I wouldn't want to drink toddy at
the Stockmanns' house tonight!

[*The people throng towards the door; the shouting is
taken up outside; from the street cries of "Enemy of the
People! Enemy of the People!" are heard.*]

CURTAIN

QUESTIONS

1. Why are the citizens speaking at the beginning of the act so certain
Dr. Stockmann is wrong? What signs are there that the public meeting has
been "rigged"?

2. What charges does Dr. Stockmann bring against the "majority"?
According to him, who has the best right to rule? How effective is Dr.
Stockmann as an orator? Why is he branded "an enemy of the People"?

3. Why does Dr. Stockmann seem to care less and less about the polluted baths? What has he discovered about the town and society in which
he lives?

4. What is the significance of the conversation between Captain Horster
and the owner of his ship? What will happen to other supporters of Dr.
Stockmann?

5. What do you think Dr. Stockmann will do after he exposes the baths
to the whole country?

ACT FIVE

SCENE: *Dr. Stockmann's study. The walls are lined
with bookshelves and glass cabinets containing various
medicines. In the back wall is the door to the living
room. Two windows in the wall right, with all the panes
smashed in. In the center of the room is the doctor's desk
covered with books and papers. The room is in disorder.
It is morning. Dr. Stockmann in a dressing gown and
slippers and with a skullcap on his head is stooping
down and raking under one of the cabinets with an umbrella; he succeeds in raking out a stone.*

DR. STOCKMANN (*calling through the open door*). Here's another one, Katrine!

MRS. STOCKMANN (*from the living room*). You'll find a lot more, I expect.

DR. STOCKMANN (*adds the stone to a pile on the table*). I'm going to keep these stones, Katrine; they're precious relics. I want Morten and Ejlif to have them constantly before their eyes — and I'll leave them as a heritage. (*Raking about under the bookcase*) By the way, hasn't — what the devil *is* that girl's name — hasn't she been to the glazier[18] yet?

MRS. STOCKMANN (*coming in*). Yes; but he wasn't sure he could come today.

DR. STOCKMANN. I suppose he doesn't dare.

MRS. STOCKMANN. That's what Randina thinks; she thinks he's afraid of the neighbors. (*Talks to someone in the living room.*) What is it, Randina? Oh, thanks. (*Goes out and returns immediately.*) A letter for you, dear.

DR. STOCKMANN. Let's see. (*Opens the letter and reads.*) Well — it's not surprising!

MRS. STOCKMANN. Who is it from?

DR. STOCKMANN. The landlord. He's giving us notice.

MRS. STOCKMANN. Not really! He's such a nice man, too — !

DR. STOCKMANN (*glancing at the letter*). He daren't do otherwise, he says. He's very sorry; but he daren't do otherwise — public opinion — he has to earn his living — he's afraid of offending certain influential men — and so on.

MRS. STOCKMANN. That just shows you, Tomas.

DR. STOCKMANN. Oh, yes; it shows me right enough. They're all cowards in this town; no one dares do anything for fear of offending someone else. (*Flings the letter on the table.*) Well — what do we care, Katrine; we're off to the New World —

MRS. STOCKMANN. You really think that's a wise decision, Tomas?

DR. STOCKMANN. You don't expect me to stay here, do you? After being spat on? After being branded as an enemy of the People and having my windows smashed? And, look, Katrine! Somebody actually tore a hole in my black trousers!

---

[18] glazier: glass fitter.

MRS. STOCKMANN. Oh, Tomas! And they're your best ones too!

DR. STOCKMANN. Yes! Well — you should never wear your best trousers when you go out to fight for truth and freedom! But I don't care so much about the trousers — you can always patch them up for me. What I can't stomach is having that mob attack me as though they were my equals!

MRS. STOCKMANN. I know, Tomas; they've behaved abominably to you here. But does that necessarily mean we have to leave the country altogether?

DR. STOCKMANN. It'd be just as bad in all the other towns; the mob is just as insolent-minded there as here. Well — to Hell with it! Let the mongrels yap; that's not the worst of it. The worst of it is that all over the country men are nothing but abject slaves to the party bosses. Not that the so-called Free West is apt to be much better; I daresay enlightened public opinion, the solid majority, and all the rest of the trash is just as rampant there — but at least it's on a bigger scale; they may kill a man, but they don't put him to slow torture; they don't clamp a free soul into a straitjacket. And, at a pinch, there's room to get away. (*Walks up and down.*) If only I knew of some primeval forest, some little South Sea island that was going cheap —

MRS. STOCKMANN. But — what about the boys, Tomas?

DR. STOCKMANN (*comes to a standstill*). What an amazing woman you are, Katrine! You wouldn't really want the boys to grow up in a society like ours, would you? You must have seen last night that half the population of this town is raving mad — and if the other half hasn't lost its wits, it's only because they're such blockheads that they have no wits to lose!

MRS. STOCKMANN. Dear Tomas — you say such reckless things!

DR. STOCKMANN. Well — isn't it true? They turn every idea upside down; they make a hotch-potch out of right and wrong; they take lies for truth and truth for lies. But the craziest thing of all is to see a lot of grownup men calling themselves Liberals, parading about pretending to themselves and others that they're friends of freedom! You must admit that's pretty silly!

MRS. STOCKMANN. Yes; I suppose it is, but — (*Petra enters from the living room.*) Home from school already, Petra?

PETRA. I've been dismissed.

MRS. STOCKMANN. Dismissed!

DR. STOCKMANN. You too!

PETRA. Mrs. Busk gave me my notice — so I thought I'd better leave at once.

DR. STOCKMANN. You were quite right!

MRS. STOCKMANN. Fancy Mrs. Busk doing a thing like that! How disgraceful of her!

PETRA. It wasn't disgraceful of her, Mother. I could see how upset she was. But she didn't dare do otherwise, she said. So — I'm dismissed.

DR. STOCKMANN (*laughs and rubs his hands*). She didn't dare do otherwise — just like the rest! This is delightful!

MRS. STOCKMANN. I suppose — after that dreadful scene last night —

PETRA. It wasn't only that. Father — listen to this!

DR. STOCKMANN. Well?

PETRA. Mrs. Busk showed me at least three letters she'd received this morning —

DR. STOCKMANN. Anonymous, of course?

PETRA. Yes.

DR. STOCKMANN. They never dare sign their names, Katrine!

PETRA. Two of them warned her that a certain gentleman — a frequent visitor at our house, so he said — had been talking at the club last night, and telling everyone that my views on certain subjects were decidedly advanced —

DR. STOCKMANN. I hope you didn't deny it!

PETRA. Of course not! Mrs. Busk has fairly advanced views too — that is, in private; but since I'd been publicly accused, she dared not keep me on.

MRS. STOCKMANN. A frequent visitor — just think of it! You see, Tomas — that's what comes of all your hospitality!

DR. STOCKMANN. We won't stay in this pigsty any longer. Get packed as soon as you can, Katrine. We'll leave this place at once — the sooner the better!

MRS. STOCKMANN. Be quiet a moment; I thought I heard someone in the hall. See who it is, Petra.

PETRA (*opens the hall door*). Oh, it's you, Captain Horster! Do come in.

HORSTER (*from the hall*). Good morning. I thought I'd just come over and see how you were getting on.

DR. STOCKMANN (*shaking his hand*). Thanks; that's very kind of you.

MRS. STOCKMANN. And thank you, Captain Horster, for helping us last night.

PETRA. How did you ever manage to get home?

HORSTER. It wasn't bad — I'm a pretty hefty man, you know. And, anyway — there was more noise than action!

DR. STOCKMANN. Isn't it amazing what cowards those people are? Come here — I want to show you something. Here are all the stones they threw in at us last night. Just look at them! There aren't more than two decent stones among the lot; most of them are pebbles — a lot of gravel! And yet they stood out there shouting and yelling that they were going to kill me! But as for really doing it — oh, no! Nothing as positive as that!

HORSTER. Well — for once — I should think you'd have been grateful, Doctor!

DR. STOCKMANN. Oh, I am — of course! But it's tragic all the same; I sometimes think — supposing a really serious struggle of national proportions were involved; you can be sure enlightened public opinion would instantly take to its heels and run away, and the great solid majority would scatter like a herd of frightened sheep; that's the depressing part of it — it makes me sick to think of. But, damn it — why should I care what they do! They've called me an enemy of the People, so I might as well *be* an enemy of the People!

MRS. STOCKMANN. You'll never be that, Tomas.

DR. STOCKMANN. I wouldn't be too sure, Katrine. One ugly word can act as an irritant sometimes — and that damned expression — ! I can't get rid of it; it's dug its way into the pit of my stomach — I feel it gnawing away there like a bitter acid. All the magnesia tablets in the world won't make it stop!

PETRA. They're not worth taking seriously, Father.

HORSTER. Some day they'll change their minds, Doctor — you'll see.

MRS. STOCKMANN. Yes, Tomas; I'm sure of that.

DR. STOCKMANN. They may — when it's too late. Well — serve them right! Let them wallow in their filth and cry their hearts out with remorse at having driven a patriot into exile. When do you sail, Captain?

HORSTER. Hm — that's really what I wanted to talk to you about —

DR. STOCKMANN. Oh? Is anything the matter with the ship?

HORSTER. No, nothing; except — I shan't be with her.

PETRA. You surely haven't been dismissed?

HORSTER (*with a smile*). But I have, you see.

PETRA. You, too.

MRS. STOCKMANN. That just shows you, Tomas.

DR. STOCKMANN. And all for the sake of truth! If I'd thought anything like this could happen — !

HORSTER. You mustn't be upset. Some other company will take me on.

DR. STOCKMANN. And to think that a man like Vik — ! A man of means — who can afford to be completely independent — ! How disgusting!

HORSTER. He's not such a bad man, really. He told me himself he'd like to keep me on — only he didn't dare —

DR. STOCKMANN. He didn't dare! Of course not!

HORSTER. He said it wasn't always easy — when you're a member of a party —

DR. STOCKMANN. He hit the nail on the head that time! A party — ! A sausage machine — that's what a party's like! All the brains are ground up together and reduced to hash; and that's why the world is filled with a lot of brainless, empty-headed numskulls!

MRS. STOCKMANN. Tomas! Please!

PETRA (*to Horster*). If you hadn't seen us home, this mightn't have happened.

HORSTER. I don't regret it.

PETRA (*holds out her hand to him*). Thank you!

HORSTER. But I wanted to tell you this: if you're really bent on going — there's another way it could be —

MRS. STOCKMANN. Hush! I thought I heard a knock.

PETRA. I believe it's Uncle.

DR. STOCKMANN. Aha! (*Calls.*) Come in!

MRS. STOCKMANN. Now, Tomas — promise me, please — !

[*The Mayor enters from the hall.*]

THE MAYOR (*in the doorway*). Oh, you're busy. Then I'd better —

DR. STOCKMANN. No, no. Come in.

THE MAYOR. I wanted to speak to you alone.

MRS. STOCKMANN. We'll go into the living room.

HORSTER. I'll come back later, then.

DR. STOCKMANN. No, Captain Horster — don't go away. I'm anxious to hear more about —

HORSTER. Very well; I'll wait.

[*He follows Mrs. Stockmann and Petra into the living room. The Mayor says nothing, but glances at the windows.*]

DR. STOCKMANN. A bit draughty, isn't it? Better put on your hat.

THE MAYOR. Thanks — if I may. (*Does so.*) I think I caught cold last night. I felt a sudden chill —

DR. STOCKMANN. Really? I thought it was a bit on the warm side!

THE MAYOR. I regret I was unable to prevent that most unfortunate business.

DR. STOCKMANN. Is there anything special you want to say to me?

THE MAYOR (*producing a large envelope*). The management of the Baths sends you this document.

DR. STOCKMANN. My dismissal, I suppose.

THE MAYOR. Yes — as of today. We regret this decision but, frankly, we didn't dare do otherwise. Out of respect for public opinion, you understand.

DR. STOCKMANN. Didn't dare do otherwise. I seem to have heard those words before, today.

THE MAYOR. I think you should face the fact that from now on you won't be able to count on any practice here.

DR. STOCKMANN. To hell with my practice! But why are you so sure of that?

THE MAYOR. The Homeowners Association is circulating a petition urging all respectable citizens to refrain from

calling on your services. Of course everyone will sign it —
they wouldn't dare do otherwise.

DR. STOCKMANN. I don't doubt that. What else?

THE MAYOR. If you take my advice, you'll leave town for a
while.

DR. STOCKMANN. Yes; I've already given serious thought to
that.

THE MAYOR. You're wise. Then — after six months or so —
when you've had time to think things over, you might perhaps feel ready to write us a few words of apology, admit-
ting your mistake —

DR. STOCKMANN. And then I might be reinstated, do you
think?

THE MAYOR. You might; it's by no means impossible.

DR. STOCKMANN. But what about public opinion? Aren't you
forgetting that?

THE MAYOR. Public opinion has a way of changing; and, quite
frankly, it would be greatly to our advantage to have a
signed statement from you to that effect.

DR. STOCKMANN. Yes — I daresay it would be most convenient! I've already told you how I feel about that kind of
crookedness.

THE MAYOR. You were in a very different position then. At
that time you imagined you had the whole town at your
back —

DR. STOCKMANN. And now, it seems, I have the whole town
on my back! (*Flaring up*) But I don't care if the devil himself
were on my back, I'll never consent to — ! Never, I tell you;
never!

THE MAYOR. As a family man you have no right to take this
stand, Tomas. You simply have no right!

DR. STOCKMANN. I have no right, have I? There's only one
thing in this world a free man has no right to do; you don't
know what that is, do you?

THE MAYOR. No, I don't.

DR. STOCKMANN. Of course not; then I'll tell you. A free man
has no right to wallow in filth. A free man has no right to
debase himself to the point of wanting to spit in his own
face!

THE MAYOR. That might sound quite convincing if there were

no other explanation for your pigheadedness; but of course we know there is —

DR. STOCKMANN. What do you mean?

THE MAYOR. You know quite well what I mean. However as your brother, and as a man of some experience, I advise you not to put too much faith in certain hopes and prospects that may prove disappointing.

DR. STOCKMANN. What on earth are you getting at?

THE MAYOR. Don't try to tell me you're unaware of the terms of old Morten Kiil's will!

DR. STOCKMANN. I only know he's left what little he has to a home for indigent workmen. It's no business of mine.

THE MAYOR. To begin with, "what little he has" amounts to a considerable sum. Morten Kiil is a very wealthy man.

DR. STOCKMANN. I had no idea of that —

THE MAYOR. No? Are you sure? Perhaps you had no idea either that a large part of his fortune is to be placed in a trust fund for your children; and that during your lifetime you and your wife are to enjoy the income from this trust. Did he never tell you that?

DR. STOCKMANN. He never breathed a word of it! In fact he does nothing but complain how poor he is, and grumble about taxes. Peter — are you quite sure of this?

THE MAYOR. Quite sure. My information is most reliable.

DR. STOCKMANN. But — good heavens! Then the children are provided for — and Katrine too! I must tell her this at once — (*Calls.*) Katrine, Katrine!

THE MAYOR (*holding him back*). No, wait! Don't tell her yet.

MRS. STOCKMANN (*opens the door*). What is it, dear?

DR. STOCKMANN. It's nothing; never mind.

[*Mrs. Stockmann closes the door again.*]

DR. STOCKMANN (*pacing up and down*). To think of it — provided for! All of them provided for — and for life too. How wonderful to feel one is provided for!

THE MAYOR. But that's just what you're not, you see. Morten Kiil can change his will whenever he sees fit.

DR. STOCKMANN. Oh, but he won't, Peter! The old badger's much too pleased with me for unmasking you and your precious friends.

THE MAYOR (*starts and looks at him intently*). I see! That puts things in quite a different light.

DR. STOCKMANN. What things?

THE MAYOR. So it was all a put-up job! Those violent attacks you made on the leading men of the town — all in the name of truth, of course — were actually nothing but — !

DR. STOCKMANN. But what?

THE MAYOR. — nothing but a kind of sop to that vindictive old miser Morten Kiil. That was his reward for leaving all that money to you in his will!

DR. STOCKMANN. Peter — upon my word you are the lowest of the low!

THE MAYOR. I shall have no further dealings with you; your dismissal is irrevocable. We are well armed against you now. (*He goes out.*)

DR. STOCKMANN. Of all the filthy — ! (*Calls.*) Katrine! Have this floor scrubbed at once! Tell the girl — what the devil's her — *you* know — the girl with the smutty nose — to bring her pail and scrub brush!

MRS. STOCKMANN (*in the doorway*). Tomas, Tomas! Hush!

PETRA (*also in the doorway*). Father; Grandfather's here. He wants to know if he can speak to you alone.

DR. STOCKMANN. Of course he can. (*By the door*) Come in, sir.

[*Morten Kiil enters. Stockmann closes the door behind him.*]

DR. STOCKMANN. Well, what is it? Won't you sit down?

MORTEN KIIL. No thanks. (*He looks round.*) Well, Stockmann — things look very cozy here.

DR. STOCKMANN. Yes, don't they?

MORTEN KIIL. Very cozy indeed; a nice lot of fresh air too; plenty of that oxygen you talked so much about. Your moral fiber must be flourishing.

DR. STOCKMANN. It is.

MORTEN KIIL. Yes, to be sure. (*Tapping his breast pocket*) But do you know what I have here?

DR. STOCKMANN. Plenty of moral fiber too, I hope.

MORTEN KIIL. Something much better than that, I can assure you. (*Takes out a large wallet, opens it, and shows Stockmann a bundle of papers.*)

DR. STOCKMANN (*looks at him in amazement*). Shares? Shares
  in the Baths?

MORTEN KIIL. They were easy enough to get today.

DR. STOCKMANN. Do you mean to say you've bought up — ?

MORTEN KIIL. All I could lay my hands on!

DR. STOCKMANN. But, my dear sir — you know the present
  situation at the Baths — !

MORTEN KIIL. If you behave like a sensible man, you'll soon
  set that right again.

DR. STOCKMANN. You know I've tried to do everything I can
  — but these people are all lunatics!

MORTEN KIIL. You said last night that the worst filth came
  from my tannery. Now supposing that were true — it means
  that my father and my grandfather before me, and I myself
  for many years, have been poisoning the town — like three
  demons of destruction. You don't expect me to accept that
  accusation calmly, do you?

DR. STOCKMANN. I'm afraid you'll have to.

MORTEN KIIL. No thank you; my good name and reputation
  mean too much to me. People call me "the badger," so I'm
  told; and a badger's a kind of a pig, they tell me. But I intend to prove them wrong. While I live and after I die, my
  name shall be kept spotless.

DR. STOCKMANN. How are you going to manage that?

MORTEN KIIL. *You* are going to manage that for me, Stockmann. You are going to clear my name for me.

DR. STOCKMANN. I!

MORTEN KIIL. Do you know what money I used to buy these
  shares? No, of course you don't — but now I'm going to tell
  you. I used all the money Katrine, Petra, and the boys were
  to inherit from me. For, in spite of everything, I have managed to save quite a bit, you see.

DR. STOCKMANN (*flaring up*). Do you mean to say you used
  Katrine's money to do this!

MORTEN KIIL. Yes — I've invested every penny of it in the
  Baths. Now let's see how much of a madman you really are,
  Stockmann. Now if you keep on spreading this story that
  a lot of filthy animals seep into the water from my tannery,
  you'll just be flaying pieces of skin off Katrine, and off Petra
  too — to say nothing of the boys, of course. No decent father
  would dream of doing that — unless he were a madman.

DR. STOCKMANN (*pacing up and down*). But I am a madman; I *am* a madman, don't you see?

MORTEN KIIL. Sacrifice your wife and children? You couldn't be as stark raving mad as that!

DR. STOCKMANN (*stopping in front of him*). Why in God's name didn't you talk to me before buying all this rubbish?

MORTEN KIIL. What's done is done; it's too late now.

DR. STOCKMANN (*walking about restlessly*). If only I weren't so absolutely certain — ! But I'm absolutely positive I'm right.

MORTEN KIIL (*weighing the wallet in his hand*). If you persist in this lunacy, these things won't be worth much, will they? (*Puts the wallet back in his pocket.*)

DR. STOCKMANN. Damn it! Surely there must be some scientific way of purifying the water — some sort of disinfectant —

MORTEN KIIL. To kill those animals, you mean?

DR. STOCKMANN. Yes — or at least to make them harmless.

MORTEN KIIL. You might try rat poison.

DR. STOCKMANN. Oh! Don't talk nonsense! — And since everyone says it's merely an illusion on my part — why not let it be an illusion then! Let them have their way! Ignorant, damnable mongrels that they are! They've called me an enemy of the People — torn the clothes off my back —

MORTEN KIIL. And smashed in all your windows!

DR. STOCKMANN. And one has a duty toward one's family, after all. I must talk it over with Katrine. She's better at these things than I am.

MORTEN KIIL. A good idea; she'll give you sensible advice.

DR. STOCKMANN (*turns on him angrily*). How could you behave in this fantastic manner? Gambling with Katrine's money; putting me through this agony — this torment! What kind of a devil are you!

MORTEN KIIL. If I'm a devil, perhaps I'd better go. But I want your decision — either yes or no — by two o'clock. If the answer's "no," I'll make these over to charity at once — this very day.

DR. STOCKMANN. And what will Katrine get?

MORTEN KIIL. Not a damn penny! (*The door to the hall opens; Hovstad and Aslaksen are seen outside.*) I certainly never expected to meet them here!

DR. STOCKMANN (*staring at them*). What does this mean? How dare you come to see me?

HOVSTAD. We have our reasons.

ASLAKSEN. We've something to discuss with you.

MORTEN KIIL (*in a whisper*). Yes or no — by two o'clock.

ASLAKSEN (*with a glance at Hovstad*). Aha!

[*Morten Kiil goes out.*]

DR. STOCKMANN. Well, what do you want? Be quick about it.

HOVSTAD. It's natural you should resent the attitude we were forced to take last night —

DR. STOCKMANN. So that's what you call an attitude, is it? A fine attitude! Behaving like a couple of cowards — a couple of old women — !

HOVSTAD. Call it what you like; but, you see, we have no alternative —

DR. STOCKMANN. You didn't dare do otherwise, I suppose!

HOVSTAD. If that's how you choose to put it.

ASLAKSEN. You should have given us some inkling, Dr. Stockmann. The slightest hint to Mr. Hovstad or to me —

DR. STOCKMANN. Hint? What about?

ASLAKSEN. About your real motive in this matter.

DR. STOCKMANN. I don't know what you mean.

ASLAKSEN (*nods confidentially*). Of course you do, Dr. Stockmann.

HOVSTAD. Why make a mystery of it now?

DR. STOCKMANN (*looks from one to the other*). What the devil's all this about — ?

ASLAKSEN. You know your father-in-law's been all over town buying up shares in the Baths — isn't that so?

DR. STOCKMANN. Yes, he has — but what of that?

ASLAKSEN. It might have been wiser to choose somebody else to do it for you; the connection is a bit too obvious.

HOVSTAD. And wouldn't it have been more prudent if you hadn't mixed yourself up personally in this affair? The attack on the Baths should have been made by someone else. Why didn't you take me into your confidence, Dr. Stockmann?

DR. STOCKMANN (*staring straight in front of him; a light seems to dawn on him, and he says as though thunderstruck*). This is incredible! Can such things be!

ASLAKSEN (*smiling*). Well — obviously! But they should be handled with more delicacy, it seems to me.

HOVSTAD. And it was unwise to attempt it single-handed; it's always easier to avoid responsibility for a matter of this sort, if you have others working with you.

DR. STOCKMANN (*calmly*). Come to the point, gentlemen. What is it you want?

ASLAKSEN. Perhaps Mr. Hovstad had better —

HOVSTAD. No; you explain it, Aslaksen.

ASLAKSEN. It's simply this: Now that we know how matters really stand, we feel safe in venturing to place *The People's Monitor* at your disposal.

DR. STOCKMANN. You feel safe, do you? What about public opinion? Aren't you afraid of raising a storm of protest?

HOVSTAD. We are prepared to weather it.

ASLAKSEN. And, before long, you can make a sudden change of tactics, Doctor. As soon as the charges made against the Baths have the desired effect —

DR. STOCKMANN. As soon as my father-in-law and I have bought up the shares at an attractive price, I suppose you mean — ?

HOVSTAD. It's mainly for scientific reasons, I presume, that you wish to gain control of the establishment — ?

DR. STOCKMANN. That goes without saying; and of course it was for scientific reasons too that I persuaded the old badger to become my partner in this plan. We'll patch up the pipes a bit, make a few little adjustments at the beach — and it won't cost the town a penny. What do you think? That ought to do the trick!

HOVSTAD. I should think so — provided you have the *Monitor* to back you up.

ASLAKSEN. In a free community the Press is all-powerful, Doctor Stockmann.

DR. STOCKMANN. Unquestionably! And so is public opinion too. I suppose you'll answer for the Homeowners Association, Mr. Aslaksen?

ASLAKSEN. The Homeowners Association, and the Temperance Society too; you may depend on that.

DR. STOCKMANN. Now, tell me, gentlemen — I'm almost ashamed to mention such a thing — what is your price?

HOVSTAD. I beg you to believe, Doctor, that we'd be only too happy to give you our support for nothing. But, unfortunately, the status of *The People's Monitor* is somewhat precarious; it's not as financially successful as it deserves to be. And it would seem a pity, just now when there's so much to be done in the field of general politics, to have to close our doors.

DR. STOCKMANN. I understand; I realize that would be very hard for a friend of the People, like yourself. (*Flaring up*) But I'm the People's enemy! An enemy of the People — have you forgotten that? (*Striding about the room*) Where's my stick? Where the devil is my stick?

HOVSTAD. What do you mean?

ASLAKSEN. You surely don't intend — ?

DR. STOCKMANN (*comes to a halt*). And what if I refuse to give you a penny of those shares? You must remember we rich people don't like parting with our money!

HOVSTAD. I advise *you* to remember that this business can be presented in a very ugly light.

DR. STOCKMANN. Yes; and you're just the man to do it! If I don't come to the rescue of your *Monitor,* I've no doubt you'll see to that. You'll hound me, won't you? You'll bait me — you'll slaughter me as a dog slaughters a hare!

HOVSTAD. That's the law of nature; every animal for himself, you know.

ASLAKSEN. We all have to take our food where we can find it.

DR. STOCKMANN. Then go out into the gutter, where you belong, and find it there! (*Striding about the room*) I'll show you who the strongest animal is here! (*Finds his umbrella and brandishes it at them.*) Now — get out!

HOVSTAD. You wouldn't dare attack us — !

ASLAKSEN. Be careful with that umbrella — !

DR. STOCKMANN. Out of the window with you, Mr. Hovstad!

HOVSTAD (*by the hall door*). Have you gone raving mad?

DR. STOCKMANN. Out of the window, Mr. Aslaksen! Jump, I tell you — and be quick about it!

ASLAKSEN (*running round the desk*). Moderation, Doctor Stockmann — moderation! I'm not a strong man, you know; I can't stand things like this — (*Screams.*) Help! Help!

[*Mrs. Stockmann, Horster, and Petra enter from the living room.*]

MRS. STOCKMANN. Good gracious, Tomas! What are you doing?

DR. STOCKMANN (*brandishing the umbrella*). Go on — jump, I tell you! Into the gutter where you belong!

HOVSTAD. You're a witness to this, Captain Horster! An unprovoked assault — ! (*Rushes out to the hall.*)

ASLAKSEN (*bewildered*). I must look up the law on matters of this sort — ! (*He escapes through the door to the living room.*)

MRS. STOCKMANN (*clinging to the doctor*). Tomas — for heaven's sake control yourself!

DR. STOCKMANN (*throws down the umbrella*). They both got away — damn them!

MRS. STOCKMANN. But what did they want, Tomas, dear?

DR. STOCKMANN. I'll tell you presently; I've other things to attend to now. (*Goes to his desk and writes something on a visiting card.*) Look, Katrine! I want you to see what I've written here.

MRS. STOCKMANN. Three large "No's" — what can that mean?

DR. STOCKMANN. I'll tell you that presently too. (*Giving Petra the card*) Here, Petra; tell Smudgy-face to run over to the badger and give him this. And hurry! (*Petra goes out with the card.*) I never expected to have so many visits from the devil's emissaries as I've had today! But I know how to deal with them; I'll sharpen my pen against them till it becomes a goad; I'll dip it in gall and venom; I'll hurl my entire inkpot at their brazen heads![19]

MRS. STOCKMANN. But, Tomas — aren't we going away?

[*Petra returns.*]

DR. STOCKMANN. Well?

PETRA. She's gone with it.

DR. STOCKMANN. Splendid! — Did you say going away? No, I'll be damned if we are, Katrine — we're going to stay right here!

MRS. STOCKMANN. Here in the town?

DR. STOCKMANN. Here in the town. The battlefield is here, and here the battle must be fought, and here I shall win the victory! As soon as you've patched my trousers I'll be

---

[19] **I'll hurl . . . brazen heads:** as Martin Luther was said to have done when he saw the devil.

off and try to find a place for us to live. We can't get through
the winter without a roof over our heads!

HORSTER. Will my roof do?

DR. STOCKMANN. You really mean it?

HORSTER. Of course. I've such a lot of room, and I'm hardly
ever home myself.

MRS. STOCKMANN. Oh, Captain Horster — that is kind of you!

PETRA. Thanks!

DR. STOCKMANN (*shaking his hand*). Thanks — and thanks
again! That's a great load off my mind. Now I can set to
work in earnest. Oh, there's such a lot to do, Katrine! And
I'll have all my time to myself — that's just as well; for, I
forgot to tell you — I've been dismissed —

MRS. STOCKMANN (*sighing*). Yes — I expected that!

DR. STOCKMANN. — and now they want to take away my practice, too! Well — let them! There are always the poor
people — those that can't afford to pay; they're really the
ones that need me most, you see. But, by God, they're
going to hear from me! I'll harangue them every single day
— "in season and out of season," as somebody or other
put it.

MRS. STOCKMANN. Haven't you done enough talking, Tomas,
dear?

DR. STOCKMANN. Don't be absurd, Katrine! Do you think I'd
allow public opinion, and the solid majority, and all the
rest of it to drive me from the field? No, thank you! Besides, my aim is perfectly simple and straightforward. I
just want to din into the heads of these poor misguided
mongrels that these so-called Liberals are freedom's bitter-
est enemies — that party programs do nothing but stifle
living truths — that justice and morality are being turned
upside down by expediency and greed — until eventually
life itself will scarcely be worth living! Surely I ought to
be able to make the people see that, Captain Horster? Don't
you think so?

HORSTER. Perhaps; I don't know much about such things myself.

DR. STOCKMANN. It's all quite simple — let me explain it to
you! First, the party bosses have got to be wiped out;
they're just like wolves, you see — like ravening wolves!
They batten on the small fry. In order to keep themselves

alive they devour literally hundreds of them every single year. Take Hovstad and Aslaksen, for instance — think of the small fry they devour! Or if they don't devour them, they debase them and corrupt them till all they're good for is to become Homeowners or subscribers to *The People's Monitor!* (*Sits on the edge of the table.*) Come here, Katrine! Just look at that radiant, gallant sunshine! And doesn't the air smell fresh and clear this morning?

MRS. STOCKMANN. If only we could live on air and sunshine, Tomas, dear!

DR. STOCKMANN. Oh, but we can — with a little help from you! You'll scrimp and save away and we shall manage splendidly. That's the least of my worries. One thing does worry me though; where am I to find a decent, freedom-loving man to carry on the work after I'm gone?

PETRA. Don't start worrying about that, Father; you've still got lots of time ahead of you! — Why, look; here are the boys!

[*Ejlif and Morten enter from the living room.*]

MRS. STOCKMANN. What's happened? It's not a holiday today!

MORTEN. We got into a fight with some of the other boys —

EJLIF. No, we didn't! They got into a fight with us!

MORTEN. And Mr. Rörlund said we'd better stay home for a few days.

DR. STOCKMANN (*snapping his fingers and jumping down from the table*). That gives me an idea! Yes, by heaven, that gives me an idea! You shan't set foot in that blasted school again!

THE BOYS. Not go to school!

MRS. STOCKMANN. But, Tomas —

DR. STOCKMANN. Never again, I say! I'll start teaching you myself; or, better still — you shan't be taught a blessed thing —

MORTEN. Hurrah!

DR. STOCKMANN. The only thing I'll teach you, is to become decent, freedom-loving men. — You'll help me, Petra, won't you?

PETRA. I'd love to, Father.

DR. STOCKMANN. We'll have the school in the very room where they branded me an enemy of the People. But we'll have to have more pupils — I want a dozen boys at least.

MRS. STOCKMANN. You'll never get them to come, Tomas; not in this town.

DR. STOCKMANN. Wait and see. (*To the boys*) You must know a few street urchins — some regular guttersnipes — ?

MORTEN. Oh, yes, Father! I know lots of them!

DR. STOCKMANN. Then find a few good specimens and bring them to me. I'm going to experiment with a few mongrels for a change; there's plenty of good raw material there.

MORTEN. What are we to do, Father, when we grow up to be decent, freedom-loving men?

DR. STOCKMANN. Drive the wolves away to the Far West, my boys!

MRS. STOCKMANN. But suppose it's the wolves who drive you away, Tomas, dear?

DR. STOCKMANN. Drive *me* away! Are you stark raving mad, Katrine? I'm the strongest man in the town! Don't you know that?

MRS. STOCKMANN. The strongest — ? You mean, *now*?

DR. STOCKMANN. Yes! I'll even go so far as to say that I'm one of the strongest men in the whole world!

MORTEN. Are you really, Father?

DR. STOCKMANN (*dropping his voice*). Hush! You mustn't say a word about it yet; I've made a great discovery, you see.

MRS. STOCKMANN. Not another, Tomas, dear!

DR. STOCKMANN. Another, yes — another! (*Gathers them round him and speaks in a confidential tone.*) And I'll tell you what it is: the strongest man in the world is the man who stands alone.

MRS. STOCKMANN (*smiles and shakes her head*). Oh, Tomas, dear — !

PETRA (*grasps his hands and says with eyes full of faith*). Father!

CURTAIN

QUESTIONS

1. Why is Petra fired? Why are the Stockmanns turned out of their house? Ibsen uses the principal and the landlord to represent the behavior

of average people during a time of stress and instability. Whom do they side with?

2. The Mayor offers to reinstall Dr. Stockmann as Medical Director of the baths if he will apologize for his "error," then withdraws his offer. Why? How do both these actions characterize Peter Stockmann? Why did Ibsen make these two men brothers?

3. Why does Kiil buy up stocks in the baths? What choice does he present Dr. Stockmann with? Why does Dr. Stockmann see in Kiil the devil himself?

4. What scheme do Hovstad and Aslaksen suspect Dr. Stockmann and Kiil to be partners in? Why would this suspicion occur naturally to them?

5. Dr. Stockmann finally decides to stay in his own town. Why? Has he compromised his principles?

AFTER THE CURTAIN

Conflict and Structure

Drama is made of quarrels — but quarrels so ordered and patterned as to arouse emotion and heighten the meaning of events.

The dramatic pattern of *An Enemy of the People* is expressed in a five-act structure, each act serving to develop or advance the action in an important way. To discover the meaning of this structure, we can label each act, noting the key events.

ACT ONE: The Truth Discovered. (The baths are found to be polluted.)

ACT TWO: The Gathering of Forces. (The liberal press and small homeowners join Dr. Stockmann against the power structure of the town.)

ACT THREE: Collapse of Support. (The consequences of the discovery of the bath's pollution — high taxes, loss of tourists — causes support to drop away.)

Can you complete the outline for Acts Four and Five?

In the conflict between Dr. Stockmann and those that oppose him, at what point do the Stockmann forces reach a peak? At what point do Dr. Stockmann's fortunes begin to decline? Why may it be said that the structure of this play is symmetrical?

If Dr. Stockmann's outward fortunes undergo a decline, his inner spirit, on the other hand, follows a different pattern. Losing his allies in Act Three only seems to strengthen the Doctor's determination. But with his job gone, his friends alienated, his wife's inheritance lost, and he himself the object of public scorn, Dr. Stockmann reaches a point of spiritual anguish at which the temptation to abandon his principles becomes all but irresistible. This peak of dramatic tension may be called the play's *climax*. Where does it occur? How does the timing of the climax contribute to its dramatic power? (The question posed at the climax seems to be: "How much can an honorable man be expected to lose before he is willing to sacrifice his integrity?" What answer does the play seem to give to this question?)

Irony of Language and Situation

To understand *Enemy* fully, a reader must appreciate the effects of irony in the language and situations in the play. *Verbal irony* occurs when the author intentionally says the opposite of what he means. This kind of irony takes place in everyday life as well as in art, and it can be light — "Great weather, isn't it?" we say in the midst of a driving rainstorm — or it can be bitter, as when a vicious gangster and murderer was termed "Pretty Boy" Floyd.

Is Ibsen's title ironic? Is Dr. Stockmann really "an enemy of the People"? If not, what is he? In the play, who are the real enemies of the people? Is the irony light or bitter?

Situational, or *dramatic*, *irony* occurs when a speaker is less aware than the audience of the full impact or meaning of what he has said. In the play by Sophocles, King Oedipus vows to find and punish the slayer of Thebes' last king, unaware that he himself was the murderer.

In view of what we later learn about Dr. Stockmann and his town, explain the irony of Stockmann's speech from Act One:

BILLING. Hovstad, don't you think the town should get up some sort of a demonstration in Dr. Stockmann's honor?

HOVSTAD. I shall certainly propose it.

BILLING. I'll talk it over with Aslaksen.

DR. STOCKMANN. No, no — my dear friends! friends! You musn't bother with such nonsense; I won't hear of it! And, I warn you, Katrine — if the Board of Directors should think of offering me a raise in salary — I shall refuse it. I simply won't accept!

Is the speaker aware of the irony of his words? What kind of irony are we dealing with? What is ironic about Aslaksen's insistence that he is a moderate? About Stockmann's remark that it is "very flattering to have the support of an enlightened, independent paper"?

What other example of irony can you find in the play? Are all these instances of irony equally effective?

Theme and Symbol

Although *An Enemy of the People* is basically a realistic play, it employs dramatic symbolism. A symbol is an object that stands both for itself and for something additional beyond itself. An example from everyday life is the wedding ring which — while certainly a gold band — also stands for the love and commitment which bind a marriage together. Similarly, the American flag — literally a piece of colored cloth — also stands for Washington, Lincoln, Bull Run, the Peace Corps — for all the sacrifices, ideals, and ordeals our country has experienced.

The difference between symbols of this kind and literary symbols is that a writer will often take a neutral object and endow it with symbolic overtones by his treatment of it. This is not always a conscious process; it often happens that something absorbs or disturbs a writer so much that he has to write about it, to relieve his feelings. In doing so, he begins to see that the thing he is dealing with has the power to suggest wider implications. Thus Dr. Stockmann (and perhaps Ibsen as well) finally saw that the baths were symbolic of the spiritual corruption in the town. The pollution of the water becomes the overwhelming symbol of the decay infecting the town's soul. (Is the fact of the baths' pollution also ironic? Why do people go to health spas?)

But Ibsen's symbolism goes beyond this. He supports the central symbol of corruption by devising appropriate names — the meanings are lost in translation — for his people, to emphasize their essential traits of character. Here are the English equivalents:

STOCKMANN: Chastiser, punisher.

ASLAKSEN (ALLSLAGS): Of various kinds, a mongrel.

BILLING: Low priced, cheap.

HOVSTAD: Capital city. (Ironically appropriate for a small-town newspaper tycoon.)

Can you think of any other elements of symbolism in the play? Are Peter's cap and stick symbolic? If so, what do they stand for? Consider also the stress given to the meat eaten in Act One; the drinks and the cigars. Why is there such attention paid to furniture in the stage directions? Do the material possessions of Stockmann's world threaten to interfere with people's moral progress? Do their belongings wall in their principles as well as their bodies?

Reading, Writing, and Dramatization

1. In the final act, Dr. Stockmann can be seen either as a saint or a madman for sacrificing his life and family to a community that doesn't have the courage to recognize the truth. If a director felt Stockmann was a fool, how would the actors "play" the final two pages of the text? How would the actor's interpretation differ if the director saw Stockmann as a kind of saint? How would the voice, looks, and gestures of the actor playing Stockmann differ between the first and second interpretations? Give dramatic readings to illustrate these contrasting interpretations.

2. You are a reporter working for Hovstad and have been asked to cover the town meeting for *The People's Monitor*. Write a 200-word account from Hovstad's view of what occurred at the meeting.

Now you are a friend and supporter of Dr. Stockmann working for a liberal out-of-town paper. Write a 200-word account from Stockmann's side of what happened there.

Write headlines for each of the stories.

3. You are Dr. Stockmann. Write a letter to your sons explaining to them in language they would understand why you have decided to remain in a town that hates you.

4. Explain to someone who has not read the play how Dr. Stockmann's view of democracy and majority rule changes during the course of the drama. Support your paper with short quotations.

5. In *The Saturday Evening Post* for May 25, 1963, look up Charles McCarry's report on the winter ski season at Zermatt, Switzerland. Report on what ways Zermatt is like the town in Ibsen's play. In what ways does it differ? Why did Zermatt hide the news of its epidemic?

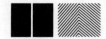

Cyrano de Bergerac

BEFORE THE CURTAIN

To understand the disfigured warrior-poet named Cyrano de Bergerac, we must remember that — above all else — he sees himself as a knight and therefore expects himself to follow a knightly code of chivalric conduct, even though the world in which he exists is largely corrupt, immoral, petty, and backbiting. For Cyrano lives in the world of seventeenth-century France, a country ruled by the brilliant and cynical Cardinal Richelieu, who gained power through the favoritism of the King's mother, only to replace her minister with his own. But if France was riddled by intrigue, this did not dampen the enthusiasm of the educated for elegance in dress, carriage, and — especially — language. As if to hide decay behind a glittering surface, the fashionable talked in elevated and refined language, attempting to purge their speech of baseness: epigrams, puns, and elaborate metaphors were greeted with delight, and a man was expected to be quick and accurate with both his rapier and his tongue. While Cyrano was such a man, he was also more than that. For in essence Cyrano believes and acts on values that the rest of the world pretends to respect but actually despises because it can't live up to them. These beliefs that so set Cyrano apart from his surroundings, that make his white plume glow so brightly amid a world of pickpockets and hypocrites, are the faith he has in truth, in courage, and in courtesy. These are his real masters.

A special kind of knight, Cyrano pledges his loyalties to these ideals rather than to kings: he views the intrigues of the French court with bemused contempt. Whenever he senses sham or hypocrisy, Cyrano exposes and denounces it, creating enemies by the fistful. Yet he must always speak the truth, never lie or hedge, for his integrity is at stake each time he speaks. More than a talker, Cyrano is also a doer: he duels with those who offend or challenge him — or with those who threaten the weak and friendless — relying on his personal skill and courage to enforce his words. But above all, Cyrano is courteous in his treatment of women. In the tradition of chivalry, he makes them the object of his adoration. He views them as semi-divine creations to be praised, honored, pampered, and — above all — kept from hurt and ugliness. And here is the great irony of Cyrano's life, for his own face, deformed by a huge, protruding nose, is hideous and grotesque.

How can Cyrano, so dedicated to beauty, overcome his own ugliness? He tries by his deeds and by his words — words that prance and soar and shine as he writes love letters for another man to the woman they both love, or as he runs an enemy through to punctuate the conclusion of a poem he has been composing while dueling. But Cyrano is also scarred by his disfigurement: afraid of ridicule, he strikes out at others before they have a chance to snicker at him, and with reckless wit mocks his own ugliness while forbidding others to so much as sneeze in his presence.

All of Cyrano's virtues as well as his vices — his courage, vanity, bitterness, eloquence, and loyalty — seem somehow to emanate from a single source or quality, symbolized by his lofty white plume. If you can grasp its meaning, you will come close to touching the heart of Cyrano's mystery.

As you will see from the stage settings, *Cyrano* was designed to overwhelm the eyes as well as the ears of its audiences: the first act occurs in a tennis court converted into a theater complete with its own audience and stage; the second act takes place in a bakery with fireplace, ovens, piles of pastries, and a chandelier from which hang pheasants, ducks, partridges, and geese; and act four is set on a battlefield with a rampart or protective wall looming across the entire rear stage, while nearer the audience are tents, scattered weapons, sentries, and campfires. This is the kind of spectacular theatrical display largely reserved now for the movies, especially in the startling effects possible through Cinerama or other multi-screen processes. Yet the largeness of *Cyrano's* sets and cast — forty-three characters plus a crowd of extras, soldiers, citizens, fops, etc. — reflects the larger-than-life characteristics of a hero who would take on a hundred opposing swordsmen or run the gauntlet of enemy fire twice a day to mail a love letter.

While reading *Cyrano,* try to widen your mind's eye. Here, all is bigger and grander than in real life: sets, battles, gestures, speeches, colors, and — especially — one lone and protuberant nose.

Cyrano de Bergerac

EDMOND ROSTAND

Translated by Harold Whitehall

Characters

Cyrano de Bergerac	A Light-Horseman
Christian de Neuvillette	The Doorkeeper
Count de Guiche	The Citizen
Ragueneau	His Son
Le Bret	A Pickpocket
De Valvert	A Spectator
Lignière	A Member of the Watch
Montfleury	The Capuchin
Bellerose	Two Musicians (Pages)
Jodelet	Poets
cuigy	Pastry Cooks
Brissaille	Roxane
Carbon de Castel-Jaloux	Mother Margüerite
The Gascony Cadets	Sister Marthe
First Fop	Lise
Second Fop	A Refreshment Girl
Third Fop	The Duenna
An Annoying Bore	Sister Claire
Two Musketeers	An Actress
Pages	The Soubrette
A Spanish Officer	The Flower Girl

The crowd, citizens of Paris, tradesmen, fops, musketeers, pickpockets, pastry cooks, poets, Gascony cadets, actors, violinists, pages, children, Spanish soldiers, spectators, *précieuses*, actresses, citizens' wives, nuns, etc.

TIME: *The first four acts in 1640; the fifth in 1655.*

ACT ONE

A THEATRICAL PERFORMANCE AT THE HÔTEL DE BOURGOGNE

SCENE 1

The Hall of the Hôtel de Bourgogne, Paris, in 1640. A sort of "real" tennis court adapted and decorated for use as a theater. It was, in actual fact, the first theater in the French capital. The auditorium is oblong, but we see it as a triangle; one of its sides runs from downstage right to upstage left and forms an angle with the stage, which is seen obliquely. The wings on both sides of this stage are cluttered with benches. Its curtain is two tapestries which can be drawn apart. Above the Harlequin draperies[1] (covering the top and sides of the stage front) are the Royal Arms of Louis XIII. Wide steps lead down from the stage platform to the auditorium. On each side of these steps, places for the violinists of the orchestra. The footlights are candles.

Two tiers of galleries in the auditorium, one above the other; the lower is divided into boxes. No seats in the pit,[2] our stage proper. At the back of the pit, that is to say downstage right, a few tiered benches; under a staircase leading to the upper seats and visible only in its lowest portion is a sort of refreshment stand furnished with small candelabra, vases of flowers, glasses, plates of cakes, bottles, etc.

[1] **Harlequin draperies:** name given to the frames at the right and left of the stage, supporting a drapery which comes down above the front part of the stage.

[2] **pit:** sunken space in front of the stage, where the theatergoers with the cheapest tickets would stand for the performance.

The entrance to this theater is center backstage under the boxes. It is a large door, halfway open to admit the audience. On the door panels, in several corners and above the refreshment stand, are red posters reading LA CLORISE.[3]

At the rise of the curtain, the auditorium is in half darkness and empty. Chandeliers have been lowered to the center of the pit in readiness for lighting.

The audience arriving gradually: cavaliers, citizens, lackeys, pages, a pickpocket, the doorkeeper, etc. Then the fops (Fr. les Marquis), Cuigy, Brissaille, the Refreshment Girl, violinists of the orchestra, etc.

(An uproar of voices behind the door. A cavalier enters suddenly.)

DOORKEEPER *(following him)*. Hey! Your fifteen cents!
CAVALIER. I come in free.
DOORKEEPER. Why?
CAVALIER. I belong to the King's Light Horse.
DOORKEEPER *(to another cavalier just entering)*. And you?
SECOND CAVALIER. I don't have to pay.
DOORKEEPER. But —
SECOND CAVALIER. I'm a musketeer.
FIRST CAVALIER *(to second)*. The play doesn't start till two o'clock. The pit is empty. Let's fence a while.

[*They fence with foils they have brought.*]

LACKEY *(entering)*. Pst — Flanquin!
ANOTHER *(already in)*. You, Champagne?
FIRST LACKEY *(revealing articles drawn from his doublet)*. Cards. Dice. *(Sits on the ground.)* Let's go.
SECOND *(also sitting)*. All right, my lad.
FIRST LACKEY *(unpocketing a candle end which he lights and sticks on the floor)*. I've stolen a little of my master's luster.
MEMBER OF THE WATCH *(to a flower girl walking in)*. It's a treat to come in before they light up. *(Puts his arm around her.)*

[3] *La Clorise:* name of the play being performed — a pastoral drama by Balthazar Baro, a writer popular in his day, but now forgotten.

CAVALIER (*hit by a foil*). Touché!

CARD PLAYER. Clubs!

MEMBER OF THE WATCH (*pursuing girl*). A kiss!

FLOWER GIRL (*evading him*). They'll see us.

MEMBER OF THE WATCH (*dragging her into a dark corner*). Not a chance!

A MAN (*joining others on the ground who have brought refreshments*). When you come in early, it's nice to have a snack.

A CITIZEN (*leading in his son*). Let's stand here, son.

CARD PLAYER. Aces — Three of a kind!

A MAN (*sitting down on the ground with the others already seated and taking a bottle from under his cloak*). Your genuine toper[4] will gulp down bourgogne (*drinks*) in the Hôtel de Bourgogne.

CITIZEN (*to his son*). You'd think we were in the stews.[5] (*Points at the drinker with his cane.*) Boozers! (*One of the fencers, recoiling, jostles him.*) Brawlers! (*Stumbles among the card players.*) Gamblers!

MEMBER OF THE WATCH (*behind him, pestering the girl*). Kiss?

CITIZEN (*hurriedly drawing his son away*). Good Heavens! To think that in a place like this they actually played Rotrou!

HIS SON. Even Corneille.[6]

A BAND OF PAGES (*entering hand in hand, singing and dancing*). Tra la la la la la la la lu!

DOORKEEPER (*severely, to the pages*). No nonsense, lads.

FIRST PAGE (*with wounded dignity*). Sir, the very idea! (*To the second page as soon as the doorkeeper has turned his back*) Got some string?

SECOND PAGE. And a fishhook.

FIRST PAGE. We could fish for wigs (*pointing*) up there.

A PICKPOCKET (*calling together around him several tough-looking men*). Now, young crooks, here's the lay. Seeing as it's your first try at lifting purses, you —

SECOND PAGE (*calling others already in the upper gallery*).

---

[4] **toper:** hard drinker.

[5] **the stews:** district of brothels.

[6] **Corneille** (cŏr·nā'): Pierre Corneille (1606–84), the French Shakespeare. His masterpiece, *The Cid*, was the first great classic French drama.

Hey! Got your blow guns?

THIRD PAGE (*from above*). I'll say. Peas, too. (*Peppers them with peas.*)

CITIZEN'S SON (*to citizen*). What's the play?

CITIZEN. *Clorise.*

SON. Who wrote it?

CITIZEN. Monsieur Balthazar Baro. A masterpiece that —

[*Walks towards the back arm in arm with his son.*]

PICKPOCKET (*to his confederates*). You cut the lace knee-ruffles just like this —

A SPECTATOR (*to another, pointing towards an upper corner*). Look, I was up there, the first night of *The Cid.*

PICKPOCKET (*motioning as if picking pockets*). Snitch the watches —

CITIZEN (*coming forward again with his son*). You'll see some famous actors —

PICKPOCKET (*his hands suggesting furtive little jerks*). Then the handkerchiefs —

CITIZEN. Montfleury —

SOMEONE (*shouting from the upper gallery*). Light up!

CITIZEN. Bellerose, l'Épy, la Beaupré, Jodelet —

A PAGE (*in the pit*). Here's the refreshment girl.

REFRESHMENT GIRL (*behind the refreshment stand*). Oranges, milk, raspberry press, citronade.

[*Confusion at the door.*]

TENOR VOICE. Room, you louts!

A LACKEY (*surprised*). Fops? In the pit?

ANOTHER LACKEY. Oh, for the moment.

[*Enter a group of young noblemen.*]

FOP (*seeing the hall is half empty*). What! Have we come in like haberdashers? No fuss disturbing people? No stepping on their toes? Too bad. (*Finding himself among other noblemen already in*) Cuigy! Brissaille!

[*General embracing.*]

CUIGY. Faithful comrades! Yes, we came before they lit the candles.

FOP. Oh, don't mention it! It puts me in such a temper —

ANOTHER FOP. Take heart, Marquis. Here comes the lamp-lighter.

ENTIRE AUDIENCE (*hailing the entrance of the lamplighter*). Hurrah! (*They crowd around the chandeliers as he lights them. Lignière enters the pit arm in arm with Christian de Neuvillette. Lignière, somewhat untidy, has the look of an aristocratic drunkard. Christian, dressed in an elegant but somewhat old-fashioned style, appears preoccupied; his attention is fixed on the boxes.*)

SCENE 2

The same; Christian, Lignière; then Ragueneau, and Le Bret.

CUIGY. Lignière!

BRISSAILLE (*laughing*). What! Not drunk yet?

LIGNIÈRE (*in a low voice to Christian*). Shall I present you? (*Sign of assent from Christian*) Baron de Neuvillette.

[*An exchange of bows.*]

THE AUDIENCE (*cheering the rise of the first lighted chandelier*). Hurrah!

CUIGY (*to Brissaille, while looking at Christian*). Handsome fellow . . . very!

FIRST FOP (*overhearing*). Pfui!

LIGNIÈRE (*presenting them to Christian*). Messieurs de Cuigy, de Brissaille.

CHRISTIAN (*bowing*). Delighted.

FIRST FOP (*to second*). Handsome enough, but scarcely dressed in style.

LIGNIÈRE (*to Cuigy*). He is just in from Touraine.[7]

CHRISTIAN. Yes, I've not been over twenty days in town. I enter the Guards tomorrow, as Gascony Cadet.

FIRST FOP (*looking over the people entering the boxes*). There's Judge Aubrey's wife.

REFRESHMENT GIRL. Oranges, milk —

THE VIOLINISTS (*tuning up*). La! . . . La!

CUIGY (*to Christian, motioning towards the auditorium which is rapidly filling*). Quite a crowd.

[7] **Touraine:** formerly a French province.

CHRISTIAN. Quite.

FIRST FOP. All the smart set.

[*The fops identify the various elegantly turned-out ladies entering the boxes. Exchange of bows and smiles.*]

SECOND FOP. Mesdames de Guéménée . . . .

CUIGY. De Bois-Dauphin . . . .

FIRST FOP. Whom we've all loved — in our time.

BRISSAILLE. De Chavigny —

SECOND FOP. Who is playing with all our hearts.

LIGNIÈRE. Look there! Monsieur de Corneille is back from Rouen.

CITIZEN'S SON (*to his father*). Is the Academy here?[8]

CITIZEN. Several members. (*Pointing*) Boudu, Boissat, Cureau de la Chambre, Porchères, Colomby, Bourzeys, Bourdon, Arbaud — immortal, deathless names! Wonderful![9]

FIRST FOP. Attention! Our *précieuses*[10] are going to their seats. Barthénoïde, Urimédonte, Cassandace, Félixérie . . .

SECOND FOP. Exquisite names! Divine! Do you know them all, Marquis?

FIRST FOP. All their names, Marquis.

LIGNIÈRE (*drawing Christian aside*). Look, my friend, I came to do you a favor. But since the lady isn't here, I shall go back to my cups.

CHRISTIAN (*imploringly*). You must stay! You lampoon[11] the Court and Town. You know everyone. Only you can tell me her name. The one I'm dying with love for.

FIRST VIOLINIST (*striking his stand with his bow*). Ready, gentlemen! (*He raises his bow.*)

REFRESHMENT GIRL. Macaroons, lemonade . . . .

[*The violinists start playing.*]

[8] the Academy: Founded by Richelieu in 1635, the Academy consists of forty elected members (sometimes called "the forty immortals"). The Academy governs French literary effort and awards prizes.

[9] immortal, deathless names! Wonderful: forgotten writers: Rostand is being ironic. Three years later Rostand himself was elected to the Academy because of *Cyrano*.

[10] *précieuses* (prā·syœz): term applied to women affected in language and manners. In conversing with friends and suitors, these women used elaborate language, full of farfetched comparisons and witty plays on words.

[11] lampoon: ridicule.

CHRISTIAN. I'm afraid she's too experienced, too subtly cultured, for a plain and timid soldier such as I am. I have no claim to wit; no courage to address her. I'm bewildered by this fancy modern language — That's the place, back there. That empty box. That's where she always sits.

LIGNIÈRE (*starting to leave*). Well, I'll be off.

CHRISTIAN (*stopping him*). You've got to stay.

LIGNIÈRE. I can't. D'Assoucy is waiting at the tavern. I'd shrivel with thirst here.

REFRESHMENT GIRL (*passing in front of him with her tray*). Orangeade?

LIGNIÈRE. Pfui!

REFRESHMENT GIRL. Milk?

LIGNIÈRE. Pfui again!

REFRESHMENT GIRL. Muscatel?

LIGNIÈRE. Wait a minute. (*To Christian*) At that, I might stay a little longer. Let us test this muscatel. (*Sits down by the refreshment stand. The girl pours out some muscatel.*)

THE AUDIENCE (*applauding the entrance of a plump, lively little fellow*). Ragueneau! Hurrah!

LIGNIÈRE (*to Christian*). Ragueneau, the famous pastry cook.

RAGUENEAU (*in a pastry-cook's Sunday best, making a bee-line for Lignière*). Have you seen Monsieur Cyrano?

LIGNIÈRE (*introducing Ragueneau to Christian*). The pastry cook of players and of poets.

RAGUENEAU (*plainly confused*). You honor me too much.

LIGNIÈRE. Quiet, Maecenas![12]

RAGUENEAU. These gentlemen give me custom —

LIGNIÈRE. On credit. A most talented poet himself —

RAGUENEAU. So they say! So they say!

LIGNIÈRE. Mad about poetry.

RAGUENEAU. It is true that for an odelet[13] —

LIGNIÈRE. You pay a tart —

RAGUENEAU (*deprecatingly*). Oh, a tartlet.

LIGNIÈRE. Pure modesty! And what do you pay for a villanelle?[14]

[12] **Maecenas:** Lignière is mocking Ragueneau. Maecenas was "Caesar's right hand" and patron of the Roman poets Virgil and Horace. Ragueneau is "a pastry cook."

[13] **odelet:** short poem. (An ode is a lyric poem characterized by exalted feeling; its lines vary in number and length.)

[14] **villanelle:** a chiefly French verse form with a fixed rhyme scheme and repeating lines.

RAGUENEAU. Rolls —

LIGNIÈRE (*severely*). Vanilla rolls! He loves the theater, too. Don't you?

RAGUENEAU. Idolize it!

LIGNIÈRE. And pay for your seat in cakes, isn't that so? Confidentially, what did your seat cost today?

RAGUENEAU. Four custards. Fifteen cream puffs. (*Looking everywhere at once*) Monsieur Cyrano isn't here. What a surprise!

LIGNIÈRE. Why?

RAGUENEAU. Montfleury is going to act.

LIGNIÈRE. Why, yes! That walking wine-cask plays Phédon's rôle tonight. What's that to Cyrano?

RAGUENEAU. Don't you know? He has forbidden Montfleury to take the stage again for an entire month. He detests him.

LIGNIÈRE (*who has reached his fourth glass*). Well?

RAGUENEAU. Montfleury is going to act!

CUIGY (*who has drawn near with his companions*). Cyrano can't stop him.

RAGUENEAU. I have come to see.

FIRST FOP. Who is this Cyrano?

CUIGY. Quite a hand with a rapier.

SECOND FOP. A gentleman?

CUIGY. He'll do. He is a cadet in the Guards. (*Indicating a gentleman walking here and there as if in search of someone*) His friend, Le Bret, could tell you. (*Calling*) Le Bret! (*Le Bret comes up.*) Looking for Bergerac?

LE BRET. I'm uneasy —

CUIGY. I appeal to you. Isn't he quite extraordinary?

LE BRET (*affectionately*). The most exquisite spirit under the moon!

RAGUENEAU. Rhymester!

CUIGY. Swordster!

BRISSAILLE. Physicist!

LE BRET. Lutanist![15]

LIGNIÈRE. And what a strange-looking fellow to boot!

RAGUENEAU. He's scarcely the kind of man our sober Philippe de Champaigne would choose to paint. But the late Jacques

---

[15] **Lutanist:** lute player.

Callot now — he might have put Cyrano among his masques[16] as the maddest fire-eater of them all. Imagine him: triple-plumed felt hat, doublet puffed out with half a dozen skirts, cloak lifted by his sword like the insolent tailfeathers of a fighting cock. He's prouder than any bravo that Gascony, the Mother Goose of bravos, ever weaned. And, to cap all, from his Punchinello ruff[17] he sports . . . a nose. Gentlemen, what a nose! A nose to end all noses! Anyone else nosed like that and you'd say, "Impossible! A pure exaggeration!" Then you would smile and think, "He'll take it off." But Cyrano, he never takes it off.

LE BRET (*nodding his head*). He never takes it off — and you don't mention it, or else —

RAGUENEAU (*proudly*). His sword is one blade of the shears of Fate.

FIRST FOP (*shrugging his shoulders*). I'll wager he won't come.

RAGUENEAU. I'll bet a chicken à la Ragueneau he will!

FIRST FOP (*laughing*). Done!

[*Admiring murmurs. Roxane has just appeared in her box. She seats herself in front, her duenna[18] at the back. Christian, paying the Refreshment Girl, fails to see her.*]

SECOND FOP (*with inchoate cries of admiration*). Gentlemen! She is too, too ravishing!

FIRST FOP. A peach that smiles with strawberry lips.

SECOND FOP. But cold — cold. If you came close you'd catch cold — in the heart.

CHRISTIAN (*looks up, sees Roxane, and grips Lignière's arm*). That's her!

LIGNIÈRE (*looking*). So she's the one.

CHRISTIAN. Quick! Tell me. I'm afraid.

LIGNIÈRE (*sipping his muscatel*). Magdeleine Robin, called Roxane. A genuine *précieuse*.

CHRISTIAN. So I feared.

LIGNIÈRE. Heart-free. Orphan. Cousin of the Cyrano they've just mentioned —

---

[16] **masques:** short allegorical plays performed by masked actors.
[17] **Punchinello ruff:** frilled stiff collar worn by the well-known clown of Italian comedy.
[18] *duenna:* woman who serves as chaperone for a younger woman.

[*At this moment, a very fashionable nobleman, wearing the ribbon of the Order of the Holy Ghost across his chest, enters the box and stands talking for a while with Roxane.*]

CHRISTIAN (*starting*). Who is that man?

LIGNIÈRE (*blinking, a little drunk*). Well! Well! The Count de Guiche. Loves her, but married to the niece of Armand de Richelieu. Wants to marry off Roxane to a certain sorry lord, Monsieur de Valvert, a viscount[19] — and accommodating. She doesn't consent, but well — De Guiche has ways and means! He could make things unpleasant for an unprotected girl. Matter of fact, I've revealed his sly maneuvering in a song which — Ho! He ought to bear me malice! The ending was really biting. Listen! —

[*He rises staggering, lifts his glass, is about to sing.*]

CHRISTIAN. No! Good-bye!

LIGNIÈRE. You're going?

CHRISTIAN. To Monsieur de Valvert's.

LIGNIÈRE. Careful. *He'll* kill you. (*Indicating Roxane by the direction of his glance*) Wait. Someone's looking.

CHRISTIAN. So she is!

[*He muses on Roxane. The group of pickpockets, seeing his head in the air and mouth open, close in on him.*]

LIGNIÈRE. I am the one to go. I am thirsty. My friends are waiting — in the taverns. (*Goes out, unsteady on his feet.*)

LE BRET (*who has completed a turn round the auditorium, in a relieved tone to Ragueneau*). No Cyrano yet.

RAGUENEAU (*incredulously*). All the same —

LE BRET. I can only hope he didn't see the playbill.

THE AUDIENCE. Curtain! Curtain!

SCENE 3

The same, without Lignière; De Guiche, Valvert, then Montfleury. De Guiche, who has left Roxane's box, crosses the pit, surrounded by obsequious noblemen, among them the Viscount de Valvert.

---

[19] **viscount** (vī'kount'): nobleman who ranks below a count. (A count is equivalent to an English earl.)

A FOP. How they fawn on this De Guiche!

ANOTHER. Just another Gascon.

THE FIRST. A cold and subtle Gascon. That kind go far. We'd better pay respects.

[*They approach De Guiche.*]

SECOND FOP. Magnificent ribbons! What color, Count de Guiche? *Kiss-me-darling,* or *Hind's Breast?*

DE GUICHE. This is *Sick Spaniard.*

FIRST FOP. Singularly fitting! For soon, thanks to your valor, things will go ill for Spaniards there in Flanders.

DE GUICHE. I am going on the stage. Will you join me? (*Followed by all the fops and noblemen he proceeds toward the stage. He turns and calls*) Come on, Valvert!

CHRISTIAN (*listening and looking on, starts at the name*). The Viscount, eh? Well! Into that face of his I'll throw my — (*Putting his hand in his pocket, he finds the hand of a pickpocket. Turns quickly.*) What's this?

THE PICKPOCKET. Ow!

CHRISTIAN (*without letting him go*). I was looking for a glove.

PICKPOCKET (*with a piteous smile*). And you found a hand. (*Changing tone and whispering hastily*) If you'll let me go, I'll tell you a secret.

CHRISTIAN (*still keeping hold*). Well?

PICKPOCKET. Lignière. He just left you —

CHRISTIAN (*still keeping hold*). Yes?

PICKPOCKET. He's near his last gasp. A song he made displeased a certain great personage. A hundred men — I'm one of them — will ambush him tonight.

CHRISTIAN. A hundred! Who hired them?

PICKPOCKET. A secret.

CHRISTIAN (*shrugging*). Oh!

PICKPOCKET (*with great dignity*). Professional secret.

CHRISTIAN. Where will they be posted?

PICKPOCKET. Right on his way home near the Porte de Nesle. Better warn him.

CHRISTIAN (*letting his wrist go*). Where can I find him?

PICKPOCKET. Scour the taverns — the Golden Wine-Press,

the Fir Cone, the Sundered Belt, the Torches Twain, the Three Funnels — leave a note of warning everywhere.

CHRISTIAN. I'll go. Ruffians! One against a hundred! (*Looking lovingly at Roxane*) To have to leave her! (*Looking angrily at Valvert*) And him! But I've got to save Lignière. (*He runs out.*)

[*De Guiche, the Viscount, the fops, all the nobles have vanished behind the curtain, to take their seats on the benches on the stage. The pit is completely full. Not an empty seat in the galleries and boxes.*]

THE AUDIENCE. Curtain!

A CITIZEN (*whose wig, hooked by a page in the upper gallery, flies away on the end of a string*). My wig!

JOYOUS SHOUTS. He is bald! Good for the pages! Ha! ha! ha!

CITIZEN (*furious, shaking his fists*). Little demon!

LAUGHTER AND SHOUTS (*beginning very loudly, then gradually diminishing*). Ha! ha! ha! ha! ha! ha!

[*Dead silence.*]

LE BRET (*surprised*). Why this sudden silence? (*A spectator whispers to him.*) Really?

SPECTATOR. On the best possible authority.

MURMURS (*through the audience*). Goodness — Is he here? — No! — Yes! — In the box with the grille. — The Cardinal![20] — The Cardinal! — The Cardinal!

A PAGE. The devil! No more fun for us!

[*Three taps on the stage announce the rise of the curtain. Everyone silent with expectation.*]

VOICE OF A FOP (*behind the curtain, breaking the silence*). Snuff that candle!

ANOTHER FOP (*poking his head through the opening in the curtain*). A chair!

[*A chair is passed from hand to hand over the heads of the audience. A fop, taking it, disappears, after throwing several kisses at the boxes.*]

A SPECTATOR. Silence!

[20] **The Cardinal:** Richelieu.

[*The three knocks are repeated. The curtain opens. The fops sit along the sides, in impudent poses. The backdrop represents the bluish setting suited to a pastoral.*[21] *Four little crystal chandeliers light the stage. The violinists play softly.*]

LE BRET (*under his breath, to Ragueneau*). Is Montfleury coming on stage?

RAGUENEAU (*also under his breath*). Yes, he has to begin.

LE BRET. And Cyrano isn't here?

RAGUENEAU. I've lost my wager.

LE BRET. So much the better.

[*Sound of bagpipes. Montfleury appears on the stage. Enormously fat, dressed in shepherd's costume, his hat trimmed with roses over one ear, he is blowing a be-ribboned bagpipe.*]

THE PIT (*applauding*). Bravo! Montfleury! Montfleury!

MONTFLEURY (*after bowing, commences his role of Phédon*).

"Happy the man, who in some solitude,
Far from the Court, in exile self-imbued,
Can list the breath of Zephyr in the wood — "

VOICE (*from the middle of the pit*). Rascal, didn't I exile you for a month?

[*Astonishment. Everyone turns round. Murmurs.*]

DIFFERENT VOICES. Hey! — What? — What is it?

[*People in the boxes stand to look.*]

CUIGY. There he is.

LE BRET (*terrified*). Cyrano!

THE VOICE. You king of clowns, get off that stage at once!

THE WHOLE AUDIENCE (*indignant*). Oh!

MONTFLEURY. But sir! —

THE VOICE. Oh! You'll be stubborn, will you?

DIFFERENT VOICES (*from the pit and boxes*). Hush! Enough! Act, Montfleury! Nothing to fear!

MONTFLEURY (*in a trembling voice*).

"Can list the breath of Zephyr in the wood —"

[21] **pastoral:** a work of art dealing with shepherds or rural life, usually contrasting the innocence of country life with the corruption of city and court life.

THE VOICE (*more menacing*). Must I plant the wood on your shoulders, you monarch of rascals?

[*An arm furnished with a cane leaps out above the heads of the audience.*]

MONTFLEURY (*in a voice growing gradually fainter*).

"Happy the man who in —"

[*The cane waves in the air.*]

THE VOICE. Out you go!
THE PIT. Oh!
MONTFLEURY (*choking*).

"Happy the man who in some sol —"

[*Cyrano emerges from the pit and stands on a chair, arms folded, hat cocked on one side, mustache bristling. His nose is terrifying.*]

CYRANO. Oh! I shall become really vexed!

[*Sensation at the sight of him.*]

SCENE 4

The same; Cyrano, then Bellerose, Jodelet.

MONTFLEURY (*to the fops*). Come to my aid, gentlemen.
A FOP (*indifferently*). On with the play, then.
CYRANO. Paunch! If you persist, I shall have to slap your face.
THE FOP. That's enough from you!
CYRANO. The young gentlemen will be seen, not heard. Otherwise, my cane might spoil their ribbons.
ALL THE FOPS (*standing*). This is too much. Montfleury —
CYRANO. Either he goes off, or I will slash his ears off, and (*gesturing*) rip him up!
A VOICE. Say!
CYRANO. He'd better go!
ANOTHER VOICE. Now wait a moment —
CYRANO. Not gone yet? (*Making the motion of rolling up his sleeves*) I'm going to slice that fat sausage on the stage as if it were a sideboard.

MONTFLEURY (*collecting all his dignity*). Sir, when you insult me, you insult the Muse![22]

CYRANO (*with great politeness*). If this Muse, who never knew you, ever knew you as you stand there, fat and lumpish as a pot, she'd kick you with her buskin.[23]

THE PIT. Montfleury! Montfleury! Give us Baro's play!

CYRANO (*to those shouting around him*). Have pity on my scabbard.. If you persist, it must yield up its mortal soul.

[*The circle around him widens immediately.*]

THE CROWD (*drawing back*). Careful now!

CYRANO (*to Montfleury*). Off the stage with you!

THE CROWD (*approaching, grumbling*). Oh! Oh!

CYRANO (*turning around suddenly*). Any objections?

[*Another general withdrawal.*]

A VOICE (*at the back, singing*).

> Monsieur de Cyrano,
> Your tyrannous caprice,
> Turns Cyrano to Tyrano:—
> They shall act *La Clorise*.

THE WHOLE AUDIENCE (*singing*). *La Clorise, La Clorise!*

CYRANO. If I hear that song again, I will knock you all down, every man Jack of you!

CITIZEN. Do you think you are a Samson?

CYRANO. Lend me your jawbone, sir?[24]

A LADY (*in one of the boxes*). This is unheard of!

A NOBLEMAN. Scandalous!

A CITIZEN. Vexatious!

A PAGE. And they call this entertainment!

THE PIT (*hissing*). Montfleury! Cyrano!

CYRANO. Silence, everybody.

THE PIT (*in a frenzy*). Hee-haw! Baa! Woof-woof! Cock-a-doodle-doo!

CYRANO. Silence! —

---

[22] **the Muse:** one of the nine goddesses in Greek mythology presiding over song and poetry and the arts and sciences.

[23] **buskin:** laced boot reaching halfway or more to the knee, with very thick soles, used in ancient tragedy to give the appearance of elevation and height.

[24] **Lend me your jawbone, sir:** Samson slew an army with the jawbone of an ass (Judges 15:15). Cyrano, then, is calling the citizen an ass.

A PAGE. Mee-ow!

CYRANO. Silence! I must insist on silence! Good! Now here's
a general challenge to the pit. Come on, young heroes, shall
I write down your names? Each in his proper turn? I'll
give you numbered tickets. Who'll be first? You, sir? No!
You? No! I promise I'll dispatch you with due honors.
Just lift your finger if you want to die. (*Silence*) Perhaps
it's modesty. You don't like looking at a *naked* blade?
What, not a single name? Not a finger lifted? Very well, to
proceed! (*Turning toward the stage where Montfleury is
waiting in an agony of apprehension*) I want to see the
theater healed of this monstrous canker.[25] If all else fails —
(*he puts his hand on his sword*) the lancet.[26]

MONTFLEURY. I think —

[*Cyrano gets down from the chair, seats himself in the
middle of the circle his words have cleared, and makes
himself thoroughly at home.*]

CYRANO. Full moon, I shall clap three times. At the third —
eclipse!

THE PIT (*amused*). Hurrah!

CYRANO (*clapping his hands*). One!

MONTFLEURY. I —

VOICE (*from the boxes*). Stay!

THE PIT. He will stay! — He won't stay!

MONTFLEURY. Gentlemen, I think —

CYRANO. Two!

MONTFLEURY. I am sure it would be better —

CYRANO. Three!

[*Montfleury disappears, as if through a trapdoor. Burst
of laughter, whistles, and hoots.*]

THE CROWD. Coward! Come back!

CYRANO (*delighted, tips back in his chair and crosses his legs*).
Let him come back if he dares!

A CITIZEN. Ah! There's the actors' spokesman.

[*Bellerose comes forward and bows.*]

THE BOXES. There's Bellerose. (*Applauding*) Bellerose!

---

[25] **canker:** pimple.
[26] **lancet:** sharp-pointed surgical instrument used to make small incisions.

BELLEROSE (*with great elegance*). Most noble gentlemen —

THE PIT. No! No! Jodelet! Give us Jodelet!

JODELET (*advancing, speaking through his nose*). Big bunch of calves!

THE PIT. Hurrah! Bravo! Excellent! Bravo! Jodelet!

JODELET. No bravo, if you please! The fat tragedian, whose paunch you all adore, has felt —

THE PIT. He's a coward!

JODELET. — has felt obliged to leave!

THE PIT. Send him back on!

SOME. No!

OTHERS. Yes!

A YOUNG MAN (*to Cyrano*). But, after all, sir, why should you hate Montfleury?

CYRANO (*graciously, still seated*). Young gosling, for two reasons, either alone sufficient. First: he is a wretched actor, howling and grunting like a water carrier the verses that should soar away on wings. Second: that's my secret.

OLD CITIZEN (*behind him*). But you rob us of *Clorise* for no good reason. I'm stubborn enough to want to know that secret.

CYRANO (*respectfully, turning his chair to face the citizen*). Old mule, this Baro's verses count for less than zero. No harm in interrupting *them*.

THE PRÉCIEUSES (*in the boxes*). What, our own Baro! How could he say it? Heavens above!

CYRANO (*gallantly, facing his chair towards the boxes*). You lovely beings, gleaming like bepetalled flowers, you cup-bearers of dreams whose smiles make even death enchanting, you should inspire our verse, not stoop to criticise it.

BELLEROSE. But the ticket money must be given back.

CYRANO (*facing his chair towards the stage*). That's the first rational remark I've heard. I'm not the man to rend the robe of Thespis.[27]   (*Rising and throwing a bag on the stage*) Here! Catch this purse on the fly and hold your tongue.

AUDIENCE (*dazzled*). Oh! Oh!

JODELET (*hastily grabbing the purse and testing its weight*).

---

[27] **rend the robe of Thespis:** *i.e.*, disrupt the traditions of the theater. (The Greek poet Thespis was the reputed founder of tragic drama.)

For this price, sir, I freely give you leave to come every day
and cancel *La Clorise* —

AUDIENCE. Hoo! Hoo!

JODELET. — even if we're all hissed down for it.

BELLEROSE. Clear the house!

JODELET. Yes! clear the house!

[*The audience begins to go out. Cyrano looks on with a
satisfied air. But people linger to hear the ensuing scene,
and the general exit ceases. The women in the boxes,
already standing with their cloaks on, stop to listen;
finally sit down again.*]

LE BRET (*to Cyrano*). Of all the madness!

A BORE (*who has come up to Cyrano*). This is scandalous.
The great Montfleury! But the Duke de Candale is his
patron; he'll protect him! Who is your patron?

CYRANO. No one.

BORE. No one?

CYRANO. No one.

BORE. No great lord to shield you with his name?

CYRANO (*irritated*). No one! I've told you twice. Must I
repeat again? No! No protector! (*His hand on his sword*)
A protectress, yes!

BORE. You're leaving town, of course?

CYRANO. It all depends.

BORE. The Duke de Candale has a long arm.

CYRANO. Not as long as mine (*pointing to his sword*) with this
extension.

BORE. But you don't pretend to think —

CYRANO. I do pretend.

BORE. But —

CYRANO. Now about face!

BORE. But —

CYRANO. About face! Or tell me why you contemplate my
nose.

BORE (*bewildered*). I —

CYRANO (*advancing*). Why is it strange?

BORE (*recoiling*). Your honor is mistaken —

CYRANO. Is it pliant, swaying like a trunk?

BORE (*again recoiling*). I didn't say —

CYRANO. Hooked like the beak of an owl?

BORE. I —

CYRANO. With a wart on the top?

BORE. But —

CYRANO. Or a fly sauntering over it? What's so unusual?

BORE. Oh!

CYRANO. Is it so freakish?

BORE. But I know enough to keep my eyes away!

CYRANO. And why, please, should you keep your eyes away?

BORE. I heard —

CYRANO. Disgusting, eh?

BORE. Sir!

CYRANO. The color seems unwholesome — ?

BORE. Sir!

CYRANO. The shape obscene?

BORE. Oh! Not at all!

CYRANO. Why so disparaging? Perhaps you find my nose a trifle large?

BORE (*stammering*). I find it small, quite small — in fact, minute!

CYRANO. Oh! That's your line of ridicule? So! My nose is small?

BORE. Merciful Heaven!

CYRANO. My nose is huge! Enormous! Why, you pip-nosed, snub-nosed flathead, know that I glory in this appendage of mine! A large nose is the sign manifest of such a man as I am — courteous, witty, liberal in opinions, fired with courage. Such a man, poor fool, you could never hope to be, for the inglorious face my hand is going to find above your collar, is just as bare —

[*He slaps his face.*]

BORE. Ow!

CYRANO. — of pride, imagination, lyricism, romantic fancy, sparkle, and rich life — as bare, in short, of nose as that (*he turns him around by the shoulders, suiting the action to the word*) my boot will find beneath your backbone.

BORE (*running off*). Help! Help! The Watch!

CYRANO. Let this be a warning to all curious fellows making pleasantries about the middle of my face. If the jester is of

noble birth, my treatment will be different — steel instead
of boot leather, in front and higher up.

DE GUICHE (*who has descended from the stage with the fops*).
The man grows tiresome.

THE VISCOUNT DE VALVERT (*shrugging*). And boastful.

DE GUICHE. Will no one answer him?

VISCOUNT. No one? Wait. I'll launch a shaft to scare him.
(*He swaggers up to Cyrano, who is watching him, and
stands in front of him with a conceited air.*) You — you
have — your — ah — nose is very large!

CYRANO (*gravely*). Very.

VISCOUNT (*smiling*). Ha! Ha!

CYRANO (*unperturbed*). Is that all?

VISCOUNT. Sir —

CYRANO. That's a mite brief, young man. You might make,
Lord, how many remarks, merely by changing tone. For
instance, listen:— Aggressive: "Sir, if I had that nose, they
should amputate at once." Friendly interest: "It must get
in your cups; you ought to have a pitcher made for drinking." Descriptive: "It's a rock! A peak! A cape! A cape, I
said? A whole peninsula." Inquisitive: "What do you use
that oblong casket for, inkstand or scissors case?" Gracious:
"Are you so fond of birds, that in paternal fashion you
tender for their little feet that perch?" Quarrelsome:
"When you smoke your pipe, sir, does the smoke ever
leave your nostrils without some neighbor crying, 'Chimney fire'?" Warning: "With that weight pulling at your
head, take care you don't fall forward on the ground!"
Tender: "Have a little parasol made, lest the sun fade its
hue." Pedantic: "Only the beast that Aristophanes calls
Hippocampelephantocamelos could carry such flesh and
bone beneath its brows." Lordly: "What, my friend, you
say that hook is in style? Surely convenient to hang one's
hat on!" Emphatic: "No wind except the mistral,[28] O
magisterial nose, could give you cold all over." Dramatic:
"When it bleeds, there's your Red Sea!" Admiring: "What
a sign for a perfumer!" Lyrical: "Oh, art thou Triton breath-

---

[28] **mistral:** a violent, cold northerly wind of the Mediterranean provinces
of France.

ing in that conch?"[29] Naïve: "What are the visiting hours at this monument?" Respectful: "My deep respects, sir! You have, so to speak, a gable all your own, fronting the street." Rustic: "Yon's a nose what is a nose. It's a great turnip or dwarf melon else." Military: "Defense against cavalry." Practical: "Is it up in a raffle? Surely, sir, it's bound to take first prize." Finally, in weeping parody[30] of De Viau's *Pyramus:*

"There's the nose that spoiled the face endowed to him
  by Nature.
Its master's symmetries are lost. It makes him blush, the
  traitor!"

That, my friend, or something very like it, is what you might have said if you had the merest spice of letters and of wit. But of wit, most ridiculous of creatures, you never had an atom, and of letters, only the four that spell out *fool!* What's more, even if you had the necessary invention to offer such mad jests before these galleries filled with nobles, you couldn't have uttered the quarter of the half of the beginning of the first. To myself I offer them with verve; but no one else may offer them to me.

DE GUICHE (*trying to drag away the petrified Viscount*). Viscount, come away!

VISCOUNT (*stifled with anger*). Such arrogant airs he gives himself, this country lout! He — he — doesn't even wear gloves! He goes about ribbonless, bowless, braidless —

CYRANO. My elegance I keep for my character. Not foppish in my dress, I am the less vain, the more perfectly accoutered.[31] I don't go from home leaving insult uncleansed, my honor soiled with wearing, my scruples black as mourning, my conscience yellow from the slumber still unwiped from its eyes. When I go abroad, everything shines fresh and cleanly, plumed as I am with sincere independence. Not my figure but my soul I stiffen up with stays; and thus, wearing the ribbands of fulfilled achievement, curling the

---

[29] **Triton . . . conch:** A demi-god of the sea and the trumpeter of Neptune, Triton was usually represented as blowing a trumpet made of a shell.

[30] **parody:** a close imitation of an author or a work for comic effect or ridicule.

[31] **accoutered:** furnished.

mustachios of my wit, I go my way through the crowd, letting truth ring out like clanking spurs.

VISCOUNT. But, sir —

CYRANO. I have no gloves? Too bad! I had one left of a very old pair. It was much in my way; I threw it in someone's face.

VISCOUNT. Knavish rascal! Ridiculous, ill-mannered boor!

CYRANO (*taking off his hat and bowing as if the Viscount were introducing himself*). Charmed! And I am Cyrano-Savinien-Hercule de Bergerac.

[*Laughter.*]

VISCOUNT (*exasperated*). Buffoon!

CYRANO (*with a sudden cry as if seized with cramp*). Oh!

VISCOUNT (*who was going away, turning around*). What else did he say?

CYRANO (*grimacing, as if in agony*). She gets stiff when not used. This comes of idleness!

VISCOUNT. What's the matter?

CYRANO. My sword's asleep. It tingles.

VISCOUNT (*drawing his*). So be it!

CYRANO. I shall give you the most charming little thrust.

VISCOUNT (*scornfully*). Poet!

CYRANO. Precisely, sir, a poet! Such a poet that while we fence I am going to make a ballade,[32] improvised.

VISCOUNT. A ballade?

CYRANO. You don't know what that is, I suppose.

VISCOUNT. Sir —

CYRANO (*as if reciting a lesson*). The ballade, then, is composed of three stanzas of eight lines each —

VISCOUNT (*stamping*). Oh!

CYRANO (*continuing*). — with an envoy[33] of four.

VISCOUNT. You —

CYRANO. At one and the same time, I shall compose a ballade, and fight you. At the last line, I shall kill you.

VISCOUNT. No!

CYRANO. No? (*Declaiming*) "BALLADE OF THE DUEL WHICH

---

[32] **ballade:** poem with usually three stanzas, recurrent rhymes, an identical refrain for each stanza, and ending with an envoy.

[33] **envoy:** short fixed final stanza of a ballade serving as a summary or dedication.

MONSIEUR DE BERGERAC FOUGHT WITH A NINCOMPOOP IN
THE HÔTEL DE BOURGOGNE."

VISCOUNT. What might that be?

CYRANO. That is the title.

AUDIENCE (*frenzied with excitement*). Room! This is fun!
Make way! No noise!

[*Tableau.*[34] *Circle of curious spectators in the pit, the
fops and officers mixed in with citizens and common
people. Pages climb on people's shoulders to get a better
view. In the boxes, all the ladies are standing. On the
right, De Guiche and his attendant nobles. Left, Le
Bret, Ragueneau, Cuigy, etc.*]

CYRANO (*closing his eyes for a moment*). Wait! I am choosing
my rhymes. There, I've found them! (*As he recites, he suits
the action to the words.*)

> With grace I toss my plumed *chapeau:*
> With languid grace, my mantle shed.
> I draw my well-tried rapier — so! —
> And circle you with catlike tread.
> Was Céladon[35] the better-bred?
> Could Scaramouche[36] such style essay?
> Young Myrmidon,[37] your Fate's foresaid:
> The envoy's end, and then *touché!*

[*Their swords meet.*]

> If you'd kept silent, *comme il faut,*[38]
> No need to riddle you; instead,
> Now I must beat my brains to know
> Where I shall spit you — heart, or head,
> Or on that badge unmerited!
> Wait! Now I have it, clear as day!
> Your paunch shall put my point to bed!
> The envoy's end, and then *touché!*

[34] *Tableau:* scene.
[35] **Céladon:** shepherd hero of a pastoral play; also used for any lovesick
swain.
[36] **Scaramouche** (ska'rǝ·müsh'): Italian actor in Paris, who was famous as a
pantomime.
[37] **Myrmidon:** short, insignificant person. (In Greek mythology Myrmidons
were people descended from ants, who were changed into men by Zeus.)
[38] *comme il faut* (kȯm'ēl'fō'): as is necessary.

I need another rhyme in — *o!*
You disengage? Your color's fled?
Then you're a goose that daren't say "Boh,"
And that's my rhyme. Your thrust is sped;
I block it with my parry, spread
Your guard with this new counter, play
My blade till your blade drops like lead!
    The envoy's end, and then *touché!*

[*He announces solemnly.*]

Envoy.
Prince! To the living God, who bled
Upon the cross, 'tis best you pray!
I lunge! I feint! You're good as dead!

[*The Viscount staggers; Cyrano bows.*]

The duel scene. José Ferrer
in the screen version of 1950.

Penguin Photo

The envoy's end! And . . . so! . . . *touché!*

[*Cheers. Applause in the boxes. Showers of flowers and handkerchiefs. Officers mob Cyrano with congratulations. Ragueneau dances with joy. Le Bret is both happy and disconsolate. The Viscount's friends, supporting him in their arms, lead him away.*]

THE CROWD (*in a long shout*). Hurrah!

A LIGHT-HORSEMAN. Superb!

A WOMAN. So pretty!

RAGUENEAU. Wonderful!

A FOP. Novel!

LE BRET. Mad!

VARIOUS MEMBERS OF THE CROWD (*surrounding Cyrano*). Compliments! — Congratulate you! — Bravo!

A WOMAN'S VOICE. He is a hero!

A MUSKETEER (*swiftly approaching Cyrano with outstretched hand*). Sir, allow me! Exceedingly well done! I'm speaking as something of a judge. Naturally, I first expressed my approval by stamping. (*He withdraws.*)

CYRANO (*to Cuigy*). What is that gentleman's name?

CUIGY. He's D'Artagnan.[39]

LE BRET (*to Cyrano, taking his arm*). Now, let us have a talk.

CYRANO. Let this crowd thin out. (*To Bellerose*) May I stay?

BELLEROSE (*with marked respect*). Most certainly.

[*Shouting outside.*]

JODELET (*after looking out*). Montfleury. They're hooting him.

BELLEROSE (*solemnly*). *Sic transit.*[40] (*Changing tone — to the Doorkeeper and Candle-snuffer*) Sweep out! Close the doors! But don't put out the lights. We'll be back after dinner to rehearse a new farce for tomorrow.

[*Exeunt Jodelet and Bellerose after impressive bows to Cyrano.*]

THE DOORKEEPER (*to Cyrano*). Aren't you dining?

CYRANO. I? No.

[*The Doorkeeper retires.*]

[39] **D'Artagnan:** (dar'ta'nyän'): a literary joke, as D'Artagnan is a hero in a fictional work by Dumas, *The Three Musketeers.*

[40] *Sic transit* (*gloria mundi*): "Thus passes the glory of the world."

LE BRET (*to Cyrano*). Not dining? Why not?

CYRANO (*proudly*). Because (*changing his tone when the Doorkeeper has gone*) — I have no money.

LE BRET (*making the motion of throwing a bag*). Oh! The bag of crowns?

CYRANO. Paternal allowance, your life was but a day!

LE BRET. How will you live the rest of the month?

CYRANO. I have nothing left.

LE BRET. Silly to throw away that bag!

CYRANO. But what a splendid gesture.

REFRESHMENT GIRL (*coughing behind her little counter*). Hm! (*Cyrano and Le Bret turn; she comes up somewhat frightened.*) Sir, to know you're hungry — that breaks my heart. (*Indicating the refreshment stand*) I have everything needed there. (*Impulsively*) Take what you wish.

CYRANO (*taking off his hat*). Dear child, though Gascon pride forbids that I accept the smallest trifle from your fingers, I could not hurt your feelings by refusing. Therefore, I'll accept — (*he goes to the stand to select something*) — some little something: a single grape! (*She wishes to give him the bunch; he takes one grape.*) Just one! This glass of (*stopping her as she starts to pour out wine*) — water! And half a macaroon! (*He puts back the other half.*)

LE BRET. Stupid!

REFRESHMENT GIRL. Oh! Something more!

CYRANO. Why, yes! Your hand to kiss. (*He kisses the hand she extends as though it were that of a princess.*)

REFRESHMENT GIRL. I thank you, sir. (*She curtsies.*) Good night! (*Exit.*)

SCENE 5

Cyrano, Le Bret, then the Doorkeeper.

CYRANO (*to Le Bret*). Now I'll listen. (*He places the macaroon before him.*) The main course. (*The glass of water*) Beverage. (*The grape*) Dessert. (*He sits down.*) I'll sit down to my feast. Pardon, my friend, I was terribly hungry. (*Eating*) What were you saying?

LE BRET. I was saying these fops with their bellicose airs will ruin your reason if you listen only to them. Talk to sensible people; you'll soon find out the effect of your escapade.

CYRANO (*finishing his macaroon*). Terrific.

LE BRET. The Cardinal —

CYRANO (*beaming*). The Cardinal — was he there?

LE BRET. Yes. He must have found it —

CYRANO. Quite unusual.

LE BRET. Nevertheless —

CYRANO. Oh, he's a playwright himself. It wouldn't bother him to see a rival's play disturbed.

LE BRET. The trouble with you is you're getting too many enemies on your hands.

CYRANO (*starting on the grape*). How many, approximately, have I made today?

LE BRET. Forty-eight, not counting women.

CYRANO. Particularize!

LE BRET. Montfleury, the old citizen, De Guiche, the Viscount, Baro, the playwright, the entire Academy —

CYRANO. That's enough. You'll kill me with joy.

LE BRET. But this kind of life — where will it lead you? What's behind it?

CYRANO. I was wandering in a maze. Too many courses, too many complicated resolutions. So I took —

LE BRET. Well?

CYRANO. — the simplest possible. I decided — in all things and at all times — to deserve admiration.

LE BRET (*shrugging*). So that's that! But your hatred for Montfleury — what's your motive, your real motive?

CYRANO (*rising*). That fat Silenus,[41] so paunched that his own navel is beyond him, thinks he's God's gift to women. As he murders his lines, his toad's eyes turn to sheep's eyes. I've hated him since that evening when he first looked at *her.* It was like watching a slug sliding down a flower.

LE BRET (*astonished*). Good God! Is it possible —

CYRANO (*with a bitter smile*). That I should be in love? (*Changing his tone and speaking gravely*) I am in love.

LE BRET. Who? You never told me.

---

[41] **Silenus:** tutor and attendant of the Greek god Bacchus, represented with a bald head, short horns, and a flat nose; hence, any very ugly man.

CYRANO. My love? Why, just consider. This nose of mine, a quarter-hour ahead no matter where I go, would nightmare dreams of love with Nature's ugliest duckling. Whom do I love then? Why, naturally, the loveliest of all.

LE BRET. The loveliest of all?

CYRANO. The loveliest in the world. The wittiest! The subtlest! (*Dejectedly*) The fairest!

LE BRET. Good God! Who can she be?

CYRANO. A deadly peril, but without intention; exquisite beauty, without self-admiration; a musk rose, Nature's snare, with love enambushed. Whoever knows her smile, he knows perfection. Graceful she is in all things; divinity is in her merest gesture. And thou, O Venus, could never mount thy shell,[42] nor thou, Diana, walk thy flowered woods, as she mounts in her chair[43] or walks through Paris!

LE BRET. The devil! I know all now. It's very plain.

CYRANO. Plain? It's crystal clear.

LE BRET. Your cousin, Magdeleine Robin.

CYRANO. Precisely. It's Roxane.

LE BRET. Well, that's only as it should be. You love her? Tell her so. In her eyes, today has covered you with glory.

CYRANO (*indicating his nose*). My dear fellow, tell me what hope of glory, what hope of any kind, this protuberance of mine could ever leave me. I'm not a fool — don't cherish such illusions! And yet, sometimes, in the violet hour of twilight, I can be touched — even I! — with secret longings. In some still garden where the very hour is fragrant, my poor sinner of a nose senses the breath of April, and my eyes drift down a silver shaft of moonlight to trail some woman on her lover's arm. I can dream then how it would be to walk slowly in the moonlight with someone on my arm. Elated, I forget myself. But suddenly, why, there's the shadow of my profile on the wall, and then —

LE BRET (*touched*). My poor friend.

CYRANO. Friend, I'm not without my dismal hours, knowing myself so ugly, so alone.

LE BRET (*hastily, seizing his hand*). What! Tears? From you?

---

[42] **Venus . . . shell:** probably an allusion to Venus Anadyomene, who is usually represented as just risen from the sea and standing on a shell.

[43] **chair:** sedan chair (covered chair carried on poles by two men).

CYRANO. Not that! No, never that! That would be much too
ugly, if tears should glide along this nose of mine. The
divine grace of tears, while I'm their master, shall never
touch such monstrous ugliness. Nothing on earth is more
sublime than tears, and no least one, through any fault of
mine, shall find the ridicule of being laughed at.

LE BRET. Love's just a game of chance. No need for sadness!

CYRANO (*shaking his head*). I love Cleopatra. Have I the look
of Caesar? I idolize Berenice. Would you take me for
Titus?[44]

LE BRET. Where's your courage? Your spirit? Why, that little
girl, just now when she offered you refreshment — you saw
her eyes.

CYRANO (*impressed*). That's true.

LE BRET. You see! And when Roxane herself went pale as she
watched you duelling —

CYRANO. Roxane went pale?

LE BRET. — it shows her heart and mind were struck with
admiration. Why don't you speak to her?

CYRANO. I can't! It's the one thing on earth that I'm afraid of.
She'd laugh in my nose.

THE DOORKEEPER (*ushering someone in*). Someone for you,
sir.

CYRANO (*recognizing the duenna*). Oh God! Her duenna!

SCENE 6

Cyrano, Le Bret, and the Duenna.

DUENNA (*with an elaborate curtsey*). Someone wants to know
where she can meet her valiant cousin — secretly.

CYRANO (*disturbed*). Meet me?

DUENNA (*curtsies*). Meet you! There are things to be told.

CYRANO. What things?

DUENNA (*curtsies again*). Some things!

CYRANO (*staggering*). My God!

DUENNA. Someone's going early — very early — tomorrow
morning to hear mass at Saint-Roch.

[44] **Berenice ... Titus:** Berenice was a captive queen loved by Titus, Emperor of Rome; their love story is the subject of a play by Racine.

CYRANO (*hanging on Le Bret for support*). Oh, my God!

DUENNA. On the way back, where could one . . . step in . . . to have a little talk?

CYRANO (*completely distracted*). Where? O-o-oh! My God!

DUENNA. Quickly, pleasè!

CYRANO. I'm cudgeling my brains —

DUENNA. Well, where?

CYRANO. At — at — Ragueneau's, the pastry cook's.

DUENNA. Which is where?

CYRANO. In — in Rue — Oh, God! Rue St. Honoré!

DUENNA (*commencing to leave*). Someone will be there. Don't forget. Be there at seven o'clock.

CYRANO. Seven without fail!

[*Exit the Duenna.*]

SCENE 7

Cyrano, Le Bret, afterwards the actors, actresses, Cuigy, Brissaille, Lignière, the Doorkeeper, the violinists.

CYRANO (*clutching Le Bret's arm*). To me! From her! A rendezvous!

LE BRET. I shouldn't think you'd be sad now.

CYRANO. Whatever happens, she at least knows I'm alive.

LE BRET. You'll calm down now?

CYRANO (*beside himself*). Now? Now I shall fulminate frenetically! I want an entire army corps to put to flight! My heart's tenfold; my arms are twentyfold! No more killing dwarfs for me! (*Shouting his head off*) Bring on your giants!

[*During his speech, whispering shadows of the actors have been moving about the back of the stage. They begin rehearsing. The violinists are in their seats under the stage.*]

VOICE (*from the stage*). Shhh! Shut up down there! We're in rehearsal.

CYRANO (*laughing*). We're going. (*He goes upstage. Through the large door at the back enter Cuigy, Brissaille, and several officers, supporting Lignière, who is completely drunk.*)

CUIGY. Cyrano!

CYRANO. What's that?

CUIGY. A boiled owl we're bringing in to you.

CYRANO (*recognizing him*). Lignière! What's wrong with him?

CUIGY. He's looking for you.

BRISSAILLE. He can't go home.

LIGNIÈRE (*in a thick voice, showing him a crumpled note*). This note . . . warning . . . a hundred men waiting . . . because of song. Great danger . . . Porte de Nesle. Must get through 'em to get back home. Allow me — hic! — sleep at your . . . house?

CYRANO. A hundred men, you say! You'll sleep at home for all that.

LIGNIÈRE (*frightened*). I daren't —

CYRANO (*commandingly, pointing to the lighted lantern which the Doorkeeper is swinging as he listens*). Take that lantern. (*Lignière hurriedly takes it.*) And get going! I'll protect you till I get you home, if I have to tuck you in myself. (*To the officers*) You'd better follow us as witnesses.

CUIGY. But a hundred men —

CYRANO. They're none too many men for me tonight.

[*The actors and actresses approach in costume down from the stage.*]

LE BRET. But why you should protect —

CYRANO. Old grumbler again!

LE BRET. — protect that vulgar sot!

CYRANO (*clapping Lignière on the shoulder*). Why? Because this sot, this tun of muscatel, this liquor hogshead,[45] once did a noble deed! One day, when leaving mass, he saw his sweetheart dipping her fingers in the holy water; and he who always runs away from water rushed to the basin, bent his mustache down and drank it, every drop.

AN ACTRESS (*in soubrette costume*). That was real nice, that was!

CYRANO. Wasn't it, my dear?

THE ACTRESS (*to the others*). But why a hundred against one poor poet?

[45] **tun . . . hogshead:** large casks for holding wine or other liquids.

CYRANO. Let's go! (*To the officers*) When you see me rush against them, don't give me aid, no matter what the danger.

ANOTHER ACTRESS (*jumping from the stage*). I'm going to see it.

CYRANO. Come on!

ANOTHER ACTRESS (*jumping down, to an old actor*). Cassandra, are you coming?

CYRANO. Come on, and welcome. Isabelle, Leander, the Doctor — all of you. Come, join your Italian farce as subplot to this Spanish tragedy,[46] and cloak its groans with your fantastic din as jingles mask the beat of tambourines.

ALL THE ACTORS (*gleefully*). Hurrah! — Where's my cloak? — Where's my hood?

JODELET. Let us go.

CYRANO (*to the violinists*). Give us a tune, there!

[*The violinists join the forming procession, handing out candles taken from the footlights. It becomes a torchlight procession.*]

CYRANO. Splendid! Officers! Actresses in costume. And twenty steps ahead (*goes to the place he designates at the head of the procession*) — myself, alone, marching under the plumes that Glory herself has given me, proud as Scipio,[47] with three times his nose! You understand? Strictly forbidden to help me. Everyone ready? One, two, three! Doorkeeper, the door!

[*The Doorkeeper opens both sides of the double door. Through it, we glimpse a corner of picturesque old Paris under the moon.*]

CYRANO. Ah! Paris mists away before my eyes. The bluish moonlight floods the sloping roofs — exquisite setting for the coming action. The Seine below us, under its scarf of haze, is tremulant as a mystic magic-mirror. You shall see . . . what you shall see! But nothing mean or pitiful, I'm sure!

ALL. To the Porte de Nesle!

---

[46] **Italian farce . . . Spanish tragedy:** During the seventeenth century, French comic drama was largely influenced by Italy, tragic drama by Spain.

[47] **Scipio:** famous Roman general.

CYRANO (*at the threshold*). To the Porte de Nesle! (*To the soubrette*) My dear, you asked me why a hundred men have set themselves against this single poet? (*Placidly, drawing his sword*) Because, as everyone knows, the man's my friend.

[*Exit Cyrano. Under the flicker of candles, to a tune on the violins, the procession — headed by Lignière, staggering, followed by the actresses on the arms of the officers, then the actors, frolicking — goes marching off into the night.*]

CURTAIN

QUESTIONS

Scene 1. Why does the first scene contain a collection of rude and disorderly louts? How does this influence your feelings towards Cyrano when he first arrives on stage? Why didn't Rostand begin the play with Cyrano onstage?

Scene 2. Why does the playwright make Roxane an unprotected orphan? What kind of people inhabit the social world of Scenes 1 and 2? Are they honorable, decent men? Is Roxane safe among them? How does Christian differ from them? What is the significance of his name?

Scene 3. What do we know about Cyrano before he appears? Why do we first hear Cyrano's voice, then see his arm? Are these significant aspects of his character?

Scene 4. Cyrano's attitude toward his monstrous nose is crucial to his character. In the passage where he describes his nose as others might, what attitude does Cyrano take toward it? Are the lines: *There's the nose that spoiled the face endowed to him by Nature./ Its master's symmetries are lost. It makes him blush, the traitor!/* entirely ironic? Does Cyrano realize their truth as he speaks them? Describe his conflicting emotions at this moment.

After the duel, when Cyrano is criticized by Le Bret for throwing away a bag of money, he replies, "But what a splendid gesture." How does Cyrano reveal himself in this remark? Why does he take so little from the girl who offers him food? Is his pride a virtue or a flaw?

Scene 5. Knowing he is hopelessly ugly, Cyrano nevertheless chooses to love "the loveliest of all"—Roxane. Can you explain why? Is he any less a man for crying at the hopelessness of his position? What is Cyrano's greatest fear in life?

Scene 6. Why cannot Cyrano recall the address of the pastry cook? What causes him to lose his usual presence of mind in this scene?

Scene 7. Describe the dangers threatening Cyrano at the end of Act One. From what different quarters do they come? Do you feel involved in Cyrano's fortunes? Do you identify with him? In what ways is he appealing? Do any of his ways annoy you? Explain.

ACT TWO

THE POET'S COOKSHOP

The shop of Ragueneau, baker and pastry cook. It is a very large establishment situated at the corner of the Rue St. Honoré and the Rue de l'Arbre-Sec. A wide vista of these streets, gray in the first light of dawn, looms through the glass of a door, backstage. Downstage, left, a counter overhung by a wrought-iron canopy from which are suspended geese, ducks, and white peacocks. Around the counter, tall bouquets of garden flowers, chiefly sunflowers, set in high china vases. Further back, left, an enormous fireplace. In front of it, on huge andirons, each supporting a saucepan, roasts drip into grease pans. Downstage, right, a door. Further back, right, a stairway leading to a little eavesloft, its interior visible through open shutters. This eating nook, lit by a little Flemish chandelier, is furnished with a table, already laid. A wooden gallery, leading from the top of the stairway, seems to give access to other, similar nooks. In the center of the shop, an iron ring, raised or lowered by means of a rope, is festooned with large chunks of meat and makes a kind of chandelier of game.

It is the early morning rush period. Ovens glow brightly in the shadow of the stairway. Copper vessels shine; spits turn. Here and there, hams are hanging. Various kinds of food pyramid up on dishes in conventional patterns. Harried scullions,[1] fat cooks, and little cooks' assistants bustle confusedly, their caps decorated with chicken feathers and guinea-fowl wings. Some bring in

---

[1] **scullions:** kitchen servants who wash dishes.

*quincunxes[2] of muffins and whole towns of tiny cakes on
sheet-iron trays and wicker stands.*

*Some of the tables are heaped with cakes and other
kinds of eatables. Others, with chairs set around them,
await customers. A smaller table in a corner is half hidden under a litter of papers. As the curtain rises, Ragueneau is seated at it, writing.*

SCENE 1

*Ragueneau, pastry cooks, then Lise. Ragueneau, at
the small table, writing with an inspired air, and counting on his fingers.*

FIRST PASTRY COOK (*with sweetmeats arranged in patterns*).
Nougat fruits!

SECOND PASTRY COOK (*with a dish*). Custard!

THIRD PASTRY COOK (*with a roast decorated with feathers*).
Peacock!

FOURTH PASTRY COOK (*with a plate of cakes*). Rissoles![3]

FIFTH PASTRY COOK (*with an earthenware dish*). Sauced filet
of beef!

RAGUENEAU (*stops writing; raises his head*). The dawn already silvers on our coppers. Time, Ragueneau, to stifle
in your god of song. Lute time will come again; this is your
stove time. (*He rises. To a cook*) Lengthen this sauce for
me; it's far too thick.

COOK. How much?

RAGUENEAU. About three feet. (*Proceeds.*)

COOK. Hey! What's that?

FIRST PASTRY COOK. Tart!

SECOND PASTRY COOK. *Torte!*[4]

RAGUENEAU (*in front of the fireplace*). Leave me, O Muse,
that your charming eyes be not reddened by this faggot fire.
(*To a pastry cook who displays bread*) You have not cleft
these loaves in the right places; caesuras go *between* the

---

[2] *quincunxes:* groups of objects arranged in fives to form squares, one object
at each corner and one in the center.

[3] **Rissoles:** fried pastries filled with chopped meat or fish.

[4] *Torte:* cake that is often made with ground nuts or bread crumbs instead
of flour.

hemistichs.[5] (*To another, displaying an unfinished pastry*)
You must roof in this palace wall of crust. (*To a young apprentice, seated on the floor, spitting poultry*) Son, upon that
same interminable spit, alternate humble chicken and
haughty turkey, as old Malherbe[6] varied long lines with
short ones; and turn your roasts before the fire in strophes.[7]

ANOTHER APPRENTICE (*approaching with a tray covered with
a napkin*). Master, thinking of you, I had this baked. I hope
you'll like it. (*He uncovers the tray and displays a huge
pastry lyre.*)

RAGUENEAU (*dazzled*). A lyre!

APPRENTICE. Of muffin paste.

RAGUENEAU (*touched*). With candied fruit!

APPRENTICE. Look at the strings. I have made them out of
sugar.

RAGUENEAU (*giving him money*). Go, drink my health in this!
(*Enter Lise.*) Hush! My wife! Off with you! Hide that
money! (*To Lise, showing her the lyre apprehensively*)
Fine, isn't it?

LISE. Ridiculous!

[*She places a pile of paper bags on the counter.*]

RAGUENEAU. Bags? Good! So thoughtful! (*Examining them*)
What! Books I revere! The verses of my friends! Torn!
Ripped apart! To make up bags for cracknels![8] Why, it's
Orpheus and the Bacchantes[9] in revival!

LISE (*dryly*). I've the right to use as I see fit the only payment
your limp-lined scribblers ever left us.

---

[5] **caesuras** (si·zùr′ez) . . . **hemistichs** (hem′i·stiks′): A caesura is a division
within a line of verse; a hemistich, half of the divided line. Ragueneau is
referring to his cooking in the same terms a poet would use in describing
his poetry.

[6] **Malherbe:** François de Malherbe (frän·swä′ de ma·lerb′), French poet and
critic who established rules for the writing of poetry.

[7] **strophes** (strō′fēz): stanzas. (*Strophe* — a Greek word meaning *turn* —
originally referred to a section of the ancient Greek ode form in which the
chorus moved to the left as it sang.)

[8] **cracknels:** hard, brittle cakes.

[9] **Orpheus and the Bacchantes:** Orpheus, a renowned poet-musician in
Greek legend, scorned other women after his wife, Eurydice, died. Enraged,
the Bacchantes (female followers of the wine god Bacchus) tore him to
pieces.

RAGUENEAU. Ant! You're insulting poetry's grasshoppers.[10]

LISE. Till they began to eat us out of house and home, you never used to call me aunt — let alone back-auntie!

RAGUENEAU. And you did this to poetry?

LISE. Nothing but!

RAGUENEAU. What would you do if it were prose?

SCENE 2

The same. Two children have just entered the shop.

RAGUENEAU. Well, children, what do you want?

FIRST CHILD. Three patties, please.

RAGUENEAU (*serving them*). There! Crisp, brown, and piping hot.

SECOND CHILD. Could you wrap them up, please?

RAGUENEAU (*aside*). Alas, one of my precious bags! (*To the children*) You're sure you want them wrapped? (*They nod. He takes a bag, and as he starts to wrap the patties, reads aloud*)

"When Ulysses had left Penelope —"

No! Not that! (*He puts it aside and takes another. As he is putting in the patties he sees the writing and reads*) "The fair Apollo —" Nor that! (*Puts it aside.*)

LISE (*impatiently*). Well, what are you waiting for?

RAGUENEAU (*hastily*). Ah! Here we are! (*Resignedly, he takes the third.*) That sonnet to Phyllis[11] — All the same, it's rather hard.

LISE (*shrugging*). It's as well you've made up your mind. Simpleton! (*She climbs on a chair, and begins to arrange dishes on a sideboard.*)

RAGUENEAU (*as soon as her back is turned, calling the children back from the door*). Quick, children! Give me back that

[10] **Ant . . . grasshoppers:** a reference to the fable "The Grasshopper and the Ant" by Jean de la Fontaine, in which a grasshopper, having spent the summer singing, finds herself without food for the winter. She begs for some grain from her neighbor the ant. The ant refuses, telling the grasshopper that since she has sung all summer, she can dance all winter.

[11] **Phyllis:** In Greek legend, Phyllis, the daughter of King Sithon of Thrace, thought she had been abandoned by her bridegroom when she was late for their wedding. She hanged herself and was turned into an almond tree.

sonnet, and I'll give you six patties for the three. (*The children give the bag back, quickly take the cakes, and go out. Ragueneau smoothes out the paper and begins to read, declaiming*) "Phyllis." What! A fleck of butter on that charming name? "Phyllis!" (*Cyrano enters hurriedly.*)

SCENE 3

Ragueneau, Lise, Cyrano; then the musketeer.

CYRANO. What time is it?

RAGUENEAU (*bowing ceremoniously*). Six.

CYRANO (*emotionally*). In one short hour! (*He walks to and fro across the shop.*)

RAGUENEAU (*following him*). Magnificent! I saw it all.

CYRANO. You saw what?

RAGUENEAU. Your duel.

CYRANO. Which?

RAGUENEAU. At the Hôtel de Bourgogne.

CYRANO (*disdainfully*). Oh, that!

RAGUENEAU (*admiringly*). Yes! The duel in verse.

LISE. He talks of nothing else.

CYRANO. No harm in that.

RAGUENEAU (*lunging with a spit*). "The envoy's end, and then *touché!*" Magnificent! "The envoy's end! And ... so! ... *touché!*" (*He grows more and more enthusiastic.*) "The envoy's end ...."

CYRANO. What time is it?

RAGUENEAU (*stopping to look at the clock*). Five after six. "And then *touché!*" (*Straightening up*) Oh, to make a ballade like that!

LISE (*to Cyrano, who has absentmindedly shaken hands with her as he passes her counter*). What have you done to your hand?

CYRANO. Nothing. Just a scratch.

RAGUENEAU. You have been in trouble!

CYRANO. No trouble at all.

LISE (*shaking her finger at him*). I think you're lying.

CYRANO. What! Did my nose quiver? It would take a monstrous lie for that. (*Changing tone*) I'm expecting someone.

If all goes well, will you leave us alone?

RAGUENEAU. That's not so easy; my poets are coming.

LISE (*ironically*). For breakfast, on the house!

CYRANO. Get them out of here when I give the signal. What time is it now?

RAGUENEAU. Ten after six.

CYRANO (*seating himself nervously at Ragueneau's table and helping himself to paper*). I need a pen.

RAGUENEAU (*offering the one behind his ear*). The quill of a swan.

[*Enter a musketeer, splendidly mustached and stentorian voiced.*]

MUSKETEER. Hail!

[*Lise goes to him hastily.*]

CYRANO (*turning*). Who's that?

RAGUENEAU. Friend of my wife's. A terrible warrior—so he says!

CYRANO (*motioning Ragueneau away; to himself*). Come on —write it—seal it—give it her and hurry off. (*Throwing down the pen*) Coward that I am! And yet I'd gladly die if I could speak to her — speak but a single word — (*To Ragueneau*) The time?

RAGUENEAU. Quarter after six.

CYRANO (*beating his breast*).—just one lone word of all I have in here! But writing, now — (*Takes up the pen again.*) Let's write this *billet-doux*,[12] then, phrased and rephrased in my mind a hundred times, already perfect. Why, all I need to do is let my soul lie by this paper and copy what I see there.

[*He writes. Slender, hesitant shadows move behind the glass window in the door.*]

SCENE 4

Ragueneau, Lise, the musketeer, Cyrano, still writing; the poets, dressed in black, their hose falling, splashed with mud.

[12] *billet-doux* (bil'ā·dü'): love letter.

LISE (*entering, to Ragueneau*). Your mud larks[13] are here.

FIRST POET (*entering, to Ragueneau*). My colleague!

SECOND POET (*shaking Ragueneau's hand*). My dear colleague!

THIRD POET. Eagle of pastry cooks! Your eyrie[14] smells divine.

FOURTH POET. O Phoebus[15] of the spit!

FIFTH POET. Apollo of the dripping pan!

RAGUENEAU (*as they surround, embrace him, and shake his hand*). How easy it is to feel at home with them.

FIRST POET. We were delayed by the crowd at the Porte de Nesle.

SECOND POET. Eight bloody sword-ripped brigands garnished the pavement there.

CYRANO (*raising his head*). Eight? Hm! Seven, I thought. (*Continues writing.*)

RAGUENEAU (*to Cyrano*). You wouldn't happen to know the hero of this slaughter?

CYRANO (*absentmindedly*). Me? No.

LISE (*to the musketeer*). Do you?

MUSKETEER (*twirling his mustache*). Perhaps I do.

CYRANO (*writing, murmuring a word from time to time*). I adore you!

FIRST POET. They say a single man put the whole troop to flight.

SECOND POET. Amazing sight! The ground strewn with pikes[16] and clubs.

CYRANO (*writing*). As for your eyes—

THIRD POET. Hats scattered on the ground as far as Goldsmiths' quay.

FIRST POET. The deuce! He must have gone berserk—

CYRANO (*writing*). And for your lips—

FIRST POET. —the man who did all this. Some fierce, remorseless giant!

CYRANO (*writing*). I swoon with fear when my eyes rest upon you!

[13] mud larks: urchins.
[14] eyrie (īr′ē): nest.
[15] Phoebus: sun god, who inspired poets.
[16] pikes: long wooden poles with pointed metal heads, used as weapons.

SECOND POET (*snatching a cake*). What's your new poem, Ragueneau?

CYRANO (*writing*). Your devoted admirer — (*Just as he is about to sign his name, he stops writing, rises, and puts the letter in his doublet.*) No need to sign; I'll give it her myself.

RAGUENEAU (*to the second poet*). I've versified a recipe.

THIRD POET (*stationing himself near a tray of cream puffs*). Let's hear this recipe.

FOURTH POET (*looking at a muffin he has taken*). This muffin's cap is unsymmetrical. (*He takes off the top at a single bite.*)

FIRST POET. This gingerbread ogles a famished poet with almond eyes 'neath brows angelical. (*Takes a piece of gingerbread.*)

SECOND POET. We are listening.

THIRD POET (*gently squeezing a cream puff between his fingers*). This cream puff is driveling cream. It's laughing at me!

SECOND POET (*biting the big pastry lyre*). For the first time in my life, the Lyre sustains me.

RAGUENEAU (*ready to recite, coughs, settles his cap, and strikes pose*). A recipe in verse:—

SECOND POET (*nudging the first*). Stuffing for breakfast?

FIRST POET (*to the second*). Gorging for dinner?

RAGUENEAU. "HOW TO MAKE ALMOND CREAM TARTS"

Whip whites of eggs to lightest texture;
   Then next your
Egg-white strain as fine as silk,
Add juice of lemons, one or two,
   And quite a few
Spoonfuls of sweetened almond milk!

Now in every tartlet mold
   Your thumb must fold
Such dough as lightens pastry tops.
You line the sides with jellied fruit,
   Sugar to suit,
And pour your whip in careful drops

Into the waiting shells! See well
    That every shell
Suffers the stove's alchemic arts,
Whence issuing, the merry crew,
    Light brown in hue,
Will be delicious cream of almond tarts!

THE POETS (*with their mouths full*). Exquisite! Delicious!
A POET (*choking*). Mmmm—mm! (*They go backstage, eating.*)
CYRANO (*has been watching them; goes up to Ragueneau*).
    Are you lulled to sleep by your own voice? Can't you see
    how they're stuffing?
RAGUENEAU (*with a smile*). I'm not asleep. I don't look, for
    fear I'd hurt their feelings. When I recite, I get a double
    pleasure: as I satisfy my little pleasant weakness, I see
    those things eaten—by those who haven't eaten.
CYRANO (*slapping him on the shoulder*). Oh, I like that!
    (*Ragueneau rejoins his friends. Cyrano, a little brusquely*)
    You, Lise! (*Lise, in amorous conversation with the muske-
    teer, starts guiltily and comes towards him.*) Is this captain
    beleaguering you?
LISE (*offended*). Oh! With a single haughty glance I can con-
    quer anyone who dares attack my virtue!
CYRANO. Huh! For a conqueror's eyes, they are pretty badly
    battered.[17]
LISE (*stifling with rage*). I won't be ridiculed!
CYRANO (*with decision*). *He* shan't be ridicuckolded.[18] I'm
    fond of him.
LISE. Ah-h-h!
CYRANO (*raising his voice for the benefit of the musketeer*).
    A word to the wise!

[*He bows to the musketeer; looks up at the clock; takes
up a place of observation by the door.*]

LISE (*to the musketeer, who has merely returned Cyrano's
    bow*). I'm surprised! Why didn't you throw that insult back
    —in his nose?

[17] **For a conqueror's eyes . . . battered:** Cyrano is saying her eyes are heavily
made up for the purpose of attracting men. Lise is a womanly contrast to the
pure Roxane.
[18] **ridicuckolded:** ridiculed by his wife's betrayal. (To *cuckold* means to be
unfaithful to one's husband.)

MUSKETEER. In his nose—*his* nose? Not me! (*He moves away hastily. Lise follows.*)

CYRANO (*from the door at the back, giving Ragueneau the signal to take the poets out*). Pst!

RAGUENEAU (*showing them the door on the right*). We'll be better off in here . . . .

CYRANO (*impatiently*). Pst! Pst!

RAGUENEAU (*trying to herd them out*). . . . for reading verses.

FIRST POET (*mournfully, his mouth full*). What about the cakes?

SECOND POET. They go with us!

[*They make a hurried onslaught on the dishes; then follow Ragueneau in procession.*]

SCENE 5

Cyrano, Roxane, the Duenna.

CYRANO (*aside*). I'll not show my letter till I know I have a chance. (*Roxane, masked, followed by the Duenna, appears behind the window. He quickly opens the door.*)

CYRANO. Come in! (*Stepping up to the Duenna*) Two words with you, Duenna.

DUENNA. Make it four.

CYRANO. Do—you—like—goodies?

DUENNA. Adore them. I could eat them till I'm sick.

CYRANO (*hastily taking paper bags from the counter*). Good! Here are two sonnets by Benserade—

DUENNA. Pfui!

CYRANO. —which I will fill with cream tarts.

DUENNA (*changing expression*). Oh!

CYRANO. Do you like the cake called "puff"?

DUENNA. Delicious! Filled with cream!

CYRANO. I will thrust six into the heart of a poem by Saint-Amant. Into these verses by Chapelain I will put a piece of sponge cake. Hmmm! Somewhat lighter! Oh! and you like fresh cakes?

DUENNA. To distraction!

CYRANO (*filling her arms with the bags*). Then eat these in the street—

DUENNA. But—

CYRANO (*pushing her out*). —and don't come back till they are eaten up.

[*He closes the door, comes to Roxane, removes his hat, and stands at a respectful distance.*]

SCENE 6

Cyrano, Roxane, the Duenna for a moment.

CYRANO. Blest be this above all other moments, when, ceasing to forget I humbly breathe, you come here to say to me—? To tell me—?

ROXANE (*unmasking*). First let me thank you because that foppish fool your sword checked yesterday is one that a great lord, in love with me—

CYRANO. De Guiche?

ROXANE (*dropping her eyes*). — has tried to force upon me, as a husband.

CYRANO. Husband in name only? (*Bowing*) Then I have fought—and this is much the better—not for my ugly nose, but for your lovely eyes.

ROXANE. Next . . . I wished—but for this confession I'll think of you once more as the . . . almost brother I used to play in the park with near the lake.

CYRANO. When you came every summer to Bergerac.[19]

ROXANE. And the reeds gave you wood to make your swords.

CYRANO. And the corn, yellow ringlets for your dolls.

ROXANE. That was our playtime —

CYRANO. —when fruit was bittersweet.

ROXANE. The time when you did everything I wanted.

CYRANO. Short-frocked Roxane, called Magdeleine—

ROXANE. And was I pretty?

CYRANO. You were not ugly.

ROXANE. Sometimes you came running with your hand all bleeding from your climbing. Then, playing mother, I would say, trying to make my childish voice severe: (*Taking his hand*) "What is the meaning of this scratch?" (*Surprised*)

[19] **Bergerac:** town in Périgord, a region in southwestern France, from which Cyrano drew his name.

Oh, that's too bad! It really is! (*Cyrano tries to withdraw his hand.*) No, show it to me! What? The same child, still? Where did you do it?

CYRANO. Still playing, near the Porte de Nesle.

ROXANE (*sitting down at a table, and dipping her handkerchief in a glass of water*). Put it here.

CYRANO (*also sitting down*). Still prettily, still playfully maternal!

ROXANE. Tell me, while I wipe away a little of this blood, how many were against you?

CYRANO. Oh, some hundred.

ROXANE. Tell me about it.

CYRANO. No! Let it pass! But tell me what you were afraid to tell just now.

ROXANE (*holding his hand*). Now I am not afraid. The perfume of the past has given me courage. Yes, now I think I'll tell you. There's someone that I care for.

CYRANO. Oh!

ROXANE. So far, he doesn't know it.

CYRANO. Oh!

ROXANE. Not yet.

CYRANO. Oh!

ROXANE. But though he doesn't know it, soon he will do.

CYRANO. Oh!

ROXANE. The poor boy has loved me from afar, not dared to tell me—

CYRANO. Oh!

ROXANE. Give me your hand again. You see, it's feverish! I've seen avowal trembling on his lips.

CYRANO. Oh!

ROXANE (*finishes a little bandage made with her handkerchief*). And just imagine, cousin! As it happens, he's in your regiment.

CYRANO. Oh!

ROXANE (*smiling*). A cadet in your company!

CYRANO. Oh!

ROXANE. His face bears the stamp of wit and genius; proud, noble, young, intrepid, handsome—

CYRANO (*losing color, rising*). Handsome?

ROXANE. Handsome! Why, what's the matter?

CYRANO. Nothing. It's — (*smilingly indicating his hand*) — it's just a childish hurt.

ROXANE. In short, I love him. Yet I've never even seen him save at the play.

CYRANO. You two have never spoken to each other?

ROXANE. Only our eyes!

CYRANO. How can you know, then?

ROXANE. Under the lindens, in the Place Royale, there's talk. Gossips have hinted—

CYRANO. Cadet, you say?

ROXANE. In the Guards.

CYRANO. And what's his name?

ROXANE. The Baron Christian de Neuvillette.

CYRANO. He's no cadet!

ROXANE. Yes, since this morning, under Captain de Castel-Jaloux.

CYRANO. How suddenly you throw your heart away! My dear—

DUENNA (*appearing at the door*). The cakes are gone, Monsieur de Bergerac.

CYRANO. Well, read the verses printed on the bags. (*The Duenna disappears.*) My dear! But what if he should be an ignoramus—unlearned, uncultivated, lacking wit? *You* know no other love but pretty speeches.

ROXANE. No, he has hair like one of d'Urfé's[20] heroes.

CYRANO. His speech may lack the brightness of his hair.

ROXANE. No! Every word is pointed, I'm quite sure.

CYRANO. His mustache must be superfine! If he were stupid —

ROXANE (*stamping her foot*). Then I should die at once!

CYRANO (*after a pause*). And you brought me here to tell me that? I scarcely see the sense—

ROXANE. Why, yesterday my heart was put to death. They told me all your company are Gascons. All Gascons, every one of you —

CYRANO. I see. They said we challenge all those quackish youths whom influence gets admitted to our ranks, posing as Gascons but, in fact, not Gascons. That's what they told you, isn't it?

---

[20] **d'Urfé's:** Honoré d'Urfé (ō·nō·rā′ dür·fā′), sixteenth-century French author, wrote a popular pastoral novel entitled *L'Astrée*.

ROXANE (*nods*). I'm concerned!

CYRANO (*between his teeth*). As well you may be!

ROXANE. But yesterday, how invincible you seemed, punishing that rascal, coping with those brutes! I thought, supposing he, whom they all fear—

CYRANO. Enough! I will protect your little baron.

ROXANE. For me? I've always been so very fond of you!

CYRANO. Yes.

ROXANE. And always be his friend?

CYRANO. I will.

ROXANE. And he will never have to fight a duel?

CYRANO. Never! I promise.

ROXANE. You're so very kind, my dear!—I must go. (*She hastily puts back her mask; throws a veil over her forehead; absentmindedly*) To think you never got to tell about your last night's exploit! Really, it must be quite unique — Tell him to write to me. (*She kisses her hand to him.*) So fond of you, my dear!

CYRANO. Yes!

ROXANE. A hundred men against you? Well, good-bye. We're great friends, aren't we?

CYRANO. Naturally! Of course!

ROXANE. Tell him to write to me. A hundred men! You must describe it—later on. Now I must go. A hundred men! What courage!

CYRANO (*bowing*). Believe me, I've done far, far better— since!

[*Exit Roxane. Cyrano stands motionless, his eyes lowered. The door at the right opens. Ragueneau puts his head in.*]

SCENE 7

Cyrano, Ragueneau, the poets, Carbon de Castel-Jaloux, the cadets, the crowd, etc.; then De Guiche, Cuigy, and Brissaille.

RAGUENEAU. Can we come in?

CYRANO (*immobile*). Yes.

[*Ragueneau beckons, and his friends come in again. At the same time, Carbon de Castel-Jaloux, in the costume*

of a captain of the Guards, appears at the door back-
stage. Seeing Cyrano, he gestures extravagantly to some-
one outside.]

CARBON. Here he is!

CYRANO (*raising his head*). Captain!

CARBON (*exultantly*). Our hero! We know everything. Thirty
of my cadets are here—

CYRANO. But—Captain!

CARBON (*trying to get him outside*). They want to greet you.

CYRANO. No.

CARBON. They're across the street, drinking at the Crossed
Hilt.

CYRANO. No!

CARBON (*shouting out of the door in a thunderous voice*). The
hero refuses. He's out of sorts.

A VOICE (*outside*). The devil he is! (*Uproar outside; noise of
clanking swords and approaching boots.*)

CARBON (*rubbing his hands*). Here they come across the
street.

THE CADETS (*entering the cookshop*). 'Sblood! 'Struth!
'Sbones! Dog's body! 'Snavel![21]

RAGUENEAU (*recoiling in alarm*). Gentlemen! Are you all
from Gascony?

CADETS. All!

A CADET (*to Cyrano*). Bravo!

CYRANO. Baron!

ANOTHER CADET (*shaking his hands*). Vivat![22]

CYRANO. Baron!

THIRD CADET. Come to my arms!

CYRANO. Baron!

SEVERAL CADETS. Come to our arms!

CYRANO (*not knowing what to answer*). Baron!—Baron!—
Please!

RAGUENEAU. Gentlemen! Are you all barons?

THE CADETS. All!

RAGUENEAU. Are they?

FIRST CADET. You could make a tower of our coronets.

---

[21] 'Sblood . . . 'Snavel: abbreviated oaths — "God's blood," "God's truth,"
etc.

[22] Vivat: Long live (an expression of approval, like *Viva!*).

LE BRET (*entering, running to Cyrano*). They're looking everywhere for you—a delirious crowd, led by those who followed you last night.

CYRANO (*in alarm*). You didn't tell them where to find me?

LE BRET (*rubbing his hands*). I certainly did!

A CITIZEN (*entering, followed by others*). The whole world of fashion is here!

[*Outside, the street is crowded with people. Sedan chairs are stopping.*]

LE BRET (*aside to Cyrano, smiling*). What about—Roxane?

CYRANO (*hurriedly*). Be quiet, will you!

THE CROWD (*shouting*). Cyrano!! (*A crowd rushes into the cookshop. Confusion. Cheering.*)

RAGUENEAU (*standing on a table*). My shop is invaded; they are smashing everything! It's wonderful!

PEOPLE (*around Cyrano*). My friend! — My friend!

CYRANO. Yesterday, so many friends were lacking.

LE BRET. Success at last!

FOP (*running up with outstretched hands*). My dear! If you only knew—

CYRANO. Dear? Dear? Where did *we* get drunk together?

ANOTHER FOP. Sir, I'd like to introduce you to some ladies in my carriage.

CYRANO (*coldly*). And who will introduce you first to me?

LE BRET (*surprised*). What's wrong with you?

CYRANO. Be quiet!

A MAN OF LETTERS (*with a pocket inkstand*). Now if you'll just give me the details—

CYRANO. No!

LE BRET (*nudging him with his elbow*). That's Théophraste Renaudot, inventor of the *Gazette!*

CYRANO. Pfui!

LE BRET. His sheet contains a world of matters. They say it has a future!

A POET (*advancing*). Sir—

CYRANO. Another?

THE POET. I'll make a pentacrostic[23] on your name.

---

[23] **pentacrostic:** set of verses divided into five sections lengthwise, with the first or last letters of each line of verse forming a particular name, word, or phrase five times.

SOMEONE ELSE (*advancing*). Sir!—

CYRANO (*loudly*). Enough's enough! (*The crowd moves off. The people withdraw. De Guiche appears, escorted by the officers who followed Cyrano in the first act, including Cuigy and Brissaille. Cuigy hastens up.*)

CUIGY (*to Cyrano*). Monsieur de Guiche! (*Murmurs; everybody withdraws.*) Representing the Marshal de Gassion!

DE GUICHE (*bowing to Cyrano*). Who wishes to express his admiration for your current exploit, now newly brought to light!

THE CROWD. Hurrah!

CYRANO (*bowing*). The Marshal is a judge of bravery.

DE GUICHE. He would never have believed it, if these gentlemen hadn't sworn that they had seen it.

CUIGY. With our own eyes!

LE BRET (*in a low voice, to Cyrano, who seems abstracted*). Now, really!

CYRANO. Hush!

LE BRET. You seem to be suffering.

CYRANO (*starting, and hastily straightening up*). What! Before these people? (*His mustache bristles; he throws out his chest.*) Suffering? You shall see!

DE GUICHE (*in whose ear Cuigy has been whispering*). Your career already abounds in glorious deeds. You're one of these crazy Gascons, aren't you?

CYRANO. A cadet!

A CADET (*in a terrific voice*). He's one of us!

DE GUICHE (*contemplates the Gascons ranged behind Cyrano*). So! All these haughty gentlemen behind you must be the famous, the renowned —

CARBON. Cyrano!

CYRANO. Captain?

CARBON. Since my company is here complete and all accounted for, you'd better introduce them to the Count.

CYRANO (*stepping two paces towards De Guiche and indicating the cadets*).

> These are Cadets of Gascony
> In Captain Carbon's corps;
> They fight and lie outrageously,

These are Cadets of Gascony!
And boast their forebears' ancestry
Who never thieves forebore.
These are Cadets of Gascony
In Captain Carbon's corps.

Hawk-eyed, wolf-fanged, and lank of knee,
Cat-whiskered, through the crowd they pour,
Careless of curse and deaf to plea,
Hawk-eyed, wolf-fanged, and lank of knee,
Wearing their plumes beguilingly
On hats agape with holes galore.
Hawk-eyed, wolf-fanged, and lank of knee,
Cat-whiskered, through the crowd they pour.

Here's Crack-your-Phiz and Snickersnee[24] —
Such nicknames they adore —
Who'd not love Fame to such degree,
Not Crack-your-Phiz and Snickersnee,[24]
Nor trade so much in duel'ry,
Loved they not Woman more.
Here's Crack-your-Phiz and Snickersnee;
Such nicknames they adore.

These are Cadets of Gascony,
All husbands they abhor;
But welcome wives! With bonhomie,[25]
These same Cadets of Gascony
Will teach you Love's geometry
While cuckoos sing and new horns roar.[26]
These are Cadets of Gascony,
All husbands they ab-whore!

DE GUICHE (*nonchalantly sitting in an armchair brought by Ragueneau*). Poets are luxuries we all must have today! Could I be your patron?

CYRANO. Not you, sir, nor anyone.

[24] **Crack-your-Phiz . . . Snickersnee**: Phiz is an abbreviation for *physiognomy,* or face: *snickersnee* means knife or sword.

[25] **bonhomie** (bon'ə·mē'): good-naturedness.

[26] **While cuckoos . . . roar**: The word *cuckold,* meaning a man with an unfaithful wife, comes from *cuckoo.* A cuckold traditionally wore horns on his head to signify his plight.

DE GUICHE. Your spirit yesterday was vastly diverting to my uncle Richelieu. I could further you with him.

LE BRET (*dazzled*). God!

DE GUICHE. I imagine that somewhere around you must have —some—some little thing—some five acts in rhyme?

LE BRET (*whispering*). They'll produce your *Agrippina*.[27]

DE GUICHE. Take it to him.

CYRANO (*tempted, somewhat pleased*). Well, really—

DE GUICHE. He's a connoisseur in such things. In your case, I'm quite sure, he'd only need to amend a verse or two.

CYRANO (*glowering*). Impossible! To think he could change a single comma would freeze my blood.

DE GUICHE. On the other hand, when he likes a verse, he'll pay—pay rather well!

CYRANO. But not so well as I do. When I've made verses that I really like, I make the proper payment: I chant them to myself.

DE GUICHE. You're a proud soul.

CYRANO. You've noticed that — already?

A CADET (*entering, his sword strung with battered plumed hats*). Look, Cyrano. Here's strange game we bagged on the quay this morning. Runaways' hats!

CARBON. Spoils of the chase!

[*General laughter.*]

CUIGY. Faith! Whoever set the rascals on will cut up rough today.

BRISSAILLE. Who could it be, I wonder?

DE GUICHE. It was I! (*The laughter stops short.*) I told them to chastise a wretched, drunken rhymester. It's not the kind of thing to soil one's hands with.

[*Strained silence.*]

THE CADET (*in an undertone to Cyrano, pointing to the hats*). What's to be done with them? Make a game stew? They're rather high.

---

[27] *Agrippina* (ag′rɔ·pi′nə): *The Death of Agrippina*, a tragedy written by the historical Cyrano about 1647. It concerns Agrippina (13 B.C.?–33 A.D.), widow of the Roman general Germanicus Caesar, and her part in a conspiracy against Emperor Tiberius, who had ordered her husband poisoned.

[*Cyrano takes the sword strung with hats and salutes with it in such a manner that they slide off with a rush at De Guiche's feet.*]

CYRANO. Perhaps you would return these to your friends?

DE GUICHE (*rising, speaking curtly*). Quick! My chair and porters! (*To Cyrano*) As for you, sir—

A VOICE (*outside*). The porters of His Grace the Count de Guiche.

DE GUICHE (*recovering self-control, with a smile*). Have you read *Don Quixote?*[28]

CYRANO. Frequently. Hats off to the harebrained fellow!

DE GUICHE. Then you would do well to remember —

A PORTER (*appearing at the back*). Here's the chair.

DE GUICHE. —the chapter on the windmills.

CYRANO (*bowing*). Chapter thirteen.

DE GUICHE. For when you attack them, it often happens—

CYRANO. —that my opponents turn with every breeze?

DE GUICHE. —that a windmill's spinning, sail-covered arms, will hurl you in the mud.

CYRANO. Or next door to the stars! (*Exit De Guiche. He is seen getting into his chair. His companions withdraw, whispering significantly. Le Bret ushers them to the door. The crowd leaves.*)

SCENE 8

Cyrano, Le Bret; the cadets sit down at the tables, right and left, and are served with refreshments throughout the scene.

CYRANO (*bowing ironically to those who leave unceremoniously*). Gentlemen! Gentlemen! Gentlemen!

LE BRET (*returning, throwing up his hands in despair*). This is a pretty pickle!

CYRANO. Enter the old grumbler!

LE BRET. You must admit you can murder opportunity too often. You exaggerate the thing!

[28] *Don Quixote* (kwik'sət): novel by Miguel de Cervantes about a Spanish gentleman who becomes obsessed with the ideals of chivalry and attempts to right the world's wrongs. In the episode referred to by De Guiche, Don Quixote comes upon some windmills and, convinced that they are giants, attacks one with his lance.

CYRANO. Exaggerate? Well, yes —

LE BRET (*triumphantly*). There now!

CYRANO. But for the sake of principle, not to say example, sometimes there's virtue in exaggeration.

LE BRET. Relax that musketeer's soul of yours a little! Think of the sure fortune, the undoubted fame —

CYRANO. What should I do? Seek out a powerful patron as protector, and like the obscure ivy round a tree, obtain support by licking at the bark, climb up by trickery, not by forthright strength? That's not for me! To be like all the rest and dedicate my verse to men of wealth, the financiers — become a vile and spiritless buffoon in the poor hope some politician's smile might prove not too unfriendly? No, not for me! I'll not lunch every mortal day on insult, nor wear my stomach's casing thin with crawling, nor lacerate these two good knees with kneeling, nor flex my dorsal vertebrae with bowing! I'll pat no cabbage-eating goat with one hand while watering rows of cabbage with the other, nor ever suffer damns to gain faint praise, nor lather perfumed flattery on a beard. I'll never graduate from lap to lap to be the darling of some little circle, nor navigate with madrigals[29] for oars and elderly maidens' sighs to fill my mainsail, or pay my publisher to bring my poems out, or chairman idiots in a grog-shop council — such things are not for me! Some make a single sonnet serve a lifetime. That's not for me! And some are terrorized by vagrant journals, would strive abjectly for a favoring mention in papers like the *Mercury of France*. Most calculate, must always be afraid, grow pale, present petitions — would rather pay a call than write a poem. But not for me! No, never that for me! None of these things for me! Instead . . . to sing, to dream, to laugh while passing by, to be alone and free! To have the observing eye, recording hand, and vibrant voice! To wear your hat as you please and when you please! To duel for *yes* or *no* . . . or poetize them. These are my life! To neglect fame for a journey to the moon;[30] never to write but what comes out of the heart — content with flowers, and fruits, even with leaves, if you

---

[29] **madrigals:** part songs that were popular during the Renaissance.

[30] **a journey to the moon:** a reference to Cyrano's book *Voyage to the Moon*.

pluck them in your own garden plot! Then, when at length
you have made a little way, you'll never need to render unto
Caesar[31] the things that are not Caesar's but your own; and
though, in the end, you may never reach the stature of a
great spreading oak or towering linden, you'll at least not
be parasitic ivy; you'll climb — not high perhaps — but
climb alone.

LE BRET. So be it! Quite alone! But quite alone — not one
against the world! Where the devil did you get that mania
for making enemies, always, everywhere?

CYRANO. From seeing you make friends! From seeing you
smiling at your crowds of friends, your mouth tight-pursed!
As for me, I like to give few greetings as I walk. My most
joyful words are: One enemy the more!

LE BRET. Sheer lunacy!

CYRANO. Lunacy or not, that's my one vice; displeasure is
my one pleasure — the great, final pleasure of being hated!
My friend, you've no idea how much better you strut it out
under the musketry of hostile eyes; and the least unpleasant
stains upon your doublet are those of envious gall and
cowards' spite. For you, the easy friendship that surrounds
you is like a floating, loose Italian collar: your neck is too
pliant for its good — not haughty because there's no restraint, support, or stricture, and your head gives way, pays
court to everyone. But hatred irons my ruff into stiff creases
that hold my head uplifted and in place. Each enemy is
another added pleat, an inconvenience but a ray of splen-
dor. For like a Spanish ruff in every way, hate's collar is
the aureole[32] of glory.

LE BRET (*after a short pause, putting his arm through Cyrano's*). Be proud and bitter to the world, my friend; but,
privately, just say, "She doesn't love me."

CYRANO (*quickly*). Quiet!

[*Christian has entered and mingled with the cadets; they
ignore him; finally, he sits down alone at a little table,
where Lise waits on him.*]

[31] **render unto Caesar:** an allusion to the statement by Jesus, "Render therefore unto Caesar the things which are Caesar's; and unto God the things that
are God's." (See Matthew 22:21.)

[32] **aureole:** a radiant light around the head (usually associated with sacred
persons).

SCENE 9

Cyrano, Le Bret, the cadets, Christian de Neuvillette.

A CADET (*seated, glass in hand, at a table backstage*). Hey!
Cyrano! (*Cyrano turns around.*) The story!

CYRANO. Later!

[*He walks backstage arm in arm with Le Bret. They talk
quietly.*]

THE CADET (*rising and coming forward*). The story of the
fight! It will be the best possible lesson (*stopping in front
of Christian's table*) for this scared beginner.

CHRISTIAN (*looking up*). Beginner?

ANOTHER CADET. Yes, puny northerner!

CHRISTIAN. Puny?

FIRST CADET (*mockingly*). Monsieur de Neuvillette, one
thing you should know: there is one subject never mentioned in this corps, any more than rope in a hanged man's
house!

CHRISTIAN. What is it?

ANOTHER CADET (*in a terrifying voice*). Look at me! (*He
mysteriously puts his finger to his nose three times.*)
Understand?

CHRISTIAN. Oh! It's his —

ANOTHER. Hush! Never utter that word (*indicating Cyrano,
talking backstage with Le Bret*) or you will have to deal
with him.

ANOTHER (*who, while Christian's back is turned, has quietly
seated himself on the table behind him*). Quite recently,
he massacred two snufflers, just for talking through their
noses. He didn't like it.

ANOTHER (*hollowly, appearing under the table*). You can't
even allude to that fatal cartilage without deceasing long
before your time.

ANOTHER (*his hand on Christian's shoulder*). A word is
enough. What did I say — a word? A single gesture! Reach
for your handkerchief and you clutch your shroud!

[*Silence. All around Christian watch him gravely, their
arms folded. He rises and goes to Carbon de Castel-*

*Jaloux, who affects to be absorbed in a conversation with
an officer.*]

CHRISTIAN. Captain!

CARBON (*turns and looks him up and down*). Sir?

CHRISTIAN. What's to be done, when southerners are boastful?

CARBON. Prove that a northerner can be courageous! (*He
turns his back upon him.*)

CHRISTIAN. Thank you!

FIRST CADET (*to Cyrano*). Now for your story.

ALL. The story!

CYRANO (*coming towards them*). My story? Here it is!

[*All draw up stools and chairs, grouping themselves
around him, craning their necks. Christian sits astride a
chair.*]

CYRANO. As I marched out alone to meet them, the moon
gleamed like a watch; but some careful horologian[33] must
have drawn a cloud of cotton over its silver case, for the
night changed swift and strangely to the blackest night in
the world. Since the quays were unillumined, you couldn't
see your —

CHRISTIAN. Nose!

[*Dead silence. Everyone slowly rises in amazement.
They watch Cyrano with alarm. He stops, stupefied.*]

CYRANO. Who is this person?

A CADET (*in an undertone*). He joined the corps this morning.

CYRANO (*stepping towards Christian*). This morning?

CARBON (*also in an undertone*). He calls himself the Baron
de Neuvil —

CYRANO (*stops hastily*). So! That's it? (*He pales, then reddens, and starts to rush at Christian again.*) Well! (*Regaining self-control, hollowly*) Very well! — I was saying —
(*Sudden burst of rage*) 'Struth! (*Continuing in his natural
voice*) — that nothing could be seen. (*General amazement;
they all sit down again, still watching him.*) And so I
marched on thinking that a friendless rogue like myself
might displease some eminent person, some prince who
would trim my —

CHRISTIAN. Nose!

[33] **horologian:** watchmaker.

[*Everyone stands again; Christian rocks back and forth in his chair.*]

CYRANO (*his voice stifled with rage*). Claws; and his claws would be out for me. In short, I'd be placing my —

CHRISTIAN. Nose!

CYRANO. Fingers — 'twixt the hammer and the anvil, for this person might have power, to strike me in the —

CHRISTIAN. Nose!

CYRANO (*wiping sweat from his forehead*). — in the back! But I said: "On! Do what you must. On, Cyrano, come what may!" So I went my way in the darkness, until some one gave me a —

CHRISTIAN. Nose-tap!

CYRANO. I parried it — so! There I was —

CHRISTIAN. Nose to nose!

CYRANO (*rushing at him*). Hell and damnation! (*All jump up to watch; controlling himself with difficulty, he continues*) — face to face with a hundred ruffians, smelling so —

CHRISTIAN. You had to hold your nose?

CYRANO (*pale, with a determined smile*). — of onions and sour wine! Forward I rushed, head down! —

CHRISTIAN. And nose to the wind!

CYRANO. I charged! Two I ripped up standing! Another I skewered at a thrust. Then one of them lunges: Snap! I parry, and answer —

CHRISTIAN. Sniff!

CYRANO (*bursting forth*). Damnation! Out! The whole pack of you!

[*All the cadets hurry toward the door.*]

FIRST CADET. The tiger has awakened!

CYRANO. All of you! Leave me alone with this man!

SECOND CADET. Heavens! He'll make mincemeat of him.

RAGUENEAU. Mincemeat?

ANOTHER CADET. Just right for one of your pies.

RAGUENEAU. I feel pale. I'm limp as a napkin.

CARBON. Let's get out of here!

ANOTHER. Not a crumb of him left.

ANOTHER. What's going to happen here would scare anyone to death.

ANOTHER. Terrible! Terrible!

[*They are all gone — some by the back, some by the sides; a few have disappeared up the staircase. Cyrano and Christian stand face to face and stare at each other a moment.*]

SCENE 10

Cyrano, Christian.

CYRANO. Come to my arms!

CHRISTIAN. Sir —

CYRANO. Brave fellow!

CHRISTIAN. Yes, but —

CYRANO. Extremely brave. I like you.

CHRISTIAN. But why all this?

CYRANO. Your hand! I'm her brother.

CHRISTIAN. Whose?

CYRANO. Hers!

CHRISTIAN. What?

CYRANO. Roxane's.

CHRISTIAN. Heavens! You, her brother?

CYRANO. Almost! Her cousin-brother.

CHRISTIAN. And she's told you —

CYRANO. Everything.

CHRISTIAN. Does she love me?

CYRANO. Possibly.

CHRISTIAN (*shaking both his hands*). How happy I am, Sir, to get to know you!

CYRANO. That's what is called taking a sudden liking.

CHRISTIAN. I'm sorry!

CYRANO (*looking at him with his hand on his shoulder*). It's true! The man is really handsome.

CHRISTIAN. If you only knew how I admire you.

CYRANO. But those noses you threw in my face —

CHRISTIAN. I take them back!

CYRANO. Roxane expects a letter tonight.

CHRISTIAN. Impossible!

CYRANO. What?

CHRISTIAN. To write would kill my chance with her!

CYRANO. How is that?

CHRISTIAN. I am such a numbskull I could kill myself for shame.

CYRANO. You couldn't be, or else you'd never know it. That was no numbskull who bandied words with me.

CHRISTIAN. Oh, you can find words in the heat of conflict. I have a certain easy soldier's wit, but before women it's best I should be silent. Oh, their eyes may shine with kindness as I pass them —

CYRANO. And don't their hearts show kindness when you stop?

CHRISTIAN. No! I am one of those — I know it, and tremble to think of it — who can never talk of love.

CYRANO. If they'd only been more careful with the model, I I might have talked of it quite passably myself.

CHRISTIAN. Oh, to be able to express such things gracefully!

CYRANO. To be some passing musketeer — but handsome!

CHRISTIAN. Roxane is fastidious in such matters — a *précieuse*! I'm sure to disappoint her.

CYRANO (*looking intently at Christian*). If I had such an interpreter to speak my soul!

CHRISTIAN (*in despair*). If I had eloquence!

CYRANO (*brusquely*). I'll give it you! Give me your conquering presence in exchange; together we could make a hero of romance!

CHRISTIAN. What?

CYRANO. Could you repeat the things I'll teach you every day?

CHRISTIAN. What are you proposing?

CYRANO. Roxane must never know the truth. Dare you feel the soul I can inspire pass from my leather jerkin into your silken doublet?

CHRISTIAN. But Cyrano! —

CYRANO. Christian, are you willing?

CHRISTIAN. You startle me!

CYRANO. Since you think that, alone, you'll make her heart turn cold, will you let your lips collaborate with my phrases, and caress her heart into flame?

CHRISTIAN. Your eyes are shining.

CYRANO. Well?

CHRISTIAN. Would it please you so very much?

CYRANO (*intoxicated by the prospect*). That? (*Regaining self-control and speaking dispassionately as an artist*) That would . . . fascinate me strangely. A situation worthy of a poet! You as my complement, and I as yours; you in the sun, and I deep in shadow; I as the spirit, you the incarnation.

CHRISTIAN. But the letter should be sent to her at once! I could never hope to write it.

CYRANO (*taking from his doublet the letter he has written*). Here is your letter.

CHRISTIAN. What?

CYRANO. Nothing lacking, except the signature.

CHRISTIAN. Mine? No!

CYRANO. You can send it. Wait! It's quite all right.

CHRISTIAN. You had it written, already?

CYRANO. We poets are never caught without a letter in our pockets — epistles to Chloris,[34] imaginative rondels[35] for sweethearts blown from dreams into the bubble of a name. Take it and use it. Make truths of its pretences. It was more eloquent the less I was sincere. These are complaints and avowals launched at random; take them and make these errant swallows come to roost. Take it and have done with it!

CHRISTIAN. But shouldn't the words be changed? Written haphazard, will it fit Roxane?

CYRANO. Fit her like a glove.

CHRISTIAN. But —

CYRANO. Self-love is self-belief; it has no limitations. Roxane will think that this was made especially for her.

CHRISTIAN. My dearest friend!

[*He throws himself into Cyrano's arms. They remain embraced.*]

SCENE 11

Cyrano, Christian, the Gascons, the musketeer, Lise.

A CADET (*opening the door*). Not a sound — dead silence — I daren't look — (*Puts in his head.*) Why!

[34] **Chloris:** conventional name in poetry.
[35] **rondels:** poems (usually of fourteen lines with two rhymes and repetition of certain lines).

ALL THE CADETS (*entering and seeing Cyrano and Christian embracing each other*). Oh! —

A CADET. Unbelievable!

[*General consternation.*]

THE MUSKETEER (*jeering*). Well! Well!

CARBON. Our demon is gentle as a disciple, is he? Whoever shall smite him on the one nostril, doth he turn the other also?[36]

MUSKETEER. We can talk about his nose, eh? (*With an air of triumph, calling Lise to see*) Hey! Lise! Here's something you should see! (*Sniffing the air affectedly*) Oh! Oh! Shocking! What an odor! (*Going to Cyrano*) Sir, you must have sniffed it. What does it smell of here?

CYRANO (*slapping his face*). A slapdragon![37]

[*General joy. The cadets have found their own Cyrano again. They turn somersaults in relief.*]

CURTAIN

QUESTIONS

Scene 1. How does Ragueneau integrate his profession of pastry-cooking with that of versemaking? How does Cyrano integrate his profession of swordsman with that of versemaking? Is the character of Ragueneau intended in some way to reflect that of Cyrano, or to comment on it?

Scenes 3–4. Cyrano fights a hundred men and must meet one girl. Which, for him, is the greater ordeal? Why? As the poets discuss the valiant fight against the hundred, Cyrano himself is composing a love letter. Which two sides of Cyrano are presented to the audience simultaneously? Why has Cyrano chosen to put his feelings for Roxane *in writing*?

Scene 6. When Roxane begins to tell Cyrano of the "boy" she loves from afar, whom does Cyrano at first think she means? Explain how the poignancy of this scene depends on a misunderstanding. Why does

---

[36] **Whoever shall smite . . . the other also:** an allusion to the words of Christ: "But whosoever shall smite thee on thy cheek, turn to him the other also." (See Matthew 5:39.)

[37] **slapdragon:** a flower; the French word also means "a slap on the face."

Cyrano lose his color at the mention of the word "handsome"? What is the significance of his remark, "I've done far, far better — since!"

Scenes 7–8. What qualities of character and manner does Cyrano reveal in his reception of the admiring crowd? in his encounter with De Guiche? How are his actions in Scene 7 illuminated by his statement of principles in Scene 8? Is haughty hatred really essential to honor, as Cyrano implies?

Scene 9. What motivates Christian to humiliate Cyrano by calling attention to his nose? Why can't Cyrano respond by fighting him? What two aspects of Cyrano's character are at war with one another?

Scene 10. Christian is like Cyrano in many ways — in his courage, for example. Are there other similarities? What are two key differences — one physical, one intellectual — between Christian and Cyrano? What is the effect when Cyrano says of the letter he has written for Christian to Roxane, "Roxane will think that this was made especially for her."

ACT THREE

ROXANE'S KISS

A *small square in the fashionable quarter of seventeenth-century Paris, the old Marais. Old-style houses. Perspectives*[1] *of narrow streets. At the right, Roxane's house and garden wall, topped by abundant foliage. Above the door of her house, a balcony and upstairs window. The walls are ivied; the balcony is wreathed in jasmine, festooning from and to the ground. In front of the threshold of the door, a bench. By means of this bench and stones jutting irregularly from the wall, the balcony can easily be climbed.*

At *the left, another old house of brick and stone in the same architectural style. The knocker in the door is swathed in linen as though it were a sore thumb.*

At *the rise of the curtain, Roxane's balcony window is open. The Duenna is seated on the bench. Before her stands Ragueneau wearing a sort of livery. He is concluding a recital of his woes, drying tearful eyes.*

---

[1] *Perspectives:* scenes painted on canvas backcurtains.

SCENE 1

Ragueneau, the Duenna; then Roxane, Cyrano, and two pages with lutes.

RAGUENEAU. And off she went with a musketeer! Alone, ruined, I was hanging myself. I had already left this world, when Monsieur de Bergerac rushed in; cut me down; recommended me to his cousin as a steward. Thus ended my suspense.

DUENNA. But how do you explain your ruination?

RAGUENEAU. Lise loved warriors; I, poets. Mars ate all the stock of cakes that Apollo had left. After that, the end wasn't long in coming.

DUENNA (*rising and calling towards the open window*). Roxane, they are waiting for us. Are you ready?

ROXANE'S VOICE (*from the window*). I am putting on my cloak.

DUENNA (*to Ragueneau, pointing to the door leftstage*). We're stepping across to Clomire's[2] house. A little meeting in her temple of letters. Someone is going to discourse on the Tender Passion.[3]

RAGUENEAU. The Tender Passion?

DUENNA (*simpering*). To be sure. (*Calling towards the window*) Roxane, hurry down! We'll be too late for the Tender Passion!

ROXANE'S VOICE. I am coming.

[*A tune played on lutes offstage. It becomes louder as the players approach.*]

CYRANO'S VOICE (*offstage, singing*). La! la! la! la!

DUENNA (*in pleased surprise*). A serenade, for us?

[*Enter Cyrano, followed by two pages with lutes.*]

CYRANO. I tell you that is a demi-semi-quaver, you demi-semi-idiot.

FIRST PAGE (*ironically*). What, sir, you know about demi-semi-quavers?

---

[2] **Clomire's:** Clomire was among the fanciful names given to one another by the *précieuses*.

[3] **the Tender Passion:** In her book *Clélie*, Mlle. Scudéry (one of the *précieuses*) sketched the Map of Tenderness, an ideal map of love and gallantry.

CYRANO. Like all Gassendi's[4] pupils, I know my music.

THE PAGE (*playing and singing*). La la!

CYRANO (*snatching his lute and taking up the musical phrase*). I can continue it. La! la! la! la!

ROXANE (*appearing on the balcony*). Is it you?

CYRANO (*singing his words to the tune*).

"I who come to greet your fairness, pay respects unto your radiance;
I who come to praise your lilies, am enamored of your roses!"

ROXANE. I am coming down.

[*She leaves the balcony.*]

DUENNA (*indicating the pages*). Who are these two masters of the lute?

CYRANO. A wager I won from D'Assoucy. We were disputing a point of grammar — this way and that way, yes and no — when suddenly he points to these his constant shadows, these crabs whose claws are skilled in scraping strings, and says: "I'll bet you a whole day's music." He lost. So, until Apollo starts his course again,[5] I have to have these lutanists at my heels, harmonious witnesses of all I do. At first, it was delightful; now, it palls. (*To the pages*) Hey! Go and play Montfleury a pavane.[6] (*They proceed upstage. To the Duenna*) I'm here, as every night, to ask Roxane — (*To the pages*) Play a long time . . . and keep it well off key! (*To the Duenna*) — whether her heart's delight is still quite faultless.

ROXANE (*coming out of the house*). How handsome. How witty. How I love him!

CYRANO (*smiling*). Christian? Witty?

ROXANE. Even more than you are!

CYRANO. Maybe so.

ROXANE. No one alive can turn so delicately those pretty nothings which are everything. Sometimes his muse is

---

[4] **Gassendi's:** Pierre Gassendi (1592–1655) was one of the most eminent French philosophers. He was the teacher of Molière and Cyrano; from him Cyrano got his love for physics and astronomy.

[5] **until Apollo . . . again:** *i.e.*, until the sun rises again.

[6] **pavane:** solemn Spanish dance; also the music for the dance.

gone; he seems distrait. Then suddenly he says enchanting things.

CYRANO (*incredulous*). Impossible!

ROXANE. Now that's too much. That's you men all over: just because he's handsome you think he can't be clever.

CYRANO. He speaks from the heart, speaks expertly?

ROXANE. He doesn't speak at all; he lyricizes.

CYRANO. And sometimes writes you?

ROXANE. He out-writes writing. Listen to this! (*Declaiming*)

> "The more you steal my heart,
>   the more remains."

Well? Good?

CYRANO. Pooh!

ROXANE. And this:

> "Since I have need of heart that
>   I may feel,
> Then keep this heart of mine,
>   but lend me yours."

CYRANO. Sometimes too much; sometimes not enough. Just how much heart does he want?

ROXANE. You're jealous!

CYRANO (*starting*). What?

ROXANE. One author's jealousy of another. And this —

> "Unto your heart, my heart sounds one clear call;
> And if my kisses could be written down,
> You'd read them with your lips, could they be read at all."

Isn't that the ultimate in delicate affection?

CYRANO (*smiling with satisfaction, in spite of himself*). Ha! Ha! Now those lines — those lines are — well! — (*with affected disdain as he remembers his rôle*) — on the insipid side.

ROXANE. And this —

CYRANO (*delighted*). You know his letters by heart, then?

ROXANE. All of them!

CYRANO. There's no denying it; the man's a flatterer.

ROXANE. Flatterer? He's a veritable master.

CYRANO (*modestly*). Oh! — a master.

ROXANE (*peremptory*). A master!

CYRANO. If you insist, then — a master!

DUENNA (*hurrying downstage*). Monsieur de Guiche! (*To Cyrano, pushing him towards the door of the house*) Into the house! He'd better not find you here. It might open his eyes —

ROXANE. Yes, to my cherished secret. He's in love with me — and powerful. He mustn't suspect. He'd knock my affair on the head — and with an axe.

CYRANO (*disappearing through the door*). All right! All right!

SCENE 2

Roxane, De Guiche; the Duenna backstage.

ROXANE (*making a curtsey to De Guiche*). I'm going out.

DE GUICHE. I've come to say good-bye.

ROXANE (*coldly*). Going away?

DE GUICHE. Going to war.

ROXANE (*without any feeling*). Oh!

DE GUICHE. Going tonight.

ROXANE. Oh!

DE GUICHE. I have my orders. Arras[7] is under siege.

ROXANE. Oh! Under siege?

DE GUICHE. Yes. I see my departure seems to leave you cold.

ROXANE. Really?

DE GUICHE. Don't you see I'm heartbroken? When and where shall we ever meet again? . . . By the way, I've been made commander of a regiment.

ROXANE (*indifferently*). Very nice.

DE GUICHE. Yes, commander. Commander of the Regiment of Guards —

ROXANE (*startled*). Of Guards! Oh!

DE GUICHE. — in which your cousin serves, he of the boastful speeches. I imagine I might pay off old scores with him out there.

ROXANE (*choking with emotion*). And the Guards are off to the front?

[7] **Arras:** city in northern France; conquered by the French in 1640.

DE GUICHE (*laughing*). Naturally! That's my regiment.

ROXANE (*aside, slipping down on to the bench*). Christian!

DE GUICHE. Is something wrong?

ROXANE (*much moved*). It's this parting. It makes me sad. To know that a loved one must go off to war!

DE GUICHE (*in pleased surprise*). So after all you can find a word of kindness? For the first time, when I'm leaving you?

ROXANE (*with a change of tone and manner*). You want your revenge against my cousin? —

DE GUICHE (*smiling*). I see. You're for him.

ROXANE. No! Against him.

DE GUICHE. But you meet him sometimes.

ROXANE. Very rarely.

DE GUICHE. He goes around everywhere with one of the cadets — a certain Neu . . . villen . . . viller . . . .

ROXANE. Tall?

DE GUICHE. Fair!

ROXANE. Red-haired.

DE GUICHE. Handsome —

ROXANE. Pfui!

DE GUICHE. — but stupid.

ROXANE. He looks it! (*Changing tone again*) This settling of old scores with Cyrano — you're going to put him under fire, aren't you? A poor revenge. He'll like that. I could suggest something really crushing.

DE GUICHE. What is it?

ROXANE. Let the regiment leave. Keep him and all his dear cadets back here in Paris, champing at the bit, until the war is over. That's the only way to hurt a man like him: to deprive him of danger is the best of all punishments.

DE GUICHE. A veritable woman after all! Only a woman could invent a trick like that!

ROXANE. He'll eat his heart out — and his friends chew their nails — not to be in the thick of it. Your revenge will count for something.

DE GUICHE (*coming close*). You must really care for me a little! (*Roxane smiles.*) Roxane, am I wrong in reading a proof of love in the fact that you second my rancor?

ROXANE. You may be right.

DE GUICHE (*showing sealed letters*). Here are the marching orders. One goes to every company except — (*taking one out*) — this one. It's for the Gascony Cadets. (*He puts it in his pocket.*) I'll see personally it is not delivered. (*Laughing*) Ha! Ha! Ha! Cyrano spoils for a fight, does he? And you, you're not above playing a trick or two?

ROXANE. Under certain circumstances.

DE GUICHE (*now very close to her*). I ought to leave tonight, but ... you drive my senses to distraction. How can I leave, knowing that I have moved you? Listen! I know! There's that convent in the Rue d'Orléans, founded by the syndic of Capuchins, Father Athanasius. A layman can't enter, but I could manage it. They'll hide me up their sleeves; they're liberal-minded. These Capuchins are of Richelieu's household; dreading the uncle, they'll obey his nephew! That's it! People will think I've gone, and I'll come back here masked. My capricious darling, grant me one more day!

ROXANE. But if it's discovered! Your reputation —

DE GUICHE. Bah!

ROXANE. What of the siege at Arras?

DE GUICHE. So much the worse! Is it a bargain?

ROXANE. No!

DE GUICHE. It must be!

ROXANE (*tenderly*). Don't you see I *must* refuse —

DE GUICHE. Oh!

ROXANE. Don't you see you'll have to go — (*Aside*) But Christian stays! (*Aloud*) — because I want you to be of heroic stature — Antoine!

DE GUICHE. Divinely uttered name! Then you really love the man who —

ROXANE. I love the man for whom I've been afraid.

DE GUICHE (*transported with joy*). Darling! I must go! (*Kisses her hand.*) Happy, now?

ROXANE. Happy? Yes, my dear! (*Exit De Guiche.*)

DUENNA (*making a mocking curtsey behind his back*). Yes, my dear!

ROXANE. Whatever you do, don't say a word of this! Cyrano will be furious if he knows I've robbed him of his silly old war. (*Calls towards the house*) Cousin!

SCENE 3

Roxane, the Duenna, Cyrano.

ROXANE. We'll go to Clomire's now. (*Indicating the door, left*) Alcandre's going to speak, and so is Lysimon.[8]

DUENNA (*putting her little finger in her ear*). A little birdie tells me we have missed them.

CYRANO (*to Roxane*). You wouldn't miss those performing monkeys, would you?

[*They reach Clomire's door.*]

DUENNA (*delighted*). Look, the knocker is swathed in linen. (*To the knocker*) Tough little fellow! They've gagged you so you shan't disturb the speeches. (*She lifts it with infinite care and knocks gently.*)

ROXANE (*as the door opens*). Let's go in. (*From the threshold, to Cyrano*) If Christian comes, as no doubt he will, tell him to wait for me.

CYRANO (*hastily, as she goes in*). By the way! (*She turns around.*) Following the usual trend, what's the interrogation for today? What will you ask him?

ROXANE. About —

CYRANO (*quickly*). About — ?

ROXANE. But you must keep mum.

CYRANO. Mum as a wall.

ROXANE. About — precisely nothing! I'm going to say to him, "Out with it! Be quite unbridled! Improvise! Talk of love! Be your splendid best!"

CYRANO (*smiling*). Good.

ROXANE. Hush.

CYRANO. Hush.

ROXANE. Not a word. (*She goes in and closes the door.*)

CYRANO (*bowing to her, after the door is shut*). Our deepest thanks! (*The door reopens; Roxane puts out her head.*)

ROXANE. He might prepare beforehand —

CYRANO. No! The devil he might!

BOTH TOGETHER. Hush!

[*The door closes.*]

CYRANO (*calling*). Christian!

[8] **Alcandre . . . Lysimon:** more of the fanciful names used by the *précieuses.*

SCENE 4

Cyrano, Christian.

CYRANO. I know all we need. Get your memory in trim. Here's a chance to cover yourself with glory. No time to lose. Don't look so sad. Quick! Let's get back to your rooms. I'm going to teach you —

CHRISTIAN. No.

CYRANO. What?

CHRISTIAN. No! I shall wait for Roxane here.

CYRANO. What's got into you? Come on, you've got to learn it quickly —

CHRISTIAN. I tell you no! I'm tired of borrowed letters and borrowed speeches, of playing a part and knowing that I'm afraid. It was all right at first, but now I feel she loves me. I'm not afraid any more; I'm going to speak for myself!

CYRANO. Careful! Look out!

CHRISTIAN. Who told you I don't know how to speak? I'm not as dull as all that. Just wait! But, my friend, your lessons have not been wasted. I shall know how to speak alone to her. And by the living God, I'll know very well how to take her in my arms! (*He sees Roxane reappearing from Clomire's house.*) Here she is now! Cyrano, don't leave me!

CYRANO (*bowing ceremoniously*). Sir, you shall speak for yourself! (*Disappears behind the garden wall.*)

SCENE 5

Christian, Roxane; the Duenna, for a moment. Roxane appears at Clomire's door with the others, from whom she is taking leave. Curtsies and bows.

ROXANE. Barthénoïde! Alcandre! Grémione!

DUENNA (*pitifully*). Oh! To have missed the discourse on the Tender Passion! (*Goes into Roxane's.*)

ROXANE (*bowing again*). Urimédonte! Farewell! (*All bow to Roxane, bow again to each other, separate, and leave by different streets. Roxane sees Christian.*) You're here! (*She goes up to him.*) Evening is falling. They have gone now; and no one else is passing. The air is mild. Let's sit down here and talk. Well, I am listening.

CHRISTIAN (*who has seated himself near her on the bench, after a pause*). I love you.

ROXANE (*closing her eyes*). Yes, speak of love.

CHRISTIAN. I love you!

ROXANE. Yes, that's the theme; what of the variations?

CHRISTIAN. I love —

ROXANE. The variations!

CHRISTIAN. I love you — very much!

ROXANE. Doubtlessly. What else?

CHRISTIAN. What else? I should be happy if you — loved me, too. Roxane, tell me that you love me!

ROXANE (*pouting*). You offer me gruel when I hoped for sweets. Tell me how you love me.

CHRISTIAN. Why, very much indeed.

ROXANE. Oh! Dislabyrinth[9] your feelings!

CHRISTIAN. I want to kiss your throat.

ROXANE. Christian!

CHRISTIAN. I love you.

ROXANE (*starting to rise*). What, again?

CHRISTIAN (*hastily, stopping her*). No! I don't love you —

ROXANE (*sitting down again*). That's just as well!

CHRISTIAN — I adore you!

ROXANE (*rising, beginning to leave him*). Oh!

CHRISTIAN. I know; I'm growing foolish —

ROXANE (*dryly*). I don't like it. No more than if you suddenly turned ugly.

CHRISTIAN. But —

ROXANE. Run after your vanished eloquence!

CHRISTIAN. I —

ROXANE. I know; you love me. Good-bye. (*Goes towards her house.*)

CHRISTIAN. Please! Not so soon! I'll tell you how —

ROXANE (*pushing the door open to go in*). — how you adore me. Yes, I know already. Best go away!

CHRISTIAN. But please! Really, I — (*She shuts the door in his face.*)

---

[9] **Dislabyrinth:** in the language of the *précieuses*, "to separate, undo." In other words, follow the thread of your feelings. Untangle them.

CYRANO (*who has looked on, unperceived, for a moment*).
A grand success!

SCENE 6

Christian, Cyrano; the pages, for a moment.

CHRISTIAN. Won't you help me?

CYRANO. I'm afraid not.

CHRISTIAN. If I can't get back her good graces, I shall die
this very instant.

CYRANO. But how the devil can I teach you this very instant?

CHRISTIAN (*seizing his arm*). See that?

[*The balcony window lights up.*]

CYRANO (*moved*). Her window! Hers!

CHRISTIAN. I'll die, I tell you.

CYRANO. Lower your voice.

CHRISTIAN (*whispering*). I'll die!

CYRANO (*thinking aloud*). Yet the night is dark —

CHRISTIAN. Yes?

CYRANO. All's not lost yet, though you don't deserve much
else. Stand there, young fool, in front of the balcony.
I'll go underneath and prompt you in a whisper.

CHRISTIAN. But —

CYRANO. Shhh!

THE PAGES (*reappearing backstage, to Cyrano*). Hey!

CYRANO. Quiet! (*Puts his finger on his lips.*)

FIRST PAGE (*in an undertone*). We've just administered the
serenade to Montfleury —

CYRANO (*low, quickly*). Go and watch for me — you at this
corner, you at that. If any inconvenient passerby should
come, play me a tune.

SECOND PAGE. What tune do you want, O follower of Gassendi?

CYRANO. Merry, if it's a woman; mournful, for a man.

[*The pages vanish, one at each corner.*]

CYRANO. Call her out!

CHRISTIAN. Roxane!

CYRANO (*gathering pebbles, and throwing them at the
window*). Wait! Let's try these pebbles.

ROXANE (*slightly opening her window*). Who called me?

CHRISTIAN. I did.

ROXANE. Which "I"?

CHRISTIAN. Christian!

ROXANE (*scornfully*). Oh, you!

CHRISTIAN. I want to speak to you.

CYRANO (*under the balcony*). Good! Good! Keep your voice down.

ROXANE. No, your words are far too halting. Go away!

CHRISTIAN. Can't you forgive?

ROXANE. No! You no longer love me.

CHRISTIAN (*as Cyrano prompts him*). Merciful Heavens! Accuse me of loving you no longer, when I love you more than ever!

ROXANE (*arrested in the act of closing the window*). Oh! That's a little better.

CHRISTIAN (*prompted*). Love waxes in me — rocked in my restless heart — my troubled heart — which the — cruel brat has taken for his — cradle.

ROXANE (*stepping out on the balcony*). That *is* better! But since this love is cruel, you were foolish not to choke it in the cradle.

CHRISTIAN (*prompted*). That I attempted also — but in vain; this — newborn child — is a little — Hercules —

ROXANE. Still better!

CHRISTIAN (*prompted*). A child newborn — who strangles as if of naught — the two writhing serpents — Pride and — Doubt.

ROXANE (*advancing, resting her elbows on the balcony*). Very good indeed! But why do you speak with so much hesitation? Have your inventive faculties succumbed to gout?

CYRANO (*pulling Christian under the balcony and taking his place*). Shhh! This is getting difficult.

ROXANE. Why are you hesitant tonight, I wonder?

CYRANO (*speaking low, like Christian*). Because it is tonight, and all my words must search in the shadowed darkness for your ear.

ROXANE. Yet mine find no such hindrance.

CYRANO. They find their way at once? Why, so they ought,

since *my* heart is here to welcome them. My heart is wide, profound; your ear is tiny. Besides, your words, descending, rush down quickly, while mine, Roxane, climb at a slower gait.

ROXANE. They climb much better in these last few moments.

CYRANO. They grow accustomed to gymnastic feats.

ROXANE. Indeed I'm far too high from where I'm speaking —

CYRANO. So high, you'd kill me, if from that great height, you dropped one hard word down upon my heart.

ROXANE. I'm coming down myself.

CYRANO (*hastily*). No!

ROXANE. Climb on that seat then, quickly.

CYRANO (*alarmed, slipping back into the darkness*). No, I daren't.

ROXANE. Why not?

CYRANO (*with rising emotion*). Let us take full advantage of this moment, when we can speak, but speaking, cannot see.

ROXANE. Not see each other?

CYRANO. Blessed, heavenly moment! Each can divine the other, nothing more. You sense the blackness of my long, trailing cloak; I glimpse the glimmering whiteness of your gown; I'm but a shadow — you, a gleam of radiance. Can you guess what all this must mean to me? If sometimes I was eloquent —

ROXANE. Oh, you were!

CYRANO. — yet, nonetheless, till this celestial minute, my words could never spring straight from the heart.

ROXANE. How could that be?

CYRANO. Because, till now, I could not speak, save through — (*Pauses.*)

ROXANE (*softly*). Through what?

CYRANO. — the veil of dizziness that mantles all who see you. Tonight, it seems, I speak for the first time.

ROXANE. It's true your voice sounds different.

CYRANO (*feverishly drawing nearer*). Yes, quite different. I'm myself at last. In this protecting darkness, I think I'd dare — (*Stops in confusion.*) Where am I? I cannot tell! Forgive this rush of feeling, so new to me —

ROXANE. So new?

CYRANO (*distracted, trying to regain composure*). New to me, yes! So new to be sincere! Fear of your laughter has always stopped me.

ROXANE. My laughter? Why?

CYRANO. Because of my — impulsiveness. My heart has hid in wit for fear of shame. Often I wished to pluck a star for you; in fear of scorn, I tendered just a flower.

ROXANE. Your flowers had virtues.[10]

CYRANO. This evening, let's forget them.

ROXANE. You never spoke like this before —

CYRANO. My dear, far from the quivers, the torches, and the arrows, let us find other words less dulled by repetition. Leave Lignon's[11] tasteless waters, drunk in drops from the puny goblet of a golden thimble, and see our souls slake their eternal thirst from the great flood of Love's eternal river.

ROXANE. But that wit of yours.

CYRANO. Oh, I made full use of it at first — to hold you. But now, to speak like some small poetaster[12] is treason to this night, this hour, this garden. Let the bright stars, in one revealing glance, rid us of artifice. By wit's fell alchemy,[13] true sentiment might puff away in vapor, the heart be emptied by its own empty pastimes, and fine refinement be — finality.

ROXANE. Then all your cleverness? —

CYRANO. In love, I hate it. Love's greatest crime is to prolong the fencing beyond the sure, inevitable moment — moment some men can never hope to know — when our hearts feel a great love ennobled beyond the dismal grasp of pretty words.

ROXANE. If this should be that moment, what words have you left for me?

CYRANO. Why, this, this, this! Every word that comes, no matter how! Words that I throw in clusters, unarranged! I love — I burn for you — I love you — I am mad! There,

---

[10] **flowers . . . virtues:** i.e., your words were effective.

[11] **Lignon's** (lēn·yonʹz'): The Lignon is a tributary of the Loire. Céladon, the hero of d'Urfé's *L'Astrée*, jumps into this stream when he is banished by Astrée.

[12] **poetaster** (pōʹət·as'tər): inferior poet.

[13] **fell alchemy:** cruel transforming power.

that's too much! I can't go on! Your name is like a bell
within my heart, and all the time I'm quivering, my Roxane,
and all the time the bell shakes with my heart, and all the
time it's pealing out your name. All of you that I love, all
I remember, comes rushing back to me. You did not know,
last year, the twelfth of May, when you left this house in
the morning, I was there! Your hair was dressed in a subtly
different fashion — your hair so long to me a blinding
radiance. And just as when you look too long in the sun,
you see vermilion circles everywhere, when I turned away
from your hair's too dazzling flame, my eyes were flecked
with shimmering golden blots.

ROXANE (*agitated*). Why! This is love itself!

CYRANO. Beyond all doubt! What else could it be, so terrible and demanding? It vibrates with love's melancholy
madness — and yet, there is no selfishness. Though I
should love and you should never know, I'd gladly sacrifice all recompense, if sometimes I could hear from far
away your gay, untroubled laughter. You understand?
Each glance of yours inspires me with new virtues, with
new courage. You must know that, and somehow sense my
soul climbing the shadows! But then, this night's too perfect as it is. To think that I can speak, that you are listening, outruns the hope of my most sanguine dreams. Since
nothing else remains to ask, I'll die. Ah! but these words
of mine have set you trembling, over my head among the
moon-flecked branches, for you *are* trembling like a leaf-
fringed flower. Whether you will or no, I feel your trembling, the adorable quiver of your outstretched hand
running along these fragrant jasmine branches.

[*He passionately kisses the tip of a hanging bough.*]

ROXANE. Yes! I am tremulous and weeping. I love you!
I am yours! Your words have cast a spell on me!

CYRANO. Then Death come when it will! It is I, I, who cast
this spell on you. I ask but one thing more of Life —

CHRISTIAN (*under the balcony*). A kiss!

ROXANE (*recoiling*). What?

CYRANO. Oh!

ROXANE. You asked for what?

CYRANO. Yes — I — (*In a low voice to Christian*) You're much too hasty!

CHRISTIAN. Since she's profoundly stirred, I'll profit by it.

CYRANO (*to Roxane*). Yes, I — I asked, it's true. But, heavens above, I was far too audacious!

ROXANE (*somewhat disappointed*). You don't insist?

CYRANO. Yes! I insist — insist without insistence. Your modesty is hurt, I know. You must not grant this kiss!

CHRISTIAN (*to Cyrano, pulling his cloak*). Why not?

CYRANO. Be quiet, Christian!

ROXANE. What are you whispering?

CYRANO. Scolding myself for having gone too far! Saying: Be quiet, Christian! (*Lutes begin to play.*) Wait! Someone's coming!

[*Roxane closes her window. Cyrano listens to the lutes, one of which plays a merry, the other a mournful air.*]

CYRANO. Sad tune! Gay tune! What's the idea? Man or woman? Oh, I understand. A monk! Some wandering monk!

[*Enter a Capuchin, lantern in hand; he goes from house to house peering at the doors.*]

Scene 7

Cyrano, Christian, the Capuchin.

CYRANO (*to the Capuchin*). Who is this new Diogenes[14] with a lantern searching for honest men in *darkness?*

CAPUCHIN. I'm looking for the house of —

CHRISTIAN. He's ruining everything!

CAPUCHIN. — of Madame Magdeleine Robin.

CHRISTIAN. What does he want?

CYRANO (*indicating one of the streets upstage*). That way. Straight ahead. Always straight ahead.

CAPUCHIN. Thank you. I'll say my rosary for you, right to the biggest bead. (*Exit backstage.*)

CYRANO. Good luck! My prayers be on your cowl! (*Returns to Christian.*)

[14] **Diogenes . . . in *darkness:*** an allusion to the Greek philosopher Diogenes, who, carrying a lantern in daylight, went looking for an honest man.

SCENE 8

Cyrano, Christian.

CHRISTIAN. Get me that kiss!

CYRANO. No!

CHRISTIAN. Sooner or later —

CYRANO. Yes, that's true. There'll come that moment of
intoxication when your lips must meet because her mouth
is red, your mustache fair. (*To himself*) I'd rather it were
because of other things.

[*Sounds of the window opening. Christian hides under
the balcony.*]

SCENE 9

Cyrano, Christian, Roxane.

ROXANE (*stepping out on the balcony*). Are you still there?
We were speaking of a — of a —

CYRANO. Kiss. The word is sweet; why are your lips afraid?
If the word burns you, what will the real thing be? No
need for fear. A moment past, insensibly, your jesting came
to an end; you passed without a qualm from smile to sigh,
and from your sighs to tears. Take one step more in the
same fearless fashion — from tear to kiss is but an added
tremor.

ROXANE. Be still!

CYRANO. A kiss! When all is said, what is a kiss? A vow
brought close, a promise more precise! A troth confirmed,
a little rosy dot we write above the letter "i" in *loving!*
A secret told the lips instead of the ear, infinite instant
murmurous of bees, fragrant communion odorous of flowers!
The breathing in, a little, of the heart, to taste, with lips,
a little of the soul!

ROXANE. Will you be still?

CYRANO. Kisses have been ennobled, my Roxane. The
Queen of France, even the Queen herself, allowed the
happiest of lords to take one!

ROXANE. Indeed!

CYRANO (*carried away*). Like Buckingham's, my sufferings

have been mute; like him, I have adored the Queen you
   are. Like him, I'm sad and true —
ROXANE. And like him, handsome.
CYRANO (*aside, sobered*). That's true; I was forgetting I am
   handsome.
ROXANE. Well, climb, and gather up this peerless flower.
CYRANO (*pushing ·Christian towards the balcony*). Climb!
ROXANE. This tasting of the soul.
CYRANO. Climb up!
ROXANE. This murmuring of bees.
CYRANO. Climb up, I say!
CHRISTIAN (*hesitating*). It seems to me it isn't quite right
   now.
ROXANE. This infinite instant.
CYRANO. Will you climb up, you idiot? (*Gives him a push.*)

[*Christian springs forward, scales the balcony by means
   of the bench and jasmines, and leaps over the balustrade.*]

CHRISTIAN. My Roxane! (*Embraces her and bends over her
   lips.*)
CYRANO. God! what is this torture in my heart? Oh feast
   of love, at which I'm Lazarus![15] A vagrant crumb comes
   falling through the darkness, brushes my lips, and slides
   into my soul! For on the lips which have enticed Roxane,
   she kisses words that only I have spoken! (*The lutes are
   heard.*) Sad tune, gay tune — the monk again! (*In a loud
   voice, pretending to run from a distance*) Hello!
ROXANE. Who's there?
CYRANO. I. I was just passing. Is Christian there?
CHRISTIAN (*astonished*). Cyrano?
ROXANE. Good evening, cousin!
CYRANO. Good evening, cousin!
ROXANE. I'm coming down.

[*She disappears into the house. Reenter the Capuchin
   backstage.*]

CHRISTIAN (*seeing him*). Him? Again? (*He follows Roxane
   inside.*)

---

[15] **Oh feast ... Lazarus:** an allusion to the parable told by Jesus in which the
beggar Lazarus ate crumbs from the rich man's feast (Luke 16).

SCENE 10

Cyrano, Christian, Roxane, the Capuchin, Ragueneau.

CAPUCHIN. It's this one. I'm certain of it. Magdeleine
Robin.

CYRANO. You said Ro*lin*.

CAPUCHIN. No! — *bin!* B, i, n — *bin!*

ROXANE (*appearing at the door followed by Ragueneau with
a lantern, and by Christian*). What is it?

CAPUCHIN. A letter.

CHRISTIAN. What?

CAPUCHIN (*to Roxane*). It can only be about some sacred
matter. It was a right worthy nobleman who —

ROXANE (*to Christian*). It's from De Guiche.

CHRISTIAN. He'd never dare!

ROXANE. Well, he won't keep on troubling me for ever.
(*Unsealing the letter*) Besides, I love you, and if he —
(*Reading by the light of Ragueneau's lantern; aside*)
"Mademoiselle: The drums are beating. My soldiers are
putting on their tunics. They leave immediately. I'm supposed to have left already, yet I'm still here — at the
convent. I've disobeyed you. I'm coming to see you, and
send this advance word by a simple sheep of a monk who
could never guess what it all means. Your smile was altogether too much for me; I *must* see it again. Please
arrange matters so that you're alone, and deign to receive
this audacious being, already pardoned as he hopes, who
signs himself your — etc." (*To the Capuchin*) Father,
here's what the letter says. Listen! (*All draw near; she
reads aloud*) "Mademoiselle: However hard it may seem,
the wishes of the Cardinal must be obeyed. That is why
I have chosen a very holy, discreet, and intelligent Capuchin to convey these lines into your charming hands. We
desire him to pronounce at once and in your own dwelling
(*she turns the page*) the nuptial benediction over you and
Christian, who will secretly become your husband. I have
sent him to you, knowing that you dislike him. Yet you
must resign yourself to the inevitable. You can be sure
that Heaven will bless your zeal, and can be assured,
Mademoiselle, òf the respect of him who has always been
your very humble and very — etc."

CAPUCHIN (*beaming*). That worthy nobleman! I said so, you remember. I wasn't afraid; I knew it must be sacred business.

ROXANE (*in an undertone to Christian*). Don't I read letters rather well?

CHRISTIAN. Hm!

ROXANE (*aloud, in mock despair*). Oh! This is terrible!

CAPUCHIN (*turning his lantern on Cyrano*). So you're the one?

CHRISTIAN. No! I'm the one!

CAPUCHIN (*turning the light on him, as if suspicious of his handsome appearance*). But — Sir! —

ROXANE (*hurriedly*). Postscript: "Give one hundred and twenty pistoles[16] for the convent."

CAPUCHIN. That worthy, worthy lord! (*To Roxane*) Resign yourself, my daughter.

ROXANE (*with the expression of a martyr*). I am resigned. (*While Ragueneau is opening the door for the Capuchin, she speaks softly to Cyrano.*) De Guiche will come. Keep him here. Don't let him come in until —

CYRANO. I understand. (*To the Capuchin*) How lengthy is this ceremony?

CAPUCHIN. A quarter of an hour.

CYRANO (*shepherding them towards the house*). Go in! I'm staying here.

ROXANE (*to Christian*). Come along. (*They enter.*)

CYRANO (*aside*). How the devil can I hold De Guiche for fifteen minutes? (*He jumps on the bench and climbs on the wall towards the balcony.*) There! Up here! I think my plan might work. (*The lutes begin to play a mournful tune.*) So? A man! (*The tune becomes tragic.*) This time a man for certain. (*He has reached the balcony; he pulls his hat over his eyes, takes off his sword, wraps his cloak about him, and leans over the balustrade.*) No, it's not too high. (*He bestrides the balustrade, grasps with both hands a branch of one of the trees over the garden wall, and prepares to let himself drop.*) A little atmospheric disturbance is forecast.

[*Enter De Guiche, masked, groping in the dark.*]

[16] **pistoles**: units of money.

SCENE 11

Cyrano, De Guiche.

DE GUICHE. What can that cursed Capuchin be doing?

CYRANO. The devil! If he should recognize my voice — (*Letting go with one hand, he pretends to turn an invisible key.*) Click, clack! (*Solemnly*) Cyrano, assume the dialect of Bergerac![17]

DE GUICHE (*looking up at the house*). Yes, that's the one. I don't see well, not with this mask on.

[*He starts towards the house; Cyrano jumps from the balcony by the aid of the branch, which bends and lets him down lightly between De Guiche and the door; he pretends to fall very heavily, as if from a height, and lies prone on the ground, motionless, as if stunned. De Guiche, startled, recoils.*]

DE GUICHE. Hey! What's this? (*By the time he looks up, the branch has already sprung back; he sees nothing but open sky.*) Where did this fellow come from?

CYRANO (*sitting up; in a broad dialect*). From the moon!

DE GUICHE. From the *what?*

CYRANO (*abruptly*). What time is it?

DE GUICHE. Is he out of his mind?

CYRANO. What time is it? What country — day — and season?

DE GUICHE. But —

CYRANO. My head is dazed!

DE GUICHE. My dear sir! —

CYRANO. I fell like a bomb — from the moon.

DE GUICHE (*impatiently*). Oh, come now! —

CYRANO (*rising, in a terrifying voice*). Fell from the moon, I tell you!

DE GUICHE (*recoiling*). All right! If you say so, you fell from the moon. (*Aside*) Probably mad!

CYRANO (*coming up to him*). Not metaphorically, either!

DE GUICHE. But —

CYRANO. But meteorically! Was it a hundred years or just a minute since? I can't tell how long I was falling — falling from that saffron planet yonder.

[17] **Bergerac:** *i.e.,* the town of Bergerac.

DE GUICHE (*shrugging*). Maybe so! Let me by!

CYRANO (*interposing*). Where am I? Be quite frank with me. No glozing over. Where — where in the universe — has my meteor fall just landed me?

DE GUICHE. The devil!

CYRANO. I couldn't pick my destination. I fell as I fell. Has my backend's weight dragged me to earth or onto a moon?

DE GUICHE. Why, sir, I assure you! —

CYRANO (*with a cry of terror that makes De Guiche recoil further*). Merciful heavens! The people have black faces here!

DE GUICHE (*feeling his face*). What?

CYRANO (*with assumed terror*). The Moors of Algeria! You're a native!

DE GUICHE (*somewhat reassured*). Oh! This mask.

CYRANO (*somewhat reassured*). Then it's Venice or Genoa!

DE GUICHE (*trying to get by him*). There's a lady expecting me —

CYRANO (*completely reassured*). Paris! That's where I am!

DE GUICHE (*smiling in spite of himself*). The fellow's amusing.

CYRANO. You're smiling!

DE GUICHE. Smiling, but you'd better let me by.

CYRANO (*beaming broadly*). So here I am in Paris? (*Brushing himself, bowing, perfectly at ease*) Excuse my appearance. That last cloudburst spattered me with ether. Quite a trip I've had. My eyes are filled with stardust, and there's still planet hair in my spurs. (*Picking something off his sleeve*) Why, here's a stray wisp from a comet's mane on my doublet. (*He makes a show of blowing it away.*)

DE GUICHE (*beside himself with anger*). Sir! —

[*Just as De Guiche is about to pass, Cyrano stretches out his leg and stops him.*]

CYRANO. If there isn't a tooth from the Great Bear in the calf of my leg! And as I skirted the Trident to avoid one of the prongs, blessed if I didn't land sitting on Libra, right on its scales! That indicator up there must still register my weight! (*Quickly preventing De Guiche from passing, he takes him by the button of his doublet.*) If you took my nose between your fingers, it would spurt out milk!

DE GUICHE. What? Milk?

CYRANO. From the Milky Way.

DE GUICHE. Hell and — !

CYRANO. Heaven sent me here. (*Folding his arms*) Would
you believe what I saw as I fell? Sirius wraps his head
every night in a turban. The Little Bear is too little yet to
bite. (*Laughing*) As I went through the Lyre I broke a
string. (*Proudly*) But I'm planning a book about it, and the
golden stars that I brought in my scorched cloak at such
great risk and peril will be useful when it's printed, as
asterisks![18]

DE GUICHE. Enough of this! I wish —

CYRANO. Naturally, you would wish —

DE GUICHE. Sir!

CYRANO. — you'd wish to know from my own lips how the
moon is made; whether any one lives within its retortlike[19]
roundness?

DE GUICHE (*shouting*). No, I don't! I wish —

CYRANO. To know how I got there? Well, the method is my
own invention.

DE GUICHE (*discouraged*). Mad!

CYRANO. I didn't use the idiotic flying machine of Regiomontanus[20] or the wooden pigeon of Archytas[21] —

DE GUICHE. Mad!! — but a scholar, nonetheless!

CYRANO. — or anything ever tried before.

[*De Guiche succeeds in getting by him and walks
towards Roxane's door. Cyrano follows, ready to hold
him forcibly.*]

CYRANO. I've found six ways to ravish the virgin skies.

DE GUICHE (*interested, turning*). Six?

CYRANO (*volubly*). My body, taper-nude, I could deck with
vials filled with the dews gathered from morning skies.
Then, when the dews were drawn up to the sun, my form
would follow and soar up with them.

[18] **asterisks:** a play on words — the literal meaning is "little stars."

[19] **retortlike:** A retort is a vessel in which substances are distilled or de-
composed by heat.

[20] **Regiomontanus** (1436–76): famous German astronomer and mathematician. Among other experiments, he made an artificial flying eagle.

[21] **Archytas:** Greek who lived in southern Italy about 400 B.C.; reputed
inventor of the screw and the crane. He also made a wooden pigeon that
could fly.

DE GUICHE (*surprised; taking a step towards Cyrano*). That's certainly one method.

CYRANO (*drawing back to lead him on*). With burning glasses in a twenty-sided frame, I'd store up air sufficient for my flight by rarefaction[22] in a cedar chest.

DE GUICHE (*taking another step*). Two!

CYRANO (*drawing further back*). I'm a pyrotechnician-machinist! I might fashion a steel-triggered cricket, which I'd hurl by successive explosions to the blue fields where stars are pastured.

DE GUICHE (*unsuspiciously following him*). Three!

CYRANO. Since smoke has the property of rising, why not rise on a globe of smoke?

DE GUICHE (*still following; increasingly astonished*). Four!

CYRANO. The Moon, when her crescent is thinnest, sucks out your marrow, O beeves![23] I'd anoint my body with marrow.

DE GUICHE (*astounded*). Five!

[*Cyrano, while talking, has gradually led De Guiche towards a seat at the other side of the square.*]

CYRANO. Lastly, mounting on an iron disc, I'd fling a lodestone magnet in the air, and as the well-thrown magnet went its way, the iron disc would soar in hot pursuit. Repeat the throw, and, faith, you'd soar indefinitely!

DE GUICHE. Six! Six excellent methods, sir! Which method did you choose?

CYRANO. A seventh.

DE GUICHE. Really? What was that?

CYRANO. You'll never guess.

DE GUICHE (*aside*). He interests me strangely!

CYRANO (*making the sound of waves, and with mysterious gestures*). Hoo-sh! Hoo-sh!

DE GUICHE. Well?

CYRANO. Can't you guess?

DE GUICHE. No!

CYRANO. The sea! The sea, of course! (*Portentously*) At the hour when the tide is surging to the moon, after my sea bath,

---

[22] **rarefaction:** process of making rare and thin.
[23] **The Moon . . . O beeves:** an allusion to the superstition that the quarter moon sucked out the marrow of animals.

lying on the sands, my head first lifting — for you see, my friend, the head holds water in its fringe of hair — upwards I drifted, upwards like an angel, ascending, rising, soaring — no sense of strain! — until I felt a shock! Then —

DE GUICHE (*carried away by curiosity, sits on the seat*). And then? What then?

CYRANO (*returning to his natural speech*). Then is now! The quarter of an hour is over. Now they are married, I'll let you go!

DE GUICHE (*springing to his feet*). What's this? Am I drunk? That voice! (*The doors of the house open. Lackeys carry out lighted candelabra. Cyrano takes off his hat.*) That nose! Cyrano?

CYRANO (*bowing*). Precisely! Cyrano! They've just exchanged rings.

DE GUICHE. They've what? Who? (*He turns round. Tableau. Behind the lackeys, Roxane and Christian holding hands. The Capuchin follows them, smiling. Ragueneau carries a torch. The flurried Duenna brings up the rear in a peignoir.*[24])

DE GUICHE. Great God in Heaven!

SCENE 12

The same; Roxane, Christian, the Capuchin, Ragueneau, the lackeys, the Duenna.

DE GUICHE (*to Roxane*). You! (*Astounded at recognizing Christian*) Him? (*Bowing to Roxane with admiration*) You are more than clever! (*To Cyrano*) My compliments, inventor of machines! Your tale would have stopped a saint from entering Paradise. I hope that you noted all the details; they deserve enshrining in a book.

CYRANO (*bowing*). That, sir, is advice I pledge myself to follow.[25]

CAPUCHIN (*indicating the lovers to De Guiche and shaking his great white beard with satisfaction*). My son, this is a

[24] **peignoir** (pān·wär′): woman's dressing gown.
[25] **That, sir ... follow:** The historical Cyrano (1619–55) wrote *The States and Empires of the Moon.*

handsome couple you united.

DE GUICHE (*frostily*). Indeed! (*To Roxane*) Madame, it's time you said good-bye to your husband.

ROXANE. What?

DE GUICHE (*to Christian*). Your regiment is on the march. Join it at once!

ROXANE. To go to war?

DE GUICHE. Naturally!

ROXANE. But, Sir, the cadets are not to go!

DE GUICHE. They'll go, all right! (*Taking out the paper which he had put into his doublet*) Here are their orders. (*To Christian*) Deliver that, Baron.

ROXANE (*throwing herself into Christian's arms*). Christian!

DE GUICHE (*sneeringly, to Cyrano*). The wedding night is still a long way off.

CYRANO (*aside*). To think he thinks that hurts me terribly!

CHRISTIAN (*to Roxane*). Oh, your lips again!

CYRANO. Come! Enough's enough.

CHRISTIAN (*continuing to kiss Roxane*). It's hard to leave her; you couldn't possibly know —

CYRANO (*trying to pull him away*). I know.

[*Drums beat a march in the distance.*]

DE GUICHE (*going upstage*). The regiment is leaving.

[*For the remainder of the scene, Cyrano tries to pull Christian away; Roxane to hold him back.*]

ROXANE (*to Cyrano*). I trust him to your care. Promise me that nothing shall put his life in danger.

CYRANO. I'll try my best, but still I cannot promise —

ROXANE. Promise that he'll be very careful.

CYRANO. I'll do all possible, but —

ROXANE. That during this terrible siege, he'll never take cold.

CYRANO. I'll do my best, but —

ROXANE. And that he'll be faithful —

CYRANO. Yes, yes, certainly! But —

ROXANE. And that he'll write me often!

CYRANO. That I can really promise you!

CURTAIN

QUESTIONS

Scene 1. Roxane says of Christian: "Sometimes his muse is gone. . . . Then suddenly he says enchanting things." How do you explain this? How does Cyrano respond to Roxane's praise of Christian's verses? How do you think Cyrano really feels about them?

Scene 2. Roxane employs a ruse to frustrate De Guiche's intention of sending Cyrano and the cadets into battle. What is the motive behind De Guiche's plan? What is Roxane's true motive in spoiling it? Roxane and Cyrano both deceive for love. Are their deceptions equally honorable?

Scenes 3–4. At the beginning of Scene 3, Cyrano promises Roxane to remain "mum as a wall" if Christian comes. What is the effect of these words in the light of what follows? Does Roxane really love Christian, or merely his words that praise her? Is she worthy of Cyrano's love?

Scenes 5–6. Why is Cyrano willing to prompt Christian from under the balcony? At what point does he begin to speak his own true feelings to Roxane? Why doesn't Cyrano at first allow Christian to kiss Roxane? Why does he later change his mind?

Scene 10–12. How does Roxane's quick wit succeed in bringing about her marriage to Christian? During the ceremony Cyrano holds De Guiche at bay with a fantastic tale of falling from the skies. Are the escapades he relates merely random fancies or do they in some way symbolize Cyrano's recent experiences? (In what sense has he been among the stars and now come back to earth?) Comment on the dramatic effectiveness of the tableau which ends Scene 11.

ACT FOUR

THE CADETS OF GASCONY

The post occupied at the Siege of Arras in 1640 by the company of cadets commanded by Carbon de Castel-Jaloux. A talus, or face-slope of an earthwork, crosses the entire backstage area. Beyond it, and extending to the horizon, a broad vista of a plain. The whole country-side is dotted with breastworks and trenches; in the far distance, the walls and roofs of Arras are silhouetted against the sky. There are tents, scattered arms, drums, etc.; sentries posted at even intervals; campfires. Day is just dawning — a Chinese yellow dawn.

The Gascony cadets are fast asleep, wrapped in their cloaks. Carbon de Castel-Jaloux and Le Bret, both very pale and very thin, keep watch. Christian, frontstage, is asleep in his cape among his comrades; his face is visible in the firelight.

SCENE 1

Christian, Carbon de Castel-Jaloux, Le Bret, the cadets; then Cyrano.

LE BRET. This is dreadful.

CARBON. Not a thing left.

LE BRET. God!

CARBON (*his finger on his lips*). Curse in whispers; you'll wake them up. (*To the cadets*) Hush! Sleep on. (*To Le Bret*) Those who sleep have no need of food.

LE BRET. Insomnia is a double hunger. We're suffering from a veritable famine!

[*Shots in the distance.*]

CARBON. Oh, the deuce take their firing. They'll wake my lads. (*To the cadets, who have raised their heads*) Go back to sleep.

[*The heads go down again. More shooting, closer.*]

A CADET (*stirring*). Lord! Again?

CARBON. It's all right. Just Cyrano coming back.

[*Heads fall back again.*]

SENTRY (*offstage*). Who goes there?

CYRANO'S VOICE. Bergerac.

ANOTHER SENTRY (*on the talus slope*). The devil! Who goes there?

CYRANO (*appearing on the rampart*). Bergerac, you idiot. (*He approaches. Le Bret goes to meet him.*)

LE BRET. Thank God you're back.

CYRANO (*motioning for quiet*). Hush!

LE BRET. Wounded?

CYRANO. You know well enough they make a habit of missing me every morning.

LE BRET. Still, it's farfetched to risk your life every morning just to carry a letter.

CYRANO (*stopping in front of Christian*). I promised he'd write often. (*Looking down at him*) Asleep, pale, dying of hunger — still handsome in spite of everything! If she only knew, poor girl, how he's starving to death.

LE BRET. Go and get some sleep.

CYRANO. Don't grouse, Le Bret. Here's one comfort for you: to get through the Spanish ranks, I've found a place where they're drunk every night.

LE BRET. Some night you ought to bring us back some food.

CYRANO. I have to travel light to get through. But something is going to happen tonight, I feel it in my bones. If I'm a judge, we French must dine or die.

LE BRET. What do you mean?

CYRANO. I'm not quite sure. You'll soon see —

CARBON. It's a crime what a hungry business this besieging is.

LE BRET. Well, this siege of Arras is a complicated matter. We besiege the town; then, caught like rats in a trap, we're besieged in turn by the Cardinal Prince of Spain.

CYRANO. To finish it off, someone ought to come out and besiege him!

LE BRET. I'm past laughing.

CYRANO. Oh! Oh!

LE BRET. It makes me boil to think that every day you risk a life like yours just to carry — (*Cyrano moves off towards one of the tents.*) Where are you off to?

CYRANO. I'm going to write another! (*He lifts the tent flap and disappears inside.*)

SCENE 2

The same; without Cyrano.

Dawn has brightened from yellow to rose. Arras, on the horizon, is steeped in morning gold. Offstage, far left, the sudden report of a cannon, followed by the beating of drums. Another roll of drums close at hand. The near and far drums answer each other, become merged in a single continuous roll, come very close to the camp, and die away gradually, offstage right. It is the reveille. Noises of the camp awakening. In the distance, voices of officers uttering commands.

CARBON (*sighing*). The reveille — oh me! (*The cadets stir in their cloaks; stretch themselves.*) Succulent slumbers, why must you end? I know only too well what their first words will be!

A CADET (*sitting up*). I'm famished.

ANOTHER. Dying.

ALL (*groaning*). Oh!

CARBON. Get up!

THIRD CADET. I can't take a step.

FOURTH CADET. I can't move a muscle.

THE FIRST (*observing his reflection in his breastplate*). My tongue is yellow; today's air doesn't eat so well.

ANOTHER. My baron's coronet for a speck of Cheshire cheese.

ANOTHER. If they won't put enough in my breadbasket to work up a pint of gastric juice, I'll sulk in my tent all day — like Achilles.[1]

ANOTHER. Oh, for a little bread.

CARBON (*in an undertone, going to Cyrano's tent*). Cyrano!

OTHERS. We're going to die.

CARBON (*still in an undertone, at the door of the tent*). Cyrano, I need your help! You always have a merry quip for them. Come and cheer them up.

SECOND CADET (*dashing at the first, who seems to be chewing something*). What are you nibbling?

THE FIRST. Gun tow, fried with axle grease in a helmet. This Arras district is a little short of game.

ANOTHER (*entering*). I've just been hunting.

ANOTHER (*entering*). I've been fishing in the Scarpe.[2]

ALL (*rising and rushing towards them*). What! What have you got — pheasant, carp? Come on, show us.

THE FISHERMAN. A minnow.

THE HUNTER. A sparrow.

ALL (*exasperated*). Enough of this! Let's mutiny!

CARBON. Cyrano, you've got to help! (*It is now broad daylight.*)

---

[1] **Achilles:** a reference to Achilles' "sulking in his tent" when he lost the maiden Briseis to Agamemnon.

[2] **Scarpe:** tributary of the Scheldt that flows by Arras.

SCENE 3

The same; and Cyrano.

CYRANO (*calmly issuing from his tent, book in hand, a pen behind his ear*). What's wrong here? (*Silence. To the first cadet*) What are you dragging around for?

THE CADET. I've something in my heels that hampers me.

CYRANO. What's that?

THE CADET. My stomach.

CYRANO. The same goes for me.

THE CADET. Doesn't it worry you?

CYRANO. The contrary! It adds inches to my stature.

SECOND CADET. My teeth are sure sharp-set.

CYRANO. The better to bite with — in good time.

A THIRD. My stomach is limp as a rag.

CYRANO. We'll use it for spare drum skins.

ANOTHER. My ears buzz —

CYRANO. That's not true. Famished stomach: deaf ears.[3] You don't believe me? There, deaf ears! A hungry man won't ever listen to reason.

ANOTHER. Oh, for a few leaves — and a little oil.

CYRANO (*taking off his helmet and quickly thrusting it in his hands*). Why, here's a whole sallet![4]

ANOTHER. I could devour anything, no matter how tough and dry.

CYRANO (*throwing him his book*). Try the *Iliad.*

ANOTHER. I'll bet the Cardinal has his four meals a day.

CYRANO. A cardinal sin you should avoid! You want him to talk turkey?

THE SAME. I'd not grouse if he sent some wine.

CYRANO. By a portly friar?[5]

THE SAME. Chartreuse or Benedictine[6] —

CYRANO. A cordial emissary!

ANOTHER. I could eat nails.

[3] **Famished stomach: deaf ears:** an allusion to the proverb "Hunger has no conscience."

[4] **sallet:** a pun on *salad* and *sallet,* a helmet of the time. This sets the tone for the food puns that follow as Cyrano tries to perk up the spirits of the starving Cadets.

[5] **portly friar:** a play on words—"port" is a sweet, rich wine.

[6] **Chartreuse** (shär´trüz´) **or Benedictine:** liqueurs (alcoholic beverages).

CYRANO. Where's the iron in your soul?

FIRST CADET (*shrugging*). Go on. Always witty! Always punning! Always words to the point!

CYRANO. Yes! the point — the pointed word. That above all! I should like to die under sunset skies some evening making a last *bon mot*[7] for a noble cause, to sink to the turf, far from the bed of sickness, struck by a worthy sword and adversary; to die with a point at my heart and a pointed word on my lips.

ALL. We're hungry!

CYRANO (*folding his arms*). Is there nothing on earth but food? Come here, old Bertrandou! I know you've been a shepherd. Take from your double leather case one of your shepherd pipes. Blow it! Play for this pack of gormandizers and gluttons the old airs of our homeland, with their ancient, haunting rhythms. Each note a little sister, or the sound of familiar voices — the cadence slow as the lazy smoke from our native village roofs, and the tune pitched to the lilt of our childhood's Gascon patois.[8] (*The old man sits down and takes out a flute.*) Let the warlike pipe, which mourns today, remember for a moment — as your fingers flutter a sarabande,[9] birdlike upon its stops — that its shrill martial ebony was once a rustic reed. Surprise it with old songs again, the songs of its peaceful youth. (*The old man begins to play Languedocian tunes.*) You weary Gascons, listen! It changes in his fingers. The shrill fife of the roaring camp is the flute of our quiet woods; the stirring call to battle turns to a goatherd's song, to the spirit of moor and forest and our little red-capped shepherds, to the tender green of evening on the reaches of Dordogne.[10] Listen, you weary Gascons! This is your Gascony.

[*All heads are bent; all eyes dreamy. Tears are furtively wiped away on the backs of sleeves and corners of cloaks.*]

---

[7] *bon mot* (bōⁿ·mō'): clever remark.

[8] **patois** (pa'twä'): dialect of a certain region.

[9] **sarabande:** music for a stately court dance of the same name.

[10] *Languedocian* (lang'gə·dō'shen) ... **Dordogne** (dȯr·dōn'): Languedoc (läⁿg·dȯk') is a region in southern France; the Dordogne River is a tributary of the Garonne, which flows through Languedoc and Gascony.

CARBON (*in an undertone, to Cyrano*). You're making them weep.

CYRANO. Nostalgia's a nobler pain than hunger. Mental, not physical. Let their sufferings leave their stomachs for a while; it's their hearts that are aching now.

CARBON. You'll weaken them by plucking at their heartstrings.

CYRANO (*signalling a drummer to approach*). Nonsense! They have heroism in their blood. It doesn't take much rousing. All that's needed is — (*At his signal, the drum rolls.*)

ALL (*leaping up and rushing to their arms*). Hey! — What! — What's all this?

CYRANO (*smiling*). — just the beat of a drum! Then, farewell dreams, regrets, homesickness, love. What the flute stirred, vanished with the drum.

A CADET (*looking backstage*). Well, well! If it isn't Monsieur de Guiche.

ALL THE CADETS (*in a low murmur*). Boo!

CYRANO (*smiling*). Such flattering murmurs!

A CADET. He bores us.

ANOTHER. Trying to make an impression with that broad point-lace collar over his armor!

ANOTHER. As if anyone wore linen on armor!

THE FIRST. It's a good thing when you've a carbuncle on your neck.

THE SECOND. He's proper nephew to that uncle.

ANOTHER. Always the perfect courtier.

CARBON. A Gascon, nonetheless.

THE FIRST. A false Gascon. I don't trust him. Real Gascons ought to be crazy; nothing's more dangerous than a Gascon who can keep his head.

LE BRET. He looks pale.

ANOTHER. He's hungry as any other poor devil. But his breast-plate has studs of silver gilt. *His* stomach cramps can glitter in the sun.

CYRANO (*hurriedly*). Don't show your sufferings, either! Get out your cards, your pipes, your dice — (*All start playing with cards and dice, on drums, stools, and cloaks spread*

on the ground. They light long tobacco pipes.) For my part,
I'll be reading Descartes.[11]

[*He walks to and fro, reading a little volume he has
taken from his pocket. Tableau. Everyone looks con-
tented and absorbed. Enter De Guiche. He approaches
Carbon.*]

SCENE 4

The same; De Guiche.

DE GUICHE (*to Carbon*). Oh! — Good morning! (*They look at
each other with open satisfaction; aside*) Green as a corpse!

CARBON (*aside*). His face all eyes!

DE GUICHE (*surveying the cadets*). So these are the wrong-
headed rascals? Gentlemen, I hear from all sides that you
scoff at me! That the cadets, those scions of the hillsides,
squireens of Béarn,[12] *pâté de fois gras* barons,[13] have no
words too bad for their colonel! That this point-lace collar
on my breastplate shocks them profoundly! That nothing
restrains their indignation to see a Gascon who is not a
beggar! (*Silence. The cadets continue smoking and playing.*) A punishment is indicated! Perhaps your captain —

CARBON. I hold a free commission. No punishment is
contemplated.

DE GUICHE. So!

CARBON. I maintain my own company. They are mine
alone — otherwise answerable only to general orders.

DE GUICHE (*struck by an idea*). Ah? Indeed? So that's it?
Enough! (*To the cadets*) I shall treat your blustering with
contempt. My conduct under fire needs no boasting adver-
tisement. Take yesterday's action at Bapaume — my
repulse of the Count of Bucquoi. Pouring in my men like
an avalanche, I charged three times —

CYRANO (*without looking up from his book*). And lost your
white scarf?

[11] **Descartes** (dā·kärt′): René Descartes (1596–1650), celebrated French philosopher who founded modern philosophy. In the seventeenth century his
works were very popular, and the *précieuses* read him enthusiastically.

[12] **squireens of Béarn:** country squires from Bcarn, a region near Gascony.

[13] *pâté de fois gras* (pä′ta′de·fwä′grä′) **barons:** *i.e.,* barons from Périgord,
noted for its goose liver paste.

DE GUICHE (*surprised and pleased*). Oh, you knew about that? Yes, as I wheeled my horse and rallied my men, a sudden rush of fugitives swept me to the enemy lines. There was danger I'd be shot or taken prisoner. Then, I had an idea. I dropped my white scarf, my only badge of rank. The trick worked. In the general confusion, the Spaniards didn't notice who I was. I got back safely to our lines, rallied my men, pressed home the charge, and won the skirmish. Well? What do you think of it?

[*The cadets have not appeared to listen; at this point, however, their cards and dice boxes remain in the air; their pipe-puffing stops. Pause*]

CYRANO. I'd say — that Henry IV,[14] no matter what the odds, would never have lowered his stature by the loss of his white plume.

[*Silent joy. The cards and dice fall. Pipes puff again.*]

DE GUICHE. Yet the stratagem succeeded!

[*The same pause and action as before.*]

CYRANO. Possibly! Possibly! But who'd decline the honor of being a target? (*Cards and dice fall; pipes puff as before.*) There's a difference in our notions of courage. If I'd been present when you dropped your scarf, I'd have picked it up and worn it myself.

DE GUICHE. More of your Gascon bluster!

CYRANO. Bluster? Lend it to me! I'll be first in tonight's attack, wearing it on my shoulder.

DE GUICHE. A typical Gascon offer! You know very well where the scarf is. Back there by the river where the enemy lines are under a hail of grapeshot. No one could get it and survive.

CYRANO (*takes a white scarf from his pocket and hands it to De Guiche*). Yet here it is!

[*Silence. The cadets smother laughter by means of cards and dice boxes. De Guiche turns round and looks at them; they recover gravity and continue gambling. One*

---

[14] **Henry IV:** Henry of Navarre (1553–1610), the first Bourbon king of France, known for his bravery in war.

*of them unconcernedly whistles the Languedocian air
played earlier by the piper.*]

DE GUICHE (*taking the scarf*). Many thanks! Now I have it
back, I can give the signal I was hesitant to give.

[*He goes to the breastwork, scrambles up, and waves the
scarf several times.*]

ALL. What's that for?

THE SENTRY (*on the breastwork*). That man down there! He's
running to the enemy, making his escape —

DE GUICHE. Very useful, too! He's a counterfeit Spanish spy.
I plant the information he carries to the enemy. They
make their dispositions according to my wishes.

CYRANO. The man's a cheat!

DE GUICHE (*returning, coolly knotting his scarf*). A convenient cheat! What were we saying? Oh yes! I was about
to tell you something. In the last supreme effort to bring in
supplies, the Marshall made a secret sortie to Dourlens.
The King's sutlers[15] are there. He'll join them by way of
the fields. But to force his way back, he has taken troops in
strength. The Spaniards would have an easy time of it,
if they'd attack us now with half our army gone.

CARBON. Lucky they don't know it! Too bad if they attack.

DE GUICHE. They do know it. They're going to attack.

CARBON. What!

DE GUICHE. That spy came to tell me. "Where do you want
it?" he said. "I can make them attack at any point you
choose. Tell me where you want them to think you're
weakest, and that's where their main smash will come."
"Good," I said. "Leave camp at once, but keep your eyes
on our lines. Where you see my signal, have them attack."

CARBON (*to the cadets*). Gentlemen, to arms!

[*All leap to their feet. Noise of buckling on of belts and
swords.*]

DE GUICHE. They'll be on you in an hour.

FIRST CADET. What! An hour?

[*They all sit down again and continue their gambling.*]

---

[15] **sutlers:** men who provide supplies for an army.

DE GUICHE (*to Carbon*). The Marshal's forces are on their way back now. You've got to gain us time.

CARBON. And to gain time?

DE GUICHE. You will oblige us by getting killed!

CYRANO. So this is your revenge!

DE GUICHE. I won't claim that if I had liked you, I'd have chosen you and your men for this duty! But your bravery is incomparable. Serving my spite, I also serve my King.

CYRANO. Permit me to express my gratitude.

DE GUICHE. You love to fight, one against a hundred. You'll not complain of lack of opportunity.

[*He walks backstage with Carbon.*]

CYRANO (*to the cadets*). Gentlemen, we shall add to the Gascon coat of arms, which bears six chevrons of azure and of or,[16] the missing chevron — red for blood!

[*Backstage De Guiche talks in an undertone with Carbon. Orders. Preparations for defence. Cyrano goes up to Christian, who stands motionless, arms folded.*]

CYRANO (*laying his hand on his shoulder*). Christian?

CHRISTIAN (*shaking his head*). Roxane!

CYRANO. Poor lad.

CHRISTIAN. I wish my heart's last farewell could be written down in a final, moving letter.

CYRANO. I guessed you'd need it for today. (*He takes a note from his doublet.*) I've written it already.

CHRISTIAN. Let me see!

CYRANO. You really want to?

CHRISTIAN (*taking the note*). Why, yes. (*He opens it, reads, suddenly stops.*) Oh!

CYRANO. What's wrong?

CHRISTIAN. This little spot?

CYRANO (*hastily taking the letter and looking it over with every sign of innocence*). Spot?

CHRISTIAN. It's a tear!

CYRANO. Yes. A poet gets caught at his own game; that's its charm! You understand — this note was very moving. Tears came into my eyes as I wrote it.

CHRISTIAN. Tears?

[16] **or**: gold.

CYRANO. Yes. To die is nothing. But — never to see her again, that's horrible! For I couldn't — (*Christian looks at him searchingly.*) We couldn't — (*hastily*) you couldn't —

CHRISTIAN (*snatching the note*). Give me that note!

[*A noise in the distance.*]

A SENTRY'S VOICE. What the hell! Who goes there?

[*Shooting. Voices. Bells*]

CARBON. What is it?

A SENTRY (*on the breastwork*). A carriage.

[*They all rush to see.*]

VARIOUS VOICES. What! In the camp? It's coming in. It's coming from the enemy. The devil! Fire! No, the coachman is shouting. Shouting what? Listen: Service of the King!

[*The bells come closer.*]

DE GUICHE. What? Service of the King?

[*Everybody comes down and falls in ordered ranks. De Guiche disappears over the breastwork.*]

CARBON. Hats off, all of you!

DE GUICHE (*offstage*). From the King! Get that crowd out of the way! Make room to draw up!

[*A carriage enters at a trot. It is covered with mud and dust. The curtains are drawn. Two lackeys behind. It comes to a sudden stop.*]

CARBON (*shouting*). Beat a salute! (*The drums roll. All the cadets remove their helmets.*)

DE GUICHE. Lower the steps!

[*Two cadets rush to the carriage. The door opens.*]

ROXANE (*jumping out of the coach*). Good morning!

[*At the sound of her voice, all the cadets, who were bowing low, jerk up their heads. Complete astonishment.*]

SCENE 5

The same; Roxane.

DE GUICHE. Service of the King! You?

ROXANE. Of Love, the only King!

CYRANO. God in Heaven!

CHRISTIAN (*rushing towards her*). You! Why are you here? Why did you come?

ROXANE. The siege was much too long.

CHRISTIAN. But why did you —

ROXANE. I'll tell you privately.

[*Since she first spoke, Cyrano has stood immobile, not daring to look up at her.*]

CYRANO. My God! Dare I look at her?

DE GUICHE. You can't stay here!

ROXANE. Indeed I can! Will someone bring me a drum? (*When it is brought, she sits down on it.*) There, thank you! (*She laughs.*) A patrol fired on my coach! (*Proudly*) It looks as if it were made out of a pumpkin, doesn't it, as in Cinderella? And the lackeys transmogrified[17] from rats? (*Blowing a kiss to Christian*) Good morning! (*Surveying them all*) You don't look very gay. Do you know it's rather far to Arras? (*Noticing Cyrano*) Cousin, I'm enchanted!

CYRANO (*approaching*). Oh, indeed! How did you —

ROXANE. How did I find the army? Gracious me! Very easy: I drove wherever the country was laid waste. I had to see such horrors to believe them. Gentlemen, if this is *your* King's service, mine is better.

CYRANO. Plain madness. Where the devil could you get through?

ROXANE. Where? Through the Spaniards.

FIRST CADET. Trust a woman to find the weakest point!

DE GUICHE. How did you manage to get across their lines?

LE BRET. It must have been difficult.

ROXANE. Not very. I drove through as fast as possible. If some hidalgo[18] showed his arrogant face, I let my sweetest smile beam through the door. And since these gentlemen — you French won't mind this — are the most gallant mortals in the world, I had no trouble at all in passing through.

CARBON. Yes, that smile of yours is a certain passport. But they must often have asked you where you were going?

ROXANE. Quite often. I answered, "I'm going to see my lover." Immediately, the fiercest Spaniard closed the

---

[17] **transmogrified:** transformed, often with comic effect.
[18] **hidalgo:** member of the lower nobility of Spain.

carriage door with a gesture a King would envy, motioned away the pointed muskets, and — superb in grace and stateliness, his legs stiff under the fluted lace — swept the air with his plumed hat, and bowed, and said: "Pass on, my señorita!"

CHRISTIAN. But Roxane —

ROXANE. I said, "My lover," yes — forgive me! You see, if I'd said, "My husband," they would never have let me pass.

CHRISTIAN. Roxane —

ROXANE. What's wrong?

DE GUICHE. You'll have to get away from here!

ROXANE. I?

CYRANO. Immediately.

LE BRET. As soon as possible!

CHRISTIAN. Yes.

ROXANE. But why?

CHRISTIAN (*embarrassed*). Because —

CYRANO (*embarrassed*). In three-quarters of an hour —

DE GUICHE (*embarrassed*). Or — an hour —

CARBON (*embarrassed*). It would be better —

LE BRET (*embarrassed*). You might —

ROXANE. I'm staying! You are going to fight.

ALL. Oh! No! Not at all!

ROXANE. He is my husband! (*She throws herself into Christian's arms.*) Let me be killed with you.

CHRISTIAN. What eyes you have.

ROXANE. I could tell you why.

DE GUICHE (*despairingly*). This is a really dangerous post.

ROXANE (*turning*). What! Dangerous?

CYRANO. That's why he gave it us.

ROXANE (*to De Guiche*). So! You wish to make me a widow?

DE GUICHE. Oh! I assure you —

ROXANE. Now I'm angry. I won't leave. Besides, this is intriguing.

CYRANO. What? Is the *précieuse* a heroine?

ROXANE. Monsieur de Bergerac! After all, I'm your cousin.

A CADET. We'll defend you well.

ROXANE (*increasingly excited*). I think you will, my friends!

ANOTHER (*carried away*). The whole camp smells of orris root.[19]

---

[19] **orris root:** root of an iris, used to make perfume.

ROXANE. Luckily I've put on a hat which will look very well in battle! (*Looking at De Guiche*) But perhaps it is time for the Count to leave. They might begin to attack.

DE GUICHE (*angry*). That's the last straw! (*Significantly*) I shall go to inspect my guns. When I come back — Well! You have still time to change your mind!

ROXANE. Never!

[*Exit De Guiche.*]

SCENE 6

The same; without De Guiche.

CHRISTIAN (*imploring*). Roxane, you must!

ROXANE. Never.

FIRST CADET (*to the others*). She'll stay.

[*The cadets hurry around, getting in each other's way, in an effort to make themselves tidy.*]

ALL. A comb! — Soap! — My jacket's torn: a needle! — A ribbon! — Your mirror! — My ruffles! — Your curling iron! — A razor!

ROXANE (*to Cyrano, who is still urging her to go*). Nothing will stir me from this place.

[*Carbon, like the others, has tightened his belt, dusted his clothes, brushed his hat, straightened his plume, and pulled down his cuffs. He approaches Roxane.*]

CARBON (*ceremoniously*). In that case, it is fitting I should present some of these gentlemen who will have the honor of dying before your eyes.

[*Roxane bows; then stands expectantly, her arm through Christian's.*]

CARBON (*in formal introduction*). Baron de Peyrescous de Colignac!

THE CADET (*bowing*). Madame —

CARBON (*continuing*). Baron de Casterac de Cahuzac. Vidame[20] de Malgouyre Estressac Lésbas d'Escarabiot — Chevalier d'Antignac-Juzet. Baron Hillot de Blagnac-Saléchan de Castel Crabioules —

ROXANE. How many names does each one have?

[20] **Vidame** (vē′dam′): minor title of nobility.

BARON HILLOT. Swarms! Galaxies!

CARBON (*to Roxane*). Open your hand. The one with the handkerchief.

ROXANE (*opens her hand; the handkerchief falls*). Why?

[*The whole company rushes forward to retrieve it.*]

CARBON (*quickly snatching it*). My company needed a flag. Faith! Now it has the finest in the camp!

ROXANE (*smiling*). It's somewhat tiny.

CARBON (*fastening the handkerchief to the staff of his captain's lance*). But lace!

A CADET (*to the others*). After looking in that face, give me a single nutshell in my stomach, and I'd die without a qualm.

CARBON (*overhearing, indignant*). Shame! To speak of eating when an exquisite woman —

ROXANE. But the air of the camp is sharp. I'm famished myself. Patties, jellied game, dry wine — that's my bill of fare. Will you bring it out?

A CADET. Nothing more?

ANOTHER. Good Lord, where could we get it?

ROXANE (*quietly*). From my carriage.

ALL. What?

ROXANE. It needs boning, carving, serving! Look at my coachman a little closer, gentlemen. You'll see he's indispensable. You can have the sauces hot if you so wish.

THE CADETS (*rushing towards the carriage*). Ragueneau! (*Cheers*) Ragueneau! Hurrah!

ROXANE (*watching them compassionately*). Poor lads.

CYRANO (*kissing her hand*). The good fairy.

RAGUENEAU (*standing on the seat like a barker at a fair*). Gentlemen! (*Wild enthusiasm*)

THE CADETS. Hurrah! Bravo!

RAGUENEAU. The Spaniards, when *she* passed, didn't investigate the *re*past!

[*Applause.*]

CYRANO (*in an undertone, to Christian*). Ahem! Christian!

RAGUENEAU. Charmed by the fair, they failed to see — (*he displays a dish which he has pulled out from under a seat*) — the fowl!

[*It is passed from hand to hand amidst applause.*]

CYRANO (*to Christian*). Just a word.

RAGUENEAU. And Venus held their eyes, while Diana brought you — (*brandishing a joint*) — venison![21]

[*Great enthusiasm. The joint is seized by twenty outstretched hands.*]

CYRANO (*to Christian*). I *must* speak to you!

ROXANE (*to the cadets, returning with their arms filled with eatables*). Put it down here! (*Assisted by the two imperturbable lackeys from the carriage, she spreads a tablecloth on the grass. To Christian, just as Cyrano is drawing him aside*) Make yourself useful!

[*Christian assists her. Cyrano shows signs of impatience.*]

RAGUENEAU. Truffled[22] peacock.

FIRST CADET (*beaming, as he cuts himself a thick slice of ham*). Thunder! We shan't run our last mile without a final guzzle. (*Hastily checking himself at the sight of Roxane*) Sorry. Er — final feed.

RAGUENEAU (*throwing cushions from the carriage*). The cushions are overstuffed — with ortolans![23]

[*Uproar. They rip the cushions open. Laughter. Delight.*]

THIRD CADET. Well, dirk my doublet![24]

RAGUENEAU (*throwing out bottles of red and white wine*). Flasks of ruby! Bottled topaz!

ROXANE (*throwing a folded tablecloth at Cyrano*). Lay out this tablecloth. Lively, now!

RAGUENEAU (*waving one of the carriage lanterns*). Each of the lanterns is a little larder!

CYRANO (*in an undertone to Christian, as they unfold the tablecloth*). I must speak to you before you speak to her.

RAGUENEAU (*increasingly rhetorical*). The handle of my whip is pure Bologna!

[21] **Diana . . . venison:** probably an allusion to the famous painting of Diane de Poitiers in the Louvre.
[22] **Truffled:** cooked with truffles, a mushroom-like delicacy.
[23] **ortolans:** small birds used as a table delicacy.
[24] **dirk my doublet:** *i.e.*, well, stab me (used as an exclamation).

ROXANE (*pouring and serving wine*). They'll kill us all off, will they? Then, *morbleu*,[25] here's a last laugh in the face of the rest of the army. This is for Gascons only. If De Guiche should come — no invitation, mind! (*Going from one to another*) There, take your time! Not so fast! Drink a little! What? Tears?

FIRST CADET. It tastes so good —

ROXANE. Hush! Red or white? Some bread for Monsieur de Carbon! A knife! Your plate! A little crust? Some more? Let me give you some! Champagne? A wing?

CYRANO (*following and helping her, aside*). I adore her. (*His arms are loaded with dishes.*)

ROXANE (*to Christian*). What will you have?

CHRISTIAN. Nothing.

ROXANE. Must! This biscuit, in some muscatel — two fingers?

CHRISTIAN (*attempting to detain her*). Why did you come? Really.

ROXANE. Wait! I must think entirely of these poor fellows now. In good time!

LE BRET (*backstage, passing bread on his lance point to the sentry on the talus*). Here's De Guiche!

CYRANO. Quick! Hide the bottles, dishes, plates, and baskets! Remember, nothing special has happened! (*To Ragueneau*) Up on your seat! Everything hidden?

[*Everything vanishes in a flash under tents, clothing, cloaks, and hats. Enter De Guiche, hurriedly. He stops suddenly, sniffs the air. Silence*]

SCENE 7

The same; De Guiche.

DE GUICHE (*sniffing*). What smells so good?

A CADET (*humming unconcernedly*). La! La! La!

DE GUICHE (*looking at him sharply*). What's wrong with you? You're red in the face.

THE CADET. Me? Nothing. Just my blood. It sniffs battle, reddens with joy.

ANOTHER. Pum — pum — pum!

DE GUICHE (*turning*). What is that?

[25] *morbleu:* a mild oath.

THE CADET (*slightly drunk*). Nothing. Nothing at all. Just a little song. The merest wisp of —

DE GUICHE. You're in high spirits, lad.

THE CADET. That's what danger does to me.

DE GUICHE (*calling Carbon to give him orders*). Captain! I — (*Stops when he sees his face.*) The devil! You don't look sad yourself!.

CARBON (*reddening; evasively hiding a bottle behind his back*). Really?

DE GUICHE. There is one cannon to spare. I've had it placed (*pointing to the side*) there, in that corner. Your men can use it, if necessary.

A CADET (*staggering*). Such attention!

ANOTHER (*smiling graciously*). Such solicitude!

DE GUICHE. Mad as March hares! (*Dryly*) You're not accustomed to artillery. Look out for the recoil; it goes back suddenly.

THE FIRST CADET. Oh! Shoot!

DE GUICHE (*furious, going towards him*). Well!

THE CADET. A Gascon's cannon never goes back on him.

DE GUICHE (*taking his arm; shaking him*). You're drunk, that's what! On what?

THE CADET (*arrogantly*). The smell of gunpowder.

DE GUICHE (*shrugs, pushes him away, and goes quietly to Roxane*). There isn't much time, madame! Have you made your decision?

ROXANE. I shall stay.

DE GUICHE. Not escape while you can?

ROXANE. No.

DE GUICHE (*after hesitating briefly*). Then give me a musket.

CARBON. What?

DE GUICHE. I'm staying too.

CYRANO. At last, Sir, you show real courage.

FIRST CADET. In spite of his lace, perhaps he *is* a Gascon.

ROXANE. But why?

DE GUICHE. I'll leave no woman in danger.

SECOND CADET (*to the first*). Don't you think we might give him something to eat?

[*The food magically reappears.*]

DE GUICHE (*his eyes brightening*). Food!

A THIRD CADET (*rubbing his stomach significantly*). Under every jacket.

DE GUICHE (*controlling himself, haughtily*). Do you think I would eat your leavings?

CYRANO (*bowing*). You show improvement.

DE GUICHE (*proudly, with the slightest trace of Gascon accent*). I shall fight on an empty stomach.

FIRST CADET. Ah! the genuine Gascon accent.

DE GUICHE (*laughing*). That to me?

THE CADET. He is one of us!

[*All begin dancing spontaneously. Carbon drops out of sight for a moment, and then reappears on the breastwork.*]

CARBON. The pikemen are set. They mean business! (*He indicates a line of pikes above the breastwork.*)

DE GUICHE (*to Roxane, bowing*). Will you honor me with your arm for the review?

[*She takes it; they proceed up the talus. Everyone uncovers and follows.*]

CHRISTIAN (*going to Cyrano, hurriedly*). Quick now!

[*When Roxane appears at the breastwork, the pikes, lowered for a salute, disappear. Cheers. She bows.*]

PIKEMEN (*offstage*). Hurrah!

CHRISTIAN. What's it all about?

CYRANO. Roxane. If by any chance she —

CHRISTIAN. Yes!

CYRANO. — should speak about your letters —

CHRISTIAN. My letters! Yes?

CYRANO. Don't be so foolish as to show surprise.

CHRISTIAN. Why?

CYRANO. Need I tell you? Good God, it's quite simple. I thought of it today when she appeared. You have — well —

CHRISTIAN. Hurry up.

CYRANO. You have — have written far more often than you realize!

CHRISTIAN. What?

CYRANO. Damnation! Can't you see it? I interpreted your passion. Sometimes I wrote without telling you about it.

CHRISTIAN. Oh?

CYRANO. It is quite simple.

CHRISTIAN. But how did you manage it? We're surrounded!

CYRANO. Oh, before daylight I could get across —

CHRISTIAN (*folding his arms*). I see! That simple! Did I write twice a week? Three times? Four?

CYRANO. More than that.

CHRISTIAN. Every day?

CYRANO. Every day! Twice a day.

CHRISTIAN (*violently*). You liked that, didn't you? Liked it so much that you'd go and risk your life —

CYRANO (*seeing Roxane return*). Hush! Not while she's here! (*He hurries off to his tent.*)

SCENE 8

Roxane, Christian; backstage, constant going and coming of cadets; Carbon and De Guiche issue orders.

ROXANE (*running up to Christian*). Christian! At last!

CHRISTIAN (*taking her hands*). And now, tell me. Tell me why you came to join me through all these awful roads, through all these lines of soldiers and desperate ruffians.

ROXANE. It was your letters.

CHRISTIAN. Do you know what you're saying?

ROXANE. It's all your doing that I had to run such risks. Your letters moved me beyond all words. Think how many you've written me this last month, and each one more eloquent than the last.

CHRISTIAN. So! For a few little love letters you have —

ROXANE. Hush! Can't you understand? God knows, I've loved you ever since that evening when your second voice came climbing to my window and made me know your soul. And this last month, your letters have brought me back the voice I heard that evening, the tender voice that enveloped me like an aura. It's all your fault that I simply had to come here! If Ulysses had written her as you did,

Penelope wouldn't have stayed at home embroidering.[26]
She'd have joined you with the heedless haste of Helen;[27]
she'd have sent her embroidery flying —

CHRISTIAN. But —

ROXANE. I read them; I was conquered; I came here —
came, utterly your own! Each of your pages was like a
petal falling from your soul, and every flaming word so
strong, sincere —

CHRISTIAN. Strong, sincere? You felt that there, Roxane?

ROXANE. God knows how I felt it!

CHRISTIAN. So you came?

ROXANE. So I came. Oh, Christian, my master, you'd raise
me up if I threw myself at your feet, but the soul that I
throw at your feet you can never raise. It is there forever.
I came to ask your pardon — this is the time to ask it with
Death so close — your pardon for the unforgivable insult
of loving you for your great good looks alone.

CHRISTIAN (*in alarm*). Roxane!

ROXANE. Later, my dear, when my love became less shallow — a fluttering bird trying its untried wings — your
beauty held me but your soul seduced me, and I loved
you for both together.

CHRISTIAN. Roxane! And now?

ROXANE. Now? You yourself are the victor over yourself:
it is only your soul I love now —

CHRISTIAN. Oh, Roxane — !

ROXANE. You should rejoice. To be loved for a transient
garment, would put an ardent and noble heart to torture.
But your dear mind eclipses your dear face, obliterates
the beauty that first won me; and now that I see, what I
saw once I see no more.

CHRISTIAN. Oh! —

ROXANE. You don't like your triumph?

CHRISTIAN (*mournfully*). Roxane! Roxane!

ROXANE. I understand! You can't believe such love —

[26] **If Ulysses ... embroidering:** an allusion to a story in the *Odyssey.*
While Ulysses was away, his wife Penelope was surrounded by suitors. To
put them off, Penelope said she would decide among them only after finishing
a piece of weaving. Each night she unraveled that day's work.

[27] **Helen:** in Greek legend, the wife of Menelaus; she ran off with Paris to
Troy, and thus started the Trojan War (described in the *Iliad*).

CHRISTIAN. I don't want such love. I want to be loved
for —

ROXANE. — for what you were always loved for till now?
You must let yourself be loved in a better fashion.

CHRISTIAN. It was better as it was before.

ROXANE. Won't you understand? It is now that I love you
better that I love you at all, loving the only you that is
really you. Though your brilliance dazzled me less —

CHRISTIAN (*anticipating the trend*). Hush!

ROXANE. — my love couldn't alter. Though all of your
handsomeness suddenly vanished —

CHRISTIAN. Don't say it!

ROXANE. But I do say it!

CHRISTIAN (*brokenly*). You mean — that if I were ugly? —

ROXANE. I swear it would make no difference.

CHRISTIAN. God!

ROXANE. Is your happiness so great then?

CHRISTIAN (*in a stifled voice*). Great? God!

ROXANE. What's wrong?

CHRISTIAN (*gently pushing her away*). Nothing! Excuse me a
moment. I have to tell someone something.

ROXANE. BUT — Christian!

CHRISTIAN (*indicating the cadets backstage*). My love is
robbing them of you. Smile on them just a little before they
die. You'd better go.

ROXANE (*deeply moved*). Dear, thoughtful Christian.

[*She goes towards the group of cadets; they collect with
respectful eagerness around her.*]

SCENE 9

*Christian, Cyrano; backstage, Roxane talking with
Carbon and the group of cadets.*

CHRISTIAN (*shouting towards Cyrano's tent*). Cyrano?

[*Cyrano comes out, armed for battle.*]

CYRANO. What is it? Why, man, you're white!

CHRISTIAN. All over! She doesn't love me any more.

CYRANO. What?

CHRISTIAN. It's you! She loves you!

CYRANO. Impossible!

CHRISTIAN. She only loves my soul.

CYRANO. No!

CHRISTIAN. Yes! You see it's you she really loves. And you love her!

CYRANO. I?

CHRISTIAN. I know you do.

CYRANO (*slowly*). It happens to be true.

CHRISTIAN. You love her to distraction.

CYRANO. More than that.

CHRISTIAN. Tell her so!

CYRANO. No.

CHRISTIAN. Why not?

CYRANO. Just look at this face of mine.

CHRISTIAN. She would love me if I were ugly.

CYRANO. She told you that?

CHRISTIAN (*pointing to the place where it happened*). There!

CYRANO. I am very glad she said it. But come, come! Don't believe such nonsense. Heavens, I'm very glad she could think a thing like that. But don't take her at her word; don't spoil that handsome face. She'd never forgive me.

CHRISTIAN. That is what I want to see.

CYRANO. No, no.

CHRISTIAN. Tell her everything! Let her make a choice between us.

CYRANO. Don't torment me!

CHRISTIAN. Should I kill your happiness because my looks are passable? That's not right.

CYRANO. And should I bury yours because the accident of birth lets me express the things you doubtless feel?

CHRISTIAN. You must tell her everything!

CYRANO. He persists in tempting me! Bad, too bad!

CHRISTIAN. I am tired of carrying a rival here inside me.

CYRANO. Christian!

CHRISTIAN. We had no witness at our secret marriage. It can be set aside, if we survive.

CYRANO. Still obstinate?

CHRISTIAN. Yes, I'll be loved for myself, or not at all! I am going to see what's happening. Wait! I shall walk down to the other end of the post; then I'll return. Meanwhile, tell her; let her make her choice.

CYRANO. It will be you.

CHRISTIAN. I hope so. (*He calls*) Roxane!

CYRANO. No! No! Christian, you mustn't!

ROXANE (*hurrying down*). What is it?

CHRISTIAN. Cyrano wants to tell you — something very important.

[*She goes quickly to Cyrano. Exit Christian.*]

SCENE 10

Roxane, Cyrano; then Le Bret, Carbon, the cadets, Ragueneau, De Guiche, etc.

ROXANE. Important?

CYRANO (*at his wit's end*). He is gone. (*To Roxane*) Nothing at all. Heavens! You of all people know how he makes something out of nothing.

ROXANE (*quickly*). Perhaps he didn't believe what I said just now? I thought he didn't believe it.

CYRANO (*taking her hand*). You were telling him the truth?

ROXANE. Yes, yes, I should love him even — (*She stops momentarily.*)

CYRANO (*smiling sadly*). The words won't come out, you see, when I'm here!

ROXANE. But —

CYRANO. I don't much mind. Even if he were ugly? Is that it?

ROXANE. Even if he were ugly! (*Shots offstage*) Listen! They are firing!

CYRANO (*ardently*). Even repulsive?

ROXANE. Repulsive!

CYRANO. Disfigured?

ROXANE. Disfigured!

CYRANO. Grotesque?

ROXANE. Nothing could make him grotesque to me.

CYRANO. You would love him still?

ROXANE. Even more — if possible!

CYRANO (*losing control; aside*). My God, perhaps it's true! Perhaps I've happiness within my grasp. (*To Roxane*) Roxane — listen! There's something —

[*Enter Le Bret hurriedly.*]

LE BRET (*in an undertone*). Cyrano!

CYRANO (*turning*). Well?

LE BRET. Sssssh! (*He whispers to Cyrano.*)

CYRANO (*with a cry, dropping Roxane's hand*). Oh, no! No!

ROXANE. What's the matter?

CYRANO (*to himself, completely overcome*). All over. That's the end.

[*Renewed firing offstage.*]

ROXANE. What is the matter? This shooting? (*She starts backstage to see for herself.*)

CYRANO. All over! I can never tell her now!

ROXANE (*trying to rush forward*). What's happening?

CYRANO (*hastily, stopping her*). It's nothing.

[*Enter a group of cadets carrying something which they try to conceal from Roxane.*]

ROXANE (*sharply*). These men —

CYRANO (*drawing her away*). Don't bother about them.

ROXANE. What were you going to say to me just now?

CYRANO. What was I going to say? Why, nothing. Nothing, I can assure you. (*Solemnly*) I assure you that Christian's spirit and his soul were — (*in alarm, trying to correct himself*) — are the greatest —

ROXANE. Were? (*With a scream*) Oh!

[*She rushes forward into the group of cadets, and thrusts them aside.*]

CYRANO. And that's the end!

ROXANE (*sees Christian lying in his cloak*). Christian!

LE BRET (*to Cyrano*). The enemy's first shot!

[*Roxane throws herself on Christian's body. More shooting. Clashing of swords. Noises of conflict. Beating of drums. Followed by the cadets, Carbon, sword in hand, goes to the far side of the talus.*]

CARBON. The attack! To arms!

ROXANE. Christian!

CARBON (*behind the breastwork*). Lively now!

ROXANE. Christian!

CARBON. Form ranks!

ROXANE. Christian!

CARBON. Measure fuses!

[*Ragueneau runs up with some water in a helmet.*]

CHRISTIAN (*in a dying voice*). Roxane!

[*The distracted Roxane dips in the water a piece of linen torn from her bosom to bandage his wound.*]

CYRANO (*hurriedly whispering in Christian's ear*). I have told her everything. You are the only one she loves. (*Christian closes his eyes.*)

ROXANE. What, dearest?

CARBON. Ramrods out!

ROXANE (*to Cyrano*). He's not dead —

CARBON. Charges ready!

ROXANE. — but his cheek is growing cold!

CARBON. Aim!

ROXANE. What? A letter in his tunic? For me!

CYRANO (*aside*). My letter!

CARBON. Fire!

[*Reports of massed musketry. Shouting. Noise of battle.*]

CYRANO (*trying to free his hand, which Roxane holds, kneeling*). But Roxane, they need me. They are fighting.

ROXANE (*detaining him*). He's dead, and you were the only one who knew him. (*She weeps gently.*) Wasn't he an exquisite soul, a marvelous being?

CYRANO (*standing, head uncovered*). Yes, Roxane.

ROXANE. An adorable poet of unheard-of powers?

CYRANO. Yes, Roxane.

ROXANE. A sublime mind?

CYRANO. Yes, Roxane.

ROXANE. A strange, deep soul, magnificent and charming?

CYRANO (*firmly*). Yes, Roxane.

ROXANE (*throwing herself on Christian's body*). He's dead!

CYRANO (*aside, drawing his sword*). Nothing is left me but to die! For without knowing, she's mourning me in him.

[*Trumpets in the distance. Enter De Guiche on the talus, head bare, a wound in his forehead.*]

DE GUICHE (*in a thundering voice*). The trumpets! That's the signal! The French are entering camp with our supplies. Hold fast just a little longer!

ROXANE. Blood. Tears! On his letter!

A VOICE (*offstage, shouting*). Surrender!

THE CADETS. Never!

RAGUENEAU (*from the top of his carriage, watching the battle*). The fight's getting hotter!

CYRANO (*to De Guiche, indicating Roxane*). Get her away. I'm going to lead a charge.

ROXANE (*kissing the letter, her voice failing*). His blood! His tears!

RAGUENEAU (*jumping down and hurrying to her*). She's fainting!

DE GUICHE (*from the talus, in a furious voice*). Stand fast!

VOICE (*offstage*). Surrender!

CADETS' VOICES. Never!

CYRANO (*to De Guiche*). Sir, you have more than proved your courage. (*Pointing to Roxane*) Escape with her! Save your own life and hers!

DE GUICHE (*runs to Roxane, lifts her in his arms*). Very well! The fight is good as won, if you'll gain us time!

CYRANO. Good! (*To Roxane, as De Guiche and Ragueneau carry her away, insensible*) Roxane! Farewell!

[*Confusion. Shouts. Wounded cadets reappear and fall upon the stage. Cyrano, hurrying into the fight, is stopped at the breastwork by Carbon, covered with blood.*]

CARBON. We're breaking! I've two halberd wounds myself —

CYRANO (*shouting to the Gascons*). Courage, lads! Stand fast! (*To Carbon*) Never fear. I have two deaths to avenge: my happiness and Christian's. (*They come down, Cyrano helping Carbon. Cyrano brandishes the lance bearing Roxane's handkerchief.*) Float, little lace; show them her monogram! (*He plants the lance in the ground, and shouts to the cadets.*) On them, lads! Crush them! (*To the piper*) Give us a tune there!

[*The piper plays. Some of the wounded get to their feet. Other cadets, rolling down the talus, group themselves around Cyrano and the little flag. The coach, covered and filled with men, bristling with arquebuses,[28] becomes*

---

[28] *arquebuses* (är′kwe·bus·ez): portable guns (now obsolete).

a redoubt. *Enter a cadet, retreating down the talus, still fighting.*]

CADET. They are coming up the slope! (*He falls dead.*)

CYRANO. Give them a rousing welcome!

[*A great array of the enemy suddenly appears above the breastwork. Over their heads, banners of the Imperial forces.*]

CYRANO. Fire!

[*A massed volley.*]

SHOUT (*from the enemy's ranks*). Fire!

[*A murderous volley in reply. Cadets fall on every side.*]

A SPANISH OFFICER (*taking off his hat*). Who are these men, so eager to be killed?

CYRANO (*in the midst of the hail of bullets, reciting*).

> "These are Cadets of Gascony
> In Captain Carbon's Corps!
> They lie and fight outrageously —"

[*He charges, followed by a few survivors.*]

> "These are Cadets of Gascony —"

[*The rest is lost in the din of battle.*]

CURTAIN

QUESTIONS

Scenes 1–3. Why is Cyrano invaluable to the starving cadets? How does he teach them to rise above the shackles of the flesh? Consider Cyrano's dream of dying with a fine phrase on his lips (page 206). Does the sentiment seem right for him? for a modern soldier?

Scene 4. De Guiche avoids capture by dropping his badge of rank, a white scarf, and escaping in the confusion. In what way is he contrasted with Cyrano? For what reasons does De Guiche choose Cyrano's regiment to bear the brunt of the Spanish attack?

Scenes 5–6. What does Roxane's trip through the enemy lines say about the power of love? What would the scene of her arrival — with a coachful of delicacies — contribute to a stage production? How does it alter the mood of the action?

Scene 7. Why does Cyrano begin to admire De Guiche? What does this indicate about the values both men possess?

Scene 8. What has Roxane said to Christian about the changed quality of her love? Whom does she really love?

Scene 10. What lie does Cyrano, who so loves the truth, tell to the wounded Christian? Why does he tell it?

ACT FIVE

CYRANO'S GAZETTE

The park of the Convent of the Sisters of the Cross in Paris, fifteen years later (1655). Magnificent shade trees. Left stage, the chapter house with several doors opening on a great terraced flight of steps. Center stage, a huge isolated tree within a small oval enclosure. Front right, a semicircular stone seat among boxwood hedges. The entire backstage is crossed by an avenue of chestnut trees leading, backstage right, to the door of a chapel half hidden among the branches. Through the double screen of trees bounding the avenue, one can catch glimpses of lawns, other avenues, small copses, remote corners of the park, the open sky. The small side door of the chapel opens on a colonnade, festooned with reddening vines, which is eventually lost to sight behind the boxwood bushes, front right.

It is autumn. Over the grass, still fresh and green, all the leaves have turned, though here and there boxwood and yew form dark islands of somber green. Under each tree there is a circle of yellow leaves. Fallen leaves strew the entire stage, crackle underfoot in the avenues, half cover the steps and seats.

Between the stone seat, front right, and the tree, center stage, is a big embroidery frame[1] set up on legs. In front

[1] *embroidery frame:* Roxane's embroidery ironically recalls Penelope's. While Penelope was waiting for her husband — missing in war — to return, Roxane thinks she is waiting for no one. Actually, Roxane's lover is approaching.

of it, a small chair and baskets filled with skeins and balls of colored wool. On the frame, a piece of embroidery has been started. At the rise of the curtain, Sisters of the convent are coming and going in the park. A few are seated on the stone seat around an older nun. Leaves are falling everywhere.

SCENE 1

Mother Marguerite, Sister Marthe, Sister Claire, other sisters.

SISTER MARTHE (*to Mother Marguerite*). Sister Claire glanced in the mirror twice this morning to see how her headdress suits her.

MOTHER MARGUERITE (*to Sister Claire*). That's very bad.

SISTER CLAIRE. Sister Marthe stole a plum out of a tart this morning. I saw her do it.

MOTHER MARGUERITE (*to Sister Marthe*). Very naughty, Sister Marthe.

SISTER CLAIRE. It was only a tiny glance.

SISTER MARTHE. It was only a tiny plum.

MOTHER MARGUERITE. This evening I shall tell Monsieur Cyrano.

SISTER CLAIRE (*alarmed*). No! He'll laugh at me.

SISTER MARTHE. He will say that nuns are very vain.

SISTER CLAIRE. Very greedy.

MOTHER MARGUERITE (*smiling*). And very good.

SISTER CLAIRE. Mother Marguerite, hasn't he come here every Saturday these last ten years?

MOTHER MARGUERITE. Longer! Ever since his cousin first brought her veil of crepe as token of worldly mourning among our linen caps. She settled among us fourteen years ago, her coif[2] a great black bird among our white ones.

SISTER MARTHE. Since she took refuge in this cloister, only Monsieur Cyrano has comforted the grief that can't be comforted.

VARIOUS SISTERS. He is so droll. So merry when he comes. He's a tease. He's nice. We're really fond of him. He likes the angelica paste[3] we make for him.

[2] **coif:** close-fitting cap tied under the chin, worn by nuns beneath a veil.
[3] **angelica paste:** paste used in candy.

SISTER MARTHE. All the same, he's not a very good Catholic!

SISTER CLAIRE. We are going to convert him.

THE SISTERS. Yes! Yes! So we are.

MOTHER MARGUERITE. I forbid you to do anything of the kind. Don't worry him; he might not come so often if you did.

SISTER MARTHE. But — Dear God! —

MOTHER MARGUERITE. God knows him very well. Be sure of that.

SISTER MARTHE. But every Saturday, he comes and says to me — and looks so proud of it — "Sister, I ate meat yesterday!"

MOTHER MARGUERITE. Oh! He tells you that? Well, the last time he came, he hadn't eaten anything for two days.

SISTER MARTHE. Mother in Heaven!

MOTHER MARGUERITE. He's poor.

SISTER MARTHE. Who told you so?

MOTHER MARGUERITE. Monsieur Le Bret.

SISTER MARTHE. Doesn't any one try to help him?

MOTHER MARGUERITE. That would offend him.

[*Enter Roxane, in widow's coif and long black veil, on one of the avenues backstage; beside her De Guiche, magnificently turned out, but growing older. They pace slowly. Mother Marguerite rises.*]

MOTHER MARGUERITE. Come, we must go inside. Madame Magdeleine is walking with a visitor.

SISTER MARTHE (*in an undertone, to Sister Claire*). Is it the Duke de Grammont?

SISTER CLAIRE (*looking*). I think it is.

SISTER MARTHE. He hasn't been to see her for months.

SISTERS. He is very busy. The Court. The Camp.

SISTER CLAIRE. The cares of the world.

[*Exit sisters. De Guiche and Roxane approach in silence and stop near the embroidery frame. A pause.*]

Scene 2

Roxane, the Duke de Grammont, formerly Count de Guiche; then Le Bret and Ragueneau.

DE GUICHE. Will you stay here forever in mourning, your blonde beauty wasted?

ROXANE. Forever.

DE GUICHE. Always faithful to his memory?

ROXANE. Always!

DE GUICHE (*after a pause*). Am I forgiven?

ROXANE (*nodding*). Since I've been here, yes!

[*Another pause.*]

DE GUICHE. He must have been a real person —

ROXANE. You had to know him.

DE GUICHE. Yes! Perhaps I never knew him well enough. I suppose his last letter is still close to your heart?

ROXANE. Hanging from this velvet like a scapulary.[4]

DE GUICHE. Dead. Yet you still love him.

ROXANE. Only half dead, it sometime seems, as though our hearts were still together and his love, still alive, hovering around me.

DE GUICHE (*after another pause*). Does Cyrano ever visit you?

ROXANE. Very often. My faithful cousin is a speaking gazette for me. He's regular as clockwork! His chair is set out for him under this tree — at least when it's fine; I embroider as I wait for him. Then, on the last stroke of the hour, not even turning my head, I hear his cane on the steps. He sits down, rallies me about my interminable embroidery, tells me the week's events, and — (*Le Bret appears on the steps.*) Ah! There's Le Bret. (*Le Bret approaches.*) How's our friend?

LE BRET. Bad!

DE GUICHE. Oh!

ROXANE (*to De Guiche*). An exaggeration!

LE BRET. Everything as I predicted: neglect, poverty, crowds of new enemies made by his epistles. He attacks everything — sham nobles, sham devotion, sham braggarts, plagiarists, everyone, everywhere.

ROXANE. But his sword still inspires profound respect. They'll never get the best of him.

DE GUICHE (*shaking his head*). Who knows?

LE BRET. It's not attacks I fear. It's loneliness and hunger, stealthy December stealing to his room. Those are assas-

---

[4] **scapulary:** shoulder covering worn by nuns and monks.

sins that will murder him. A new notch in his belt every day. His poor nose yellow as old ivory. Nothing to wear but an old serge suit.

DE GUICHE. There's one who didn't succeed. Just the same, I wouldn't pity him too much.

LE BRET (*with a bitter smile*). My lord!

DE GUICHE. No! Don't pity him too much. He has lived without concessions to the world, free in his thoughts and free in act.

LE BRET (*still bitterly smiling*). But, your Grace!

DE GUICHE (*haughtily*). Yes, I know! I've had everything, you think; he has had nothing? And yet — I'd very gladly shake his hand. (*Bowing to Roxane*) Good-bye.

ROXANE. I'll see you out.

[*De Guiche bows to Le Bret and goes with Roxane towards the steps.*]

DE GUICHE (*stopping, as she starts to ascend*). Somehow, I almost envy him. You see: too much success in life will bring, though God knows you've done nothing really wrong, a thousand little self-disgusts whose total is not remorse perhaps but a vague feeling, an obscure sense of . . . almost embarrassment. And a duke's robes may drag within their lining (even as they sweep the rising stairs to eminence) the rustle of withered illusions and dry regrets; just as in climbing slowly towards those doors, your gown of mourning drags the fallen leaves.

ROXANE (*ironically*). A dreamer? You?

DE GUICHE. Perhaps. (*Abruptly, just as he is leaving*) Monsieur Le Bret! (*To Roxane*) A word with him, if you don't mind. (*In an undertone to Le Bret*) It's true that no one would openly attack your friend, but many hate him. Only yesterday, at a card game in the Queen's Apartment, somebody said to me, "This Cyrano might die by accident."

LE BRET. So!

DE GUICHE. He should go out very seldom and be careful.

LE BRET (*throwing up his arms*). Careful! Careful! He's coming here! I've got to head him off! But how can I — ?

ROXANE (*at the head of the steps, to an approaching Sister*). What is it?

SISTER. Ragueneau, Madame. He wants to see you.

ROXANE. Have him come in. (*To De Guiche and Le Bret*) Some pitiful story of his latest plight. Starting as author, he has become by turns a singer —

LE BRET. Bath keeper.

ROXANE. Actor.

LE BRET. Beadle.

ROXANE. Wigmaker.

LE BRET. And virtuoso of the lute.

ROXANE. What will he be today, I wonder?

RAGUENEAU (*entering precipitately*). Madame! (*Seeing Le Bret*) Monsieur!

ROXANE (*smiling*). Tell all your latest troubles to Le Bret. I'll soon be back.

RAGUENEAU. Oh! Madame! —

[*She pays no further attention. Exit Roxane with De Guiche. Ragueneau hurries up to Le Bret.*]

SCENE 3

Le Bret, Ragueneau.

RAGUENEAU. Perhaps it's for the best since you are here. She oughtn't to know. I was going to see your friend. About twenty paces from his house — and he came out. I hurried up. As he started to turn the corner I started running. Then — there was the window — he was under it — and — accident? — perhaps! — a lackey lets fall a heavy log of wood.

LE BRET. The scoundrels! Cyrano!

RAGUENEAU. I rush up! I look at him!

LE BRET. Horrible!

RAGUENEAU. Our friend, our poet, prostrate on the ground, with a great wound in his head!

LE BRET. Dead?

RAGUENEAU. No. But — dear God! I carried him to his room. His room! You ought to see the place.

LE BRET. Is he suffering?

RAGUENEAU. He's unconscious.

LE BRET. What about a doctor?

RAGUENEAU. One came out of charity.

LE BRET. Poor Cyrano! Break it gently to Roxane. What does the doctor say?

RAGUENEAU. I hardly know — fever, something about the brain. You should see him — his head all bandaged. Let's go at once! There is no one with him to look after him. If he gets up, he'll die.

LE BRET (*pointing offstage right*). This way. Quick! A short-cut! Through the chapel!

[*Roxane, entering, sees them hurrying down the colonnade.*]

ROXANE. Monsieur Le Bret! (*Le Bret and Ragueneau hurry off without replying.*) Why doesn't Le Bret come back when I call him? More trouble for good old Ragueneau I suppose. (*She descends the steps.*)

SCENE 4

Roxane alone; then two Sisters for a moment.

ROXANE. The last day of September — beautiful. Even my grief, uncomfortable in spring, can find a smile these gentler autumn days. (*She sits down by her embroidery frame. Two Sisters bring a large armchair from the house and set it under the trees.*) My dear old friend's old chair?

SISTER. It's the best the convent has.

ROXANE. Thank you, Sister. (*The sisters leave.*) He'll soon be here. (*She sits before the embroidery frame. The clock strikes.*) There! It's striking now. Quick, my skeins! Why, it has finished striking. I'm quite surprised. Could he be late now the first time? That Sister at the wicket[5] — where's my thimble? Ah! I've got it! — she must be urging him to penitence. (*Pauses.*) She must be urging him at length. He can't be much longer. Apart from that, nothing could prevent — scissors? — here in my bag! — could prevent him from coming. What, a dying leaf? (*She brushes away a leaf which has fallen on the embroidery.*)

[*Enter a Sister at the head of the steps.*]

A SISTER. Monsieur de Bergerac.

[5] **wicket:** entrance into the convent.

SCENE 5

Roxane, Cyrano; then, for a short while, Sister Marthe.

ROXANE (*without turning around*). What was I saying?

[*She works at her embroidery. Enter Cyrano, very pale, his hat pulled down over his eyes. The Sister who announced him withdraws. He descends the steps slowly, leaning on his cane, visibly struggling to keep erect.*]

ROXANE. Oh! these faded shades. How can I make them match? (*To Cyrano, affecting to scold him*) For the first time in fourteen years, you're late!

[*Cyrano reaches the armchair and sits down.*]

CYRANO (*in a merry voice belying his appearance*). Yes, provoking! I am vexed. I was delayed, confound it!

ROXANE. By what?

CYRANO. A quite inopportune visit.

ROXANE (*absentminded, working*). Some disagreeable person?

CYRANO. Very disagreeable. He won't be denied.

ROXANE. Did you send him away?

CYRANO. Yes. I said: "You'll excuse me. This is Saturday. On Saturdays I visit a certain house. Nothing can prevent me. Come back in an hour."

ROXANE (*lightly*). Well! He'll have to wait to see you; I shan't let you leave before evening.

CYRANO. Perhaps I'll have to leave a little sooner.

[*He closes his eyes and is silent for a moment. Sister Marthe crosses the park from the chapel to the steps. Roxane, seeing her, beckons.*]

ROXANE (*to Cyrano*). Aren't you going to tease Sister Marthe?

CYRANO (*quickly, opening his eyes*). Why certainly! (*In a comical, blustering voice*) Sister Marthe, come here! (*The sister approaches.*) Ha! Ha! Ha! Your lovely eyes are wasted on the ground.

SISTER MARTHE (*looking up with a smile*). Really? (*Noticing his face, alarmed*) Oh!

CYRANO (*in a whisper, indicating Roxane*). Hush! It is nothing — (*Boastfully, aloud*) I ate meat yesterday.

SISTER MARTHE. I knew it. (*Aside*) So that's why he's so pale. Hungry! (*Quickly, in an undertone*) If you'll come up to the refectory, I will make you a big bowl of soup. Won't you come?

CYRANO. Yes indeed!

SISTER MARTHE. For once, you're quite reasonable today.

ROXANE (*hearing them whisper*). Is she trying to convert you?

SISTER MARTHE. Heaven forbid!

CYRANO. It's true. You're always talkative on pious matters; today you haven't preached to me at all. Surprising! (*With affected fury*) Thunderation! I must surprise you too. Wait! — (*Apparently searching for, and finding, a new method of teasing*) Yes! Something completely new. I'll let you pray for me in church tonight.

ROXANE (*smiling*). Oh! Oh!

CYRANO (*laughing*). Sister Marthe is amazed beyond all words.

SISTER MARTHE (*quietly*). I didn't need your permission. (*She leaves.*)

CYRANO (*turning to Roxane, bent over her frame*). Embroidery, alas, I'll never see you finished!

ROXANE. That's the joke I was expecting.

[*A slight gust of wind causes a flurry of falling leaves.*]

CYRANO. Ah! The leaves.

ROXANE (*lifting her head to look across at the avenues*). Venetian yellow. Watch them fall.

CYRANO. How well they fall. In this one short journey from the branch to earth, they show a final beauty. Despite their fear of rotting on the ground, they wish their fall to assume the grace of flight.

ROXANE. Melancholy?

CYRANO (*recollecting himself*). Not at all, Roxane.

ROXANE. Let the leaves fall as they will. Give me the news. Where's my today's gazette?

CYRANO. Why, here it is.

ROXANE. Good.

CYRANO (*paling rapidly, struggling against the pain*). Saturday, the nineteenth: Roxane's gazette of news. After eight full helpings of fine Cette preserves, His Majesty was stricken with a fever; twice-bled, he had his malady arrested, and now his august pulse is back to normal. At the Queen's grand ball, given on Sunday evening, they burned seven hundred and sixty-three wax candles; meanwhile, our troops have beaten John of Austria, four sorcerers have been hanged, and Madame d'Athis has had to give her ailing dog a clyster[6] —

ROXANE. Monsieur de Bergerac, let's leave that out.

CYRANO (*his face contorted*). On Monday, nothing — Lygdamire changed lovers.

ROXANE. Oh.

CYRANO. On Tuesday the Court assembled at Fontainebleau. On Wednesday, La Montglat said "No" to De Fiesque. On Thursday, Mancini was queen of France — or almost. On Friday, La Montglat said "Yes" to De Fiesque. On Saturday, the twenty-sixth —

[*His eyes close. His head drops forward. Silence.*]

ROXANE (*surprised, turns around, looks at him, and rises in alarm*). Has he fainted? (*She runs to him, calling*) Cyrano!

CYRANO (*opens his eyes again; in an uncertain voice*). What is it? What has happened? (*Seeing Roxane bending over him, he hastily readjusts his hat, and draws back in his chair in alarm.*) No! No! I assure you, it's nothing. I'll be all right.

ROXANE. Still —

CYRANO. It's the wound I had at Arras. Sometimes, you know —

ROXANE. My poor friend!

CYRANO. It's nothing. It will go away. (*He smiles with an effort.*) It's gone.

ROXANE (*straightening up, relieved*). Each of us has a wound. I have mine too. The old wound, always fresh — it's still here! (*She puts her hand on her breast.*) Here under this fading letter stained with blood and tears.

[*Twilight begins to fall.*]

CYRANO. His letter. Didn't you say that some day, perhaps, you would let me read it?

ROXANE. You want to read his letter?

CYRANO. Yes, today, now!

[6] clyster: enema.

ROXANE (*giving him the little bag which hangs around her neck*). Here!

CYRANO (*taking it*). May I open it?

ROXANE. Open it and read it.

[*She returns to her embroidery frame, folds it up, and begins to collect her skeins and balls of wool.*]

CYRANO (*reading*). "Roxane, farewell! Knowing I must die, and as it seems tonight, I send this greeting."

ROXANE (*stopping, surprised*). What, aloud?

CYRANO (*continuing*). "My heart is heavy with love that I never told, and now can never tell. My infatuate eyes —"

ROXANE. How strangely well you read it.

[*Darkness is falling imperceptibly.*]

CYRANO (*continuing*). "— those eyes which found a tremulous joy in this, shall never again embrace your familiar gestures. You can never know how your best trait of all, the way you smooth your forehead, made my cry, 'My best, my own beloved' —"

ROXANE. You are reading —

CYRANO (*continuing*). "— makes me cry —"

ROXANE. That voice —

CYRANO (*continuing*). "Now, in the recollection, 'Love, farewell!'"

ROXANE. That voice I heard long years ago.

[*She approaches very quietly without his noticing, goes behind the armchair, bends over him noiselessly, and looks at the letter. Darkness deepens.*]

CYRANO. "My heart has never left you for a moment; and, still in the other world, I shall be the one who has loved beyond all hope of loving, the one who loved —"

ROXANE (*placing her hand on his shoulder*). How can you read it now? It's dark. (*Startled, he turns round, sees her very close, makes a gesture of alarm, bends his head. A long silence. Then, slowly, clasping her hands*) And so for fourteen years, you've played this part. The old friend coming to amuse me!

CYRANO. Roxane!

ROXANE. It was you!

CYRANO. No, no, Roxane, no!

ROXANE. I ought to have known it by the way you spoke my name.

CYRANO. You're wrong.

ROXANE. It was you.

CYRANO. I assure you —

ROXANE. I see through all your generous trickery. The letters — they were yours —

CYRANO. No!

ROXANE. The dear mad words were yours.

CYRANO. No.

ROXANE. The voice in the night was yours.

CYRANO. I swear it wasn't.

ROXANE. The soul was yours.

CYRANO. I didn't love you.

ROXANE. You loved me.

CYRANO. It was the other. He was the one who loved you.

ROXANE. *You* loved me!

CYRANO. No! No!

ROXANE. You say it in a faltering voice already.

CYRANO. No! No! I never loved you — dearest love!

ROXANE. Ah! How many things, long dead, are now reborn. Why were you silent all these fourteen years, when on this letter that he never wrote these tears were yours?

CYRANO (*giving her the letter*). The blood was his.

ROXANE. Then why did you let this silence so sublime be broken now?

CYRANO. Why, Roxane?

[*Le Bret and Ragueneau rush in.*]

SCENE 6

The same; Le Bret, and Ragueneau.

LE BRET. Sheer madness! I was sure of it. Here he is!

CYRANO (*smiling and straightening up*). Why, naturally. Where else?

LE BRET. He has finished himself, madame, by getting up.

ROXANE. God alive! Then that faintness just now — ?

CYRANO. Quite so. I didn't finish my gazette. On Saturday, the twenty-sixth, an hour before his dinner, Monsieur de Bergerac was done to death.

[*He takes off his hat, revealing his bandaged head.*]

ROXANE. What does he mean? Cyrano! Your head all bandaged up? What have they done to you?

CYRANO. "Struck by a worthy sword and adversary; to die with a point at my heart and a pointed word at my lips!" And I said that. How Fate has laughed at me! Here I am murdered, trapped in an ambush, killed by a lackey, with a mere block of wood! Nothing more perfect. A failure in life, and a failure in death.

RAGUENEAU. My dear friend!

CYRANO. Ragueneau! No tears. (*Stretching out his hand to him*) What are you now, my brother?

RAGUENEAU (*through his tears*). I am candle — candle snuffer, for the plays of Molière.

CYRANO. Molière?

RAGUENEAU. I shall leave him after tomorrow; I'm quite indignant. Yesterday, when they played "Scapin," I saw he had taken an entire scene from you.[7]

LE BRET. An entire scene!

RAGUENEAU. Yes! The famous "What the devil was he doing — ?"

LE BRET (*indignantly*). And Molière stole that from you?

CYRANO. Hush! He did right. (*To Ragueneau*) Was it effective?

RAGUENEAU (*sobbing*). The people laughed — laughed and laughed!

CYRANO. That's been my life — to prompt and be forgotten. (*To Roxane*) The night Christian spoke beneath your window — you remember? My whole life's in that moment. While I stayed below within the shadows, others have climbed to take the kiss of glory. It's not unfair. From the grave's brink, I think I must approve: Molière has genius; Christian had beauty. (*Bells sound from the chapel. Sisters*

---

[7] **he had taken ... from you:** Jean Molière (1622–73), the great comic French dramatist, based two scenes of his *The Deceits of Scapin* on the historical Cyrano's *Le Pédant Joué.*

pass along the avenue backstage on their way to service.)
For whom the bell is tolling — they should pray.

ROXANE (*rising and calling*). Sister! Sister!

CYRANO (*holding her back*). No! Don't go for anyone. Too
late. When you returned, I should be no longer here. (*The
Sisters have entered the chapel; the organ is heard.*) Ah!
Harmony was missing; there it is.

ROXANE. I love you; you must live!

CYRANO. No. In the tale of Beauty and the Beast, when the
princess says, "I love you," then the prince feels all his
ugliness transformed to fairness, transmuted in the sunshine of her words. You see, I'm still the same, still un-
transformed.

ROXANE. I've been your life's misfortune —

CYRANO. Never that. Quite the reverse. I've never known
women's sweetness. My mother — she could scarcely think
me handsome. I had no sister. Later, I was afraid to meet a
sweetheart's eye. Yet, thanks to you, I've known a woman's
friendship — a woman's gown has brushed against my life.

LE BRET (*pointing to the moonlight in the branches*). Your
other friend has come to you.

CYRANO (*smiling at the moon*). I see her.

ROXANE. I've loved one man alone. Why must I lose him
twice?

CYRANO. Le Bret, I'll climb to the opaline moon tonight and
not need my machines —

ROXANE. What are you saying?

CYRANO. They'll send me there to find my Paradise. They
must. The souls I love are exiled there. I shall find Socrates
and Galileo —

LE BRET (*rebelling*). No! This end's too senseless, too unjust!
A poet like him! A heart so great, so lofty! To die! To die
like this!

CYRANO. Old grumbler to the last!

LE BRET (*in tears*). Dear friend!

CYRANO (*rising, wild-eyed*). "These are Cadets of Gascony" —
the elemental mass! — yes, there's the problem!

LE BRET (*almost proudly*). A scientist, even in delirium!

CYRANO. Copernicus — he said —

ROXANE (*weeping*). Oh!

CYRANO.

"But what the devil was he doing there,
How did he come to be in this affair?"[8]

[*Pauses.*]

Philosopher and physicist,
Musician, poet, duellist,
Planetary aerialist,
Skilled at the parry and attack,
A lover too — unhappy man!
Here lies Hercule-Savinien
De Cyrano de Bergerac,
Who failed in all a mortal can!

Forgive me. I must go now. I can't stay. Moonlight is here to take me home again. (*He falls back in his chair. Roxane's tears bring him to reality. He looks at her and touches her veil with caressing fingers.*) Don't grieve the less for your fine, charming Christian, but when the last great chill has gripped my bones, could you give double meaning to your veil, and, mourning him, mourn me a little also? Could you, Roxane?.

ROXANE. I promise — faithfully!

CYRANO (*seized by a great shivering, suddenly rises*). Not here! No! not in this armchair! (*They wish to help him.*) Never! No! Don't support me. (*He leans against the tree.*) Nothing but this tree. (*Pause*) He's on his way now. Already I'm shod in marble — and gloved with lead. But since he's on his way, I shall await him standing — (*he draws his sword*) — and standing sword in hand!

LE BRET. Cyrano!

ROXANE (*faltering*). Cyrano!

[*All draw back in terror.*]

CYRANO. I see him peering now! He dares to look at my nose, that squat-nosed Horror! (*Raising his sword*) What do you say? It's useless? Well, I know it! But the best fight is not for the hope of winning. Far better to fight when you know the fight is hopeless. Who are all these? A thousand of you? So! I know you now — my ancient adversaries. Falsehood!

[8] "But what . . . affair": lines from the scene borrowed from Cyrano by Molière.

(*Striking the empty air with his sword*) And Cowardice! And Prejudice! Compromise too? (*Striking hard*) I'll make a compact, will I? Why, never! Never! Ah! And here comes Folly! I know you'll better me tonight. No matter! I'll fight, and fight, and fight. (*He sweeps his sword in great circles, then stops, panting.*) Yes! You have robbed me of all now, the laurel and the rose.[9] Take them. Despite your malice, there are things you cannot take. When I enter the mansion of God tonight, my bow shall brush its azure sills with something erect, unspotted, that I carry in spite of you all — (*starts forward with raised sword*) — and that is — (*The sword drops from his hand; he staggers and falls into the arms of Roxane and Ragueneau.*)

ROXANE (*bending over him and kissing his forehead*). And that is?

CYRANO (*reopens his eyes, recognizes her, and smiles*). My undishonored plume!

CURTAIN

QUESTIONS

Scenes 1–2. Act Five takes place fifteen years later. Why is the season autumn, rather than spring or summer? From the conversations about Cyrano between the other characters, should we assume that time has changed Cyrano's character? Be able to defend your answer. Who has had the happier life, Cyrano or De Guiche?

Scene 4. Why does a dying leaf fall on Roxane's embroidery? What is the effect of Roxane's line: "Then, on the last stroke of the hour, not even turning my head, I hear his cane on the steps." Why is the line such a shock?

Scene 5. Who is the visitor Cyrano has delayed for an hour? Is it a human one? Explain the significance of Cyrano's "permission" to let Sister Marthe pray for him that night in church. How does Roxane discover Cyrano wrote the precious letter? Why does Cyrano read it aloud to her at just that moment? Is there a darkness beyond twilight falling over the scene?

Scene 6. Why does Le Bret refer to the rising moon as Cyrano's "other friend"? Why does Cyrano feel his manner of dying is inappropriate?

[9] **the laurel and the rose:** symbols of victory and love.

How would he have liked to die? Do you feel his death is inappropriate? Why? In his final moments of life, what has his plume come to mean to Cyrano?

AFTER THE CURTAIN

Romantic and Realistic Theater

As Cyrano the man was born too late for the chivalric age which might have valued more highly his defiant integrity, so *Cyrano* the play was conceived and written too late in the twilight of Romantic Theater for it to launch a theatrical tradition. Like its hero, *Cyrano* was a play going against the main literary current of the eighteen-nineties, realism — as exemplified by Ibsen's social problem play[1] *An Enemy of the People.* *Cyrano* looks backward to a nineteenth-century Romantic view of man rather than forward to the twentieth-century, environmentalist view of man that we term Realism. *Cyrano* was written in 1897, during Europe's pre-machine-gun era, when heroism and skill were still thought to be possible on the battlefield, and war was considered a glorious and romantic adventure. With the advent of the machine gun, however, any recruit could have cut Cyrano down a hundred yards in front of the spot where the hero's gallantry and swordsmanship would have been effective.

(Although not realistic, do you think the play may be truer to the spirit of man — at least as man would like to see himself? What ideals does Cyrano embody? Are such ideals as truth, courage, and courtesy ever practiced in life, or are they found only in the dreams of poets? Are they less in evidence today than they were in Cyrano's time? If so, explain what changes in living help to account for their decline.)

The Romantic Theater, where such a character as Cyrano becomes credible, differs from the Realistic Theater in three basic ways: first, man is shown as master of his own life, not the victim of his environment and upbringing. Will, courage,

[1] See Glossary.

and pride are the supreme virtues, for the Romantic hero believes in himself, sees himself as the measure of the universe. (This is why Cyrano never becomes converted to Catholicism, as it would mean acknowledging his dependence on and therefore inferiority to God.) Which scenes best demonstrate Cyrano's will power? courage? pride? Do you admire and identify with the Romantic hero, as exemplified by Cyrano? or do you prefer a less egoistic or invincible protagonist?[2] Draw on your reading and experience to illustrate your views.

Romantic Theater differs from Realistic Theater in a second way: the language that romantic characters use is heightened through poetry. Unlike Ibsen's Realistic Theater, where everyday language is used so that the audience is led to feel that what they are watching on stage could happen in real life, the speech in Romantic Theater cascades with poetry and metaphor. Indeed, the original French of *Cyrano* is written in rhymed couplets that are impossible to translate into English: so much rhyme would sound artificial. Even so, the heightening of language and feeling comes through in such scenes as when Cyrano, pretending to be Christian, says: "Your name is like a bell within my heart, and all the time I'm quivering, my Roxane, and all the time the bell shakes with my heart, and all the time it's pealing out your name." No lover has probably ever spoken so, yet most would wish to. Find other examples of intense and imaginative expression in Cyrano's speeches. What does each contribute to the mood of the dramatic moment?

A third difference between Romantic and Realistic Theater lies in the way scenes and situations are heightened through coincidences that would seem absurd or artificial on the Realistic stage. Improbabilities are crucial in *Cyrano:* Christian is killed at exactly the second Cyrano is about to confess his love to Roxane; De Guiche arrives precisely as the wedding between Christian and Roxane begins, and he must be detained precisely fifteen minutes; twilight falls at just the moment Cyrano reads "Christian's" love letter aloud. Do these coincidences spoil the play, or do you accept them as right, inevitable, given the mood and spirit of the play? How does each serve to advance the plot?

[2] See Glossary.

Character and Foil

Believing only in himself and in the values of his code, Cyrano owes allegiance only to himself, but that allegiance is a sacred one. Such a romantic attitude can result at best in pride, at worst in arrogance — and both may very well co-exist side by side as they do in Cyrano, who is a very great and very flawed character. Outraged at his own ugliness, Cyrano is vain, haughty, suspicious. An isolated man with only a few deep friends, Cyrano is seldom able to return love or affection, always suspecting that it contains mockery or, worse yet, the taint of pity.

Yet, however incomplete a man, he is the hero, and his good qualities are heightened by Rostand's use of *dramatic foils*. Basically, a foil character — the metaphor comes from fencing and implies the opponent's sword and hence that which one clashes with — is a character who is like the hero in many respects but differs in one important way. The foil exists as a contrast to the hero, pointing up the hero's strengths and suggesting the kind of man the hero would have been had he lacked the same qualities the foil lacks. In *Cyrano* there are three foils, three more incomplete men who surround Cyrano, making him appear the taller by comparison.

Ragueneau has Cyrano's skill with words; indeed, he is the only match for Cyrano's tongue in the whole play. Yet his character differs from Cyrano's in what ways? How courageous is Ragueneau? What aspect of Cyrano's character does he magnify?

Christian, too, is like Cyrano in his regard for honor and in his personal courage. What is his great difference from Cyrano? In what ways does Cyrano shine even more brightly in his presence? Explain how the whole idea of the play depends on the contrast between these two characters.

In what ways does De Guiche differ from Cyrano? In a sense, De Guiche is less a foil — like but unlike — than a shadow Cyrano, the realist who accepts the world's corrupt values and succeeds through using them. Bold and intelligent, Cyrano could have become like De Guiche, but chose not to. What does Cyrano possess that De Guiche lacks? How does De Guiche feel about that difference? What prevented Cyrano from becoming a De Guiche?

Reading and Writing

1. Read Eric Remarque's *All Quiet on the Western Front* and compare that novel's vision of warfare with that shown in *Cyrano de Bergerac*. How does Rostand's attitude toward war differ from Remarque's? Is this difference superficial, or is it total?

2. At the end of Act Two, Scene 7, Cyrano mentions Don Quixote with approval. Using the library, find out all you can about the career and adventures of Don Quixote. How is Cyrano like Don Quixote? How does he differ from Don Quixote?

3. The Romantic hero still exists on television in such forms as the western sheriff like *Gunsmoke*'s Matt Dillon. Compare Matt Dillon or a similar figure with Cyrano. How do they regard women? How do they feel about physical combat? Are there any significant ways in which Cyrano differs from the heroic western lawman?

You Can't Take
It With You

BEFORE THE CURTAIN

Nineteen hundred and thirty-six, the year *You Can't Take It With You* opened on Broadway, was a glum time in an era about to turn grim. At home the depression still spread its grayness over boarded-up factories and eroded hillsides. Abroad democracies faltered while totalitarian governments flourished: Hitler was firmly in control, occupying the Rhineland and linking Italy's destiny to Germany's through the Rome-Berlin Pact. In Spain, Franco's fascist forces divided the country in civil war. Some good news was sorely needed. And *You Can't Take It With You* provided it, opening on December 14, 1936, at New York's Booth Theater.

Its good news was an assertion of zany individuality when tyrannical dictatorships seemed the wave of the future. While a century earlier Thoreau had proclaimed "The mass of men lead lives of quiet desperation," it took Moss Hart and George S. Kaufman to bring the proof of Thoreau's statement to the Broadway stage. Contrasted to the Vanderhof "family" — with its entourage of fireworks makers, exiled Russians, amateur printers, and two-finger playwrights — are the Kirbys: prosperous Wall Streeters who belong to all the right clubs and vacation in all the right places — and who have lost all relish in living. Through this contrast between the opposing personalities and values of Mr. Kirby and Grandpa Vanderhof — the stodgy, snobbish millionaire vs. the fan of zoos and commencements — emerges one of the great comedies of the

American stage, showing each member of the family personally fulfilling that Constitutional guarantee ensuring each of us the right to "the pursuit of happiness."

All comedy distorts and simplifies, revealing to us the everyday absurdities we accept as the "natural" way things are. Viewing life through the special prism of comedy, which breaks up our pre-set expectations about reality and human nature, Hart and Kaufman show us the contrast between what life can be and what too often it is. In *You Can't Take It With You,* the authors' premise is that life should allow us to do just what we want to do. To dramatize this belief, Hart and Kaufman pit the square world of millionaire Kirby against Martin Vanderhof's nineteen thirties' version of a hippie family, creating the essential conflict by introducing a poor-girl-loves-rich-boy situation which forces the two worlds to clash.

But to turn these conflicts into successful comedy, the playwrights must join suspense — will the boy get the girl? — to the sharp and rapid pace of comedy. Absurdity must be piled on absurdity at such a rapid rate that the audience never becomes bored, never questions the probability that what he is seeing on stage could actually occur. For a successful comedy is like a juggler putting three, four, five . . . eight balls in the air at once, then suddenly sneezing and releasing a hailstorm of falling balls. But after this happens, the juggler retains his relaxed attitude, triumphant expression; his arms still move as though he still had complete mastery of the balls. For one basis of humor is a mechanical lack of response to a changed situation. Whatever happens, a comic figure proceeds at his accustomed pace, refusing to recognize the reality of new events. Comedy resides in the dignity of the top-hatted man refusing to acknowledge, as he stiffly reaches out to receive a gold medal for citizenship, that his pants have just fallen down. Comedy lives in the earnest lover trying to ignore the fact that, as he leans over the dinner table to embrace his beloved, half of his dangling tie has just disappeared into her cup of coffee. While reading *You Can't Take It With You*, notice how mechanically the wealthy Kirbys respond to the nuttiness of the Vanderhof household, treating the "family" as though it were that of a fellow millionaire in New Rochelle. The same comic formula underlies much of the hilarity of the play's action. It explains, for example, the response of the government agents. See if you can discover other applications of the same principle.

Since the pace of comedy is sharp and rapid — a dozen things happening simultaneously — expect little pause in the frantic ballet of bustle and activity once the Vanderhof family is on stage: Essie dances, Penny paints, Ed sets type, De Pinna explodes fireworks, Kolenkhov gestures, and Ed xylophones while Grandpa rocks and the snakes slither. It is an eight-ring circus.

You Can't Take It With You

MOSS HART and GEORGE S. KAUFMAN

Characters

PENELOPE SYCAMORE

ESSIE

RHEBA

PAUL SYCAMORE

MR. DE PINNA

ED

DONALD

MARTIN VANDERHOF

OLGA

ALICE

HENDERSON

TONY KIRBY

BORIS KOLENKHOV

GAY WELLINGTON

MR. KIRBY

MRS. KIRBY

THREE MEN

ACT ONE

SCENE 1

A Wednesday evening at the home of Martin Vander-hof — just around the corner from Columbia University, but don't go looking for it. The room we see is what is customarily described as a living room, but in this house the term is something of an understatement. The every-man-for-himself room would be more like it. For here meals are eaten, plays are written, snakes collected, ballet steps practiced, xylophones played, printing presses operated — if there were room enough, there would probably be ice skating. In short, the brood presided over by Martin Vanderhof goes on about the business of living in the fullest sense of the word. This is a house where you do as you like, and no questions asked.

At the moment, Grandpa Vanderhof's daughter, Mrs. Penelope Sycamore, is doing what she likes more than anything else in the world. She is writing a play — her eleventh. Comfortably ensconced in what is affectionately known as Mother's Corner, she is pounding away on a typewriter perched precariously on a rickety card table. Also on the table is one of those plaster-of-Paris skulls ordinarily used as an ashtray, but which serves Penelope as a candy jar. And, because Penny likes companionship, there are two kittens on the table, busily lapping at a saucer of milk.

Penelope Vanderhof Sycamore is a round little woman in her early fifties, comfortable looking, gentle, homey. One would not suspect that under that placid exterior there surges the Divine Urge — but it does, it does.

After a moment her fingers lag on the keys; a thoughtful expression comes over her face. Abstractedly she takes a piece of candy out of the skull, pops it into her mouth. As always, it furnishes the needed inspiration — with a furious burst of speed she finishes a page and whips it out of the machine. Quite mechanically, she picks up one of the kittens, adds the sheet of paper to the pile underneath, replaces the kitten.

As she goes back to work, Essie Carmichael, Mrs. Sycamore's eldest daughter, comes in from the kitchen. A girl of about twenty-nine, very slight, a curious air of the pixie about her. She is wearing ballet slippers — in fact, she wears them throughout the play.

ESSIE (*fanning herself*). My, that kitchen's hot.

PENNY (*finishing a bit of typing*). What, Essie?

ESSIE. I say the kitchen's awful hot. That new candy I'm making — it just won't ever get cool.

PENNY. Do you have to make candy today, Essie? It's such a hot day.

ESSIE. Well, I got all those new orders. Ed went out and got a bunch of new orders.

PENNY. My, if it keeps on I suppose you'll be opening up a store.

ESSIE. That's what Ed was saying last night, but I said no, I want to be a dancer. (*Bracing herself against the table, she manipulates her legs, ballet fashion.*)

PENNY. The only trouble with dancing is, it takes so long. You've been studying such a long time.

ESSIE (*slowly drawing a leg up behind her as she talks*). Only — eight — years. After all, Mother, you've been writing plays for eight years. We started about the same time, didn't we?

PENNY. Yes, but you shouldn't count my first two years, because I was learning to type.

[*From the kitchen comes a colored maid named Rheba — a very black girl somewhere in her thirties. She carries a white tablecloth and presently starts to spread it over the table.*]

RHEBA (*as she enters*). I think the candy's hardening up now, Miss Essie.

ESSIE. Oh, thanks, Rheba. I'll bring some in, Mother — I want you to try it. [*She goes into the kitchen.*]

[*Penny returns to her work as Rheba busies herself with the table.*]

RHEBA. Finish the second act, Mrs. Sycamore?

PENNY. Oh, no, Rheba. I've just got Cynthia entering the monastery.

RHEBA. Monastery? How'd she get there? She was at the El Morocco, wasn't she?

PENNY. Well, she gets tired of the El Morocco, and there's this monastery, so she goes there.

RHEBA. Do they let her in?

PENNY. Yes, I made it Visitors' Day, so of course anybody can come.

RHEBA. Oh.

PENNY. So she arrives on Visitors' Day, and — just stays.

RHEBA. All night?

PENNY. Oh, yes. She stays six years.

RHEBA (*as she goes into the kitchen*). Six years? My, I bet she busts that monastery wide open.

PENNY (*half to herself, as she types*). "Six Years Later."

[*Paul Sycamore comes up from the cellar. Mid-fifties but with a kind of youthful air. His quiet charm and mild manner are distinctly engaging.*]

PAUL (*turning back as he comes through the door*). Mr. De Pinna! ˙(*A voice from below.* "Yah?") Mr. De Pinna, will you bring up one of those new skyrockets, please? I want to show them to Mrs. Sycamore. (*An answering monosyllable from the cellar as he turns toward Penny*) Look, Penny — what do you think of these little fire-crackers? Ten strings for a nickel. Listen. (*He puts one down on the center table and lights it. It goes off with a good bang.*) Nice, huh?

PENNY. Paul, dear, were you ever in a monastery?

PAUL (*quite calmly*). No, I wasn't . . . Wait till you see the new rockets. Gold stars, then blue stars, then some bombs, and then a balloon. Mr. De Pinna thought of the balloon.

PENNY. Sounds lovely. Did you do all that today?

PAUL. Sure. We made up — oh, here we are. (*Mr. De Pinna comes up from the cellar. A bald-headed little man with a serious manner, and carrying two good-sized skyrockets*) Look, Penny. Cost us eighteen cents to make and we sell 'em for fifty. How many do you figure we can make before the Fourth, Mr. De Pinna?

DE PINNA. Well, we've got two weeks yet — what day you going to take the stuff up to Mount Vernon?

PAUL. Oh, I don't know — about a week. You know, we're going to need a larger booth this year — got a lot of stuff made up.

DE PINNA (*examining the rocket in his hand*). Look, Mr. Sycamore, the only thing that bothers me is, I'm afraid the powder chamber is just a little bit close to the balloon.

PAUL. Well, we've got the stars and the bombs in between.

DE PINNA. But that don't give the balloon time enough. A balloon needs plenty of time.

PAUL. Want to go down in the cellar and try it?

DE PINNA. All right.

PAUL (*as he disappears through the cellar door*). That's
the only way you'll really tell.

PENNY (*halting De Pinna in the cellar doorway*). Mr. De
Pinna, if a girl you loved entered a monastery, what would
you do?

DE PINNA (*he wasn't expecting that one*). Oh, I don't know,
Mrs. Sycamore — it's been so long. (*He goes.*)

[*Rheba returns from the kitchen, bringing a pile of
plates.*]

RHEBA. Miss Alice going to be home to dinner tonight,
Mrs. Sycamore?

PENNY (*deep in her thinking*). What? I don't know, Rheba.
Maybe.

RHEBA. Well, I'll set a place for her, but she's only been
home one night this week. (*She puts down a plate or
two.*) Miss Essie's making some mighty good candy today. She's doing something new with cocoanuts. (*More
plates*) Let's see — six, and Mr. De Pinna, and if Mr.
Kolenkhov comes that makes eight, don't it? (*At which
point a muffled sound, reminiscent of the Battle of the
Marne,*[1] *comes up from the cellar. It is the skyrocket, of
course. The great preliminary hiss, followed by a series
of explosions. Penny and Rheba, however, don't even
notice it. Rheba goes right on.*) Yes, I'd better set for
eight.

PENNY. I think I'll put this play away for a while, Rheba,
and go back to the war play.

RHEBA. Oh, I always liked that one — the war play.

[*Essie returns from the kitchen, carrying a plate of
freshly made candy.*]

ESSIE. They'll be better when they're harder, mother, but
try one — I want to know what you think.

PENNY. Oh, they look awfully good. (*She takes one.*) What
do you call them?

ESSIE. I think I'll call 'em Love Dreams.

PENNY. Oh, that's nice. . . . I'm going back to my war play,
Essie. What do you think?

ESSIE. Oh, are you, Mother?

---

[1] *Battle of the Marne:* World War I battle.

PENNY. Yes, I sort of got myself into a monastery and I can't get out.

ESSIE. Oh, well, it'll come to you, Mother. Remember how you got out of that brothel. . . . Hello, boys. (*This little greeting is idly tossed toward the snake solarium, a glass structure looking something like a goldfish aquarium, but containing, believe it or not, snakes.*) The snakes look hungry. Did Rheba feed them?

PENNY (*as Rheba re-enters*). I don't know. Rheba, did you feed the snakes yet?

RHEBA. No, Donald's coming and he always brings flies with him.

PENNY. Well, try to feed them before Grandpa gets home. You know how fussy he is about them.

RHEBA. Yes'm.

PENNY (*handing her the kittens*). And take Groucho and Harpo into the kitchen with you. . . . I think I'll have another Love Dream.

[*Mr. Sycamore emerges from the cellar again.*]

PAUL. Mr. De Pinna was right about the balloon. It was too close to the powder.

ESSIE (*practicing a dance step*). Want a Love Dream, Father? They're on the table.

PAUL. No, thanks. I gotta wash.

PENNY. I'm going back to the war play, Paul.

PAUL. Oh, that's nice. We're putting some red stars after the blue stars, then come the bombs and *then* the balloon. That ought to do it. (*He goes up the stairs*)

ESSIE (*another dance step*). Mr. Kolenkhov says I'm his most promising pupil.

PENNY (*absorbed in her own troubles*). You know, with forty monks and one girl, something ought to happen.

[*Ed Carmichael comes down the stairs. A nondescript young man in his mid-thirties. In shirtsleeves at the moment*]

ED. Listen! (*He hums a snatch of melody as he heads for the far corner of the room — the xylophone corner. Arriving there, he picks up the sticks and continues the melody on the xylophone. Immediately Essie is up on*

her toes, *performing intricate ballet steps to Ed's accom-
paniment.*)

ESSIE (*dancing*). I like that, Ed. Yours?

ED (*shakes his head*). Beethoven.

ESSIE (*never coming down off her toes*). Lovely. Got a lot
of *you* in it. . . . I made those new candies this afternoon,
Ed.

ED (*playing away*). Yah?

ESSIE. You can take 'em around tonight.

ED. All right. . . . Now, here's the finish. This is me. (*He
works up to an elaborate crescendo, but Essie keeps pace
with him right to the finish.*)

ESSIE. That's fine. Remember it when Kolenkhov comes,
will you?

PENNY (*who has been busy with her papers*). Ed, dear, why
don't you and Essie have a baby? I was thinking about
it just the other day.

ED. I don't know — we could have one if you wanted us to.
What about it, Essie? Do you want to have a baby?

ESSIE. Oh, I don't care. I'm willing if Grandpa is.

ED. Let's ask him.

[*Essie goes into the kitchen as Penny goes back to her
manuscripts.*]

PENNY (*running through the pile*). Labor play . . . religious
play . . . sex play. I know it's here some place.

[*Ed, meanwhile, has transferred his attention from the
xylophone to a printing press that stands handily by,
and now gives it a preliminary workout.*]
[*Mr. De Pinna comes out of the cellar, bound for the
kitchen to wash up.*]

DE PINNA. I was right about the balloon. It was too close to
the powder.

ED. Anything you want printed, Mr. De Pinna? How about
some more calling cards?

DE PINNA (*as he passes into the kitchen*). No, thanks. I've
still got the *first* thousand.

ED (*calling after him*). Well, call on somebody, will you?
(*He then gives his attention to Rheba, who is busy with*

the table again.) What have we got for dinner, Rheba? I'm ready to print the menu.

RHEBA. Cornflakes, watermelon, some of those candies Miss Essie made, and some kind of meat — I forget.

ED. I think I'll set it up in boldface Cheltenham[2] tonight. (*He starts to pick out the letters.*) If I'm going to take those new candies around, I'd better print up some descriptive matter after dinner.

PENNY. Do you think anybody reads those things, Ed — that you put in the candy boxes? . . . Oh, here it is. (*She pulls a manuscript out of a pile.*) "Poison Gas." (*The doorbell sounds.*) I guess that's Donald. (*As Rheba breaks into a broad grin*) Look at Rheba smile.

ED. The boyfriend, eh, Rheba?

PENNY (*as Rheba disappears into the hallway*). Donald and Rheba are awfully cute together. Sort of like Porgy and Bess.

[*Rheba having opened the door, the gentleman named Donald now looms up in the doorway — darkly. He is a colored man of no uncertain hue.*]

DONALD. Good evening, everybody!

ED. Hi, Donald! How've you been?

DONALD. I'm pretty good, Mr. Ed. How you been, Mrs. Sycamore?

PENNY. Very well, thank you. (*She looks at him, appraisingly.*) Donald, were you ever in a monastery?

DONALD. No-o. I don't go no place much. I'm on relief.

PENNY. Oh, yes, of course.

DONALD (*pulling a bottle out of each side pocket*). Here's the flies, Rheba. Caught a big mess of them today.

RHEBA (*taking the jars*). You sure did.

DONALD. I see you've been working, Mrs. Sycamore.

PENNY. Yes, indeed, Donald.

DONALD. How's Grandpa?

PENNY. Just fine. He's over at Columbia this afternoon. The commencement exercises.

DONALD. My, the years certainly do roll 'round.

ED (*with his typesetting*). M — E — A — T. . . . What's he go there for all the time, Penny?

---

[2] **boldface Cheltenham:** a style of printer's type.

PENNY. I don't know. It's so handy — just around the corner.

[*Paul comes downstairs.*]

PAUL. Oh, Donald! Mr. De Pinna and I are going to take the fireworks up to Mount Vernon next week. Do you think you could give us a hand?

DONALD. Yes, sir, only I can't take no money for it this year, because if the Government finds out I'm working they'll get sore.

PAUL. Oh! . . . Ed, I got a wonderful idea in the bathroom just now. I was reading Trotzky.[3] (*He produces a book from under his arm.*) It's yours, isn't it?

ED. Yah, I left it there.

PENNY. *Who* is it?

PAUL. *You* know, Trotzky. The Russian Revolution.

PENNY. Oh.

PAUL. Anyhow, it struck me it was a great fireworks idea. Remember "The Last Days of Pompeii"?

PENNY. Oh, yes. Palisades Park. (*With a gesture of her arms she loosely describes a couple of arcs, indicative of the eruption of Mt. Vesuvius.*) That's where we met.

PAUL. Well, I'm going to do the Revolution! A full hour display.

DONALD. Say!

PENNY. Paul, that's wonderful!

ED. The red fire is the flag, huh?

PAUL. Sure! And the Czar,[4] and the Cossacks!

DONALD. And the freeing of the slaves?

PAUL. No, no, Donald —

[*The sound of the front door slamming. A second's pause, and then Grandpa enters the living room. Grandpa is about seventy-five, a wiry little man whom the years have treated kindly. His face is youthful, despite the lines that sear it; his eyes are very much alive. He is a man who made his peace with the world long, long ago, and his whole attitude and manner are quietly persuasive of this.*]

[3] **Trotzky:** Leon Trotzky (1877–1940), a Russian Communist, leader of the Revolution of 1917 and author of many political works.
[4] **the Czar:** Nicholas II, the last czar, or emperor, of Russia. He reigned from 1894 to 1917.

GRANDPA (*surveying the group*). Well, sir, you should have been there. That's all I can say — you should have been there.

PENNY. Was it a nice commencement, Grandpa?

GRANDPA. Wonderful. They get better every year. (*He peers into the snake solarium.*) You don't know how lucky you are you're snakes.

ED. Big class this year, Grandpa? How many were there?

GRANDPA. Oh, must have been two acres. *Everybody* graduated. And much funnier speeches than they had last year.

DONALD. You want to listen to a good speech you go up and hear Father Divine.[5]

GRANDPA. I'll wait — they'll have him at Columbia.

PENNY. Donald, will you tell Rheba Grandpa's home now and we won't wait for Miss Alice.

DONALD. Yes'm. . . . (*As he goes through the kitchen door*) Rheba, Grandpa's home — we can have dinner.

PAUL. Got a new skyrocket today, Grandpa. Wait till you see it. . . . Wonder why they don't have fireworks at commencements.

GRANDPA. Don't make enough noise. You take a good commencement orator and he'll drown out a whole carload of fireworks. And say just as much, too.

PENNY. Don't the graduates ever say anything?

GRANDPA. No, they just sit there in cap and nightgown, get their diplomas, and then along about forty years from now they suddenly say, "Where am I?"

[*Essie comes in from the kitchen, bringing a plate of tomatoes for the evening meal.*]

ESSIE. Hello, Grandpa. Have a nice day?

GRANDPA (*watching Essie as she puts the tomatoes on the table*). Hello-have-a-nice-day. (*Suddenly he roars at the top of his voice.*) Don't I even get kissed?

ESSIE (*kissing him*). Excuse me, Grandpa.

GRANDPA. I'll take a tomato, too. (*Essie passes the plate; Grandpa takes one and sits with it in his hand, solemnly weighing it.*) You know, I could have used a couple of these this afternoon. . . . Play something, Ed.

[5] **Father Divine** (1877?–1965): famous black preacher of the thirties.

[*Ed at once obliges on the xylophone — something on the dreamy side. Immediately Essie is up on her toes again, drifting through the mazes of a toe dance.*]

ESSIE (*after a moment*). There was a letter came for you Grandpa. Did you get it?

GRANDPA. Letter for me? I don't know anybody.

ESSIE. It was for you, though. Had your name on it.

GRANDPA. That's funny. Where is it?

ESSIE. I don't know. Where's Grandpa's letter, Mother?

PENNY (*who has been deep in her work*). What, dear?

ESSIE (*dancing dreamily away*). Where's that letter that came for Grandpa last week?

PENNY. I don't know. (*Then, brightly*) I remember seeing the kittens on it.

GRANDPA. Who was it from? Did you notice?

ESSIE. Yes, it was on the outside.

GRANDPA. Well, who was it?

ESSIE (*first finishing the graceful flutterings of the Dying Swan*). United States Government.

GRANDPA. Really? Wonder what *they* wanted.

ESSIE. There was one before that, too, from the same people. There was a couple of them.

GRANDPA. Well, if any more come I wish you'd give them to me.

ESSIE. Yes, Grandpa.

[*A fresh flurry of dancing; the xylophone grows a little louder.*]

GRANDPA. I think I'll go out to Westchester tomorrow and do a little snake-hunting.

PAUL (*who has settled down with his book some time before this*). "God is the State; the State is God."

GRANDPA. What's that?

PAUL. "God is the State; the State is God."

GRANDPA. Who says that?

PAUL. Trotzky.

GRANDPA. Well, that's all right — I thought *you* said it.

ED. It's nice for printing, you know. Good and short. (*He reaches into the type case.*) G — O — D — space — I — S — space — T — H — E

[*The sound of the outer door closing, and Alice Sycamore enters the room. A lovely, fresh young girl of about twenty-two. She is plainly Grandpa's granddaughter, but there is something that sets her apart from the rest of the family. For one thing, she is in daily contact with the world; in addition, she seems to have escaped the tinge of mild insanity that pervades the rest of them. But she is a Sycamore for all that, and her devotion and love for them are plainly apparent. At the moment she is in a small nervous flutter, but she is doing her best to conceal it.*]

ALICE (*as she makes the rounds, kissing her grandfather, her father, her mother*). And so the beautiful princess came into the palace, and kissed her mother, and her father, and her grandfather — hi, Grandpa — and what do you think? They turned into the Sycamore family. Surprised?

ESSIE (*examining Alice's dress*). Oh, Alice, I like it. It's new, isn't it?

PENNY. Looks nice and summery.

ESSIE. Where'd you get it?

ALICE. Oh, I took a walk during lunch hour.

GRANDPA. You've been taking a lot of walks lately. That's the second new dress this week.

ALICE. Oh, I just like to brighten up the office once in a while. I'm known as the Kay Francis[6] of Kirby & Co. . . . Well, what's new around here? In the way of plays, snakes, ballet dancing or fireworks. Dad, I'll bet you've been down in that cellar all day.

PAUL. Huh?

PENNY. I'm going back to the war play, Alice.

ESSIE. Ed, play Alice that Beethoven thing you wrote. Listen, Alice.

[*Like a shot Ed is at the xylophone again, Essie up on her toes.*]

[*Grandpa, meanwhile, has unearthed his stamp album*

---

[6] **Kay Francis** (1903–1968): glamorous movie actress of the thirties, who wore clothes beautifully and often appeared on the lists of best-dressed women.

from under a pile of oddments in the corner and is now busy with his magnifying glass.]

GRANDPA. Do you know that you can mail a letter all the way from Nicaragua for two pesetos?

PENNY (*meanwhile dramatically reading one of her own deathless lines*). "Kenneth, my virginity is a priceless thing to me."

ALICE (*finding it hard to break through all this*). Listen, people.... Listen. (*A break in the music; she gets a scattered sort of attention.*) I'm not home to dinner. A young gentleman is calling for me.

ESSIE. Really? Who is it?

PENNY. Well, isn't that nice?

ALICE (*with quiet humor*). I did everything possible to keep him from coming here, but he's calling for me.

PENNY. Why don't you both stay to dinner?

ALICE. No, I want him to take you in easy doses. I've tried to prepare him a little, but don't make it any worse than you can help. Don't read him any plays, mother, and don't let a snake bite him, Grandpa, because I like him. And I wouldn't dance for him, Essie, because we're going to the Monte Carlo ballet tonight.

GRANDPA. Can't do *anything*. Who *is* he — President of the United States?

ALICE. No, he's vice-president of Kirby & Co. Mr. Anthony Kirby, Jr.

ESSIE. The Boss's son?

PENNY. Well!

ALICE. The Boss's son. Just like the movies.

ESSIE. That explains the new dresses.

ED. And not being home to dinner for three weeks.

ALICE. Why, you're wonderful!

PENNY (*all aglow*). Are you going to marry him?

ALICE. Oh, of course. Tonight! Meanwhile I have to go up and put on my wedding dress.

ESSIE. Is he good-looking?

ALICE (*vainly consulting her watch*). Yes, in a word. Oh dear! What time is it?

PENNY. I don't know. Anybody know what time it is?

PAUL. Mr. De Pinna might know.

ED. It was about five o'clock a couple of hours ago.

ALICE. Oh, I ought to know better than to ask you people. . . . Will you let me know the minute he comes, please?

PENNY. Of course, Alice.

ALICE. Yes, I know, but I mean the *minute* he comes.

PENNY. Why, of course. (*Alice looks apprehensively from one to the other; then disappears up the stairs.*) Well, what do you think of that?

GRANDPA. She seems to like him, if you ask me.

ESSIE. I should say so. She's got it bad.

PENNY. Wouldn't it be wonderful if she married him? We could have the wedding right in this room.

PAUL. Now, wait a minute, Penny. This is the first time he's ever called for the girl.

PENNY. You only called for me once.

PAUL. Young people are different nowadays.

ESSIE. Oh, I don't know. Look at Ed and me. He came to dinner *once* and just stayed.

PENNY. Anyhow, I think it's wonderful. I'll bet he's crazy about her. It must be he that's been taking her out every night. (*The doorbell rings.*) There he is! Never mind, Rheba, I'll answer it. (*She is fluttering to the door.*) Now remember what Alice said, and be *very* nice to him.

GRANDPA (*rising*). All right — let's take a look at him.

PENNY (*at the front door; milk and honey in her voice*). Well! Welcome to our little home! I'm Alice's mother. Do come right in! Here we are! (*She reappears in the archway, piloting the stranger.*) This is Grandpa, and that's Alice's father, and Alice's sister, and her husband, Ed Carmichael. (*The family all give courteous little nods and smiles as they are introduced.*) Well! Now give me your hat and make yourself right at home.

THE MAN. I'm afraid you must be making a mistake.

PENNY. How's that?

THE MAN. My card.

PENNY (*reading*). "Wilbur C. Henderson. Internal Revenue Department."

HENDERSON. That's right.

GRANDPA. What can we do for you?

HENDERSON. Does a Mr. Martin Vanderhof live here?

GRANDPA. Yes, sir. That's me.

HENDERSON (*all milk and honey*). Well, Mr. Vanderhof, the Government wants to talk to you about a little matter of income tax.

PENNY. Income tax?

HENDERSON. Do you mind if I sit down?

GRANDPA. No, no. Just go right ahead.

HENDERSON (*settling himself*). Thank you.

[*From above stairs the voice of Alice floats down.*]

ALICE. Mother! Is that Mr. Kirby?

PENNY (*going to the stairs*). No. No, it isn't, darling. It's — an internal something or other. (*To Mr. Henderson*) Pardon me.

HENDERSON (*pulling a sheaf of papers from his pocket*). We've written you several letters about this, Mr. Vanderhof, but have not had any reply.

GRANDPA. Oh, that's what those letters were.

ESSIE. I told you they were from the Government.

[*Mr. De Pinna comes up from the cellar, bearing a couple of giant firecrackers. He pauses as he sees a stranger.*]

DE PINNA. Oh, pardon me.

PAUL. Yes, Mr. De Pinna?

DE PINNA. These things are not going off, Mr. Sycamore. Look. (*He prepares to apply a match to one of them, as a startled income-tax man nearly has a conniption fit. But Paul is too quick for him*)

PAUL. Ah — not here, Mr. De Pinna. Grandpa's busy.

DE PINNA. Oh. (*Mr. De Pinna and Paul hurry into the hall with their firecrackers.*)

HENDERSON (*now that order has been restored*). According to our records, Mr. Vanderhof, you have never paid an income tax.

GRANDPA. That's right.

HENDERSON. Why not?

GRANDPA. I don't believe in it.

HENDERSON. Well — you own property, don't you?

GRANDPA. Yes, sir.

HENDERSON. And you receive a yearly income from it?

GRANDPA. I do.

HENDERSON. Of — (*he consults his records*) — between three and four thousand dollars.

GRANDPA. About that.

HENDERSON. You've been receiving it for years.

GRANDPA. I have. 1901, if you want the exact date.

HENDERSON. Well, the Government is only concerned from 1914 on. That's when the income tax started.

GRANDPA. Well?

HENDERSON. Well — it seems, Mr. Vanderhof, that you owe the Government twenty-two years' back income tax.

ED. Wait a minute! You can't go back that far — that's outlawed.

HENDERSON (*calmly regarding him*). What's *your* name?

ED. What difference does that make?

HENDERSON. Ever file an income tax return?

ED. No, sir.

HENDERSON. What was your income last year?

ED. Ah — twenty-eight dollars and fifty cents, wasn't it, Essie?

[*Essie gives quick assent; the income tax man dismisses the whole matter with an impatient wave of the hand and returns to bigger game.*]

HENDERSON. Now, Mr. Vanderhof, you know there's quite a penalty for not filing an income tax return.

PENNY. Penalty?

GRANDPA. Look, Mr. Henderson, let me ask you something.

HENDERSON. Well?

GRANDPA. Suppose I pay you this money — mind you, I don't say I'm going to do it — but just for the sake of argument — what's the Government going to do with it?

HENDERSON. How do you mean?

GRANDPA. Well, what do I get for my money? If I go into Macy's and buy something, there it *is* — I see it. What's the Government give me?

HENDERSON. Why, the Government gives you everything. It protects you.

GRANDPA. What from?

HENDERSON. Well — invasion. Foreigners that might come over here and take everything you've got.

GRANDPA. Oh, I don't think they're going to do that.

HENDERSON. If you didn't pay an income tax, they would. How do you think the Government keeps up the Army and Navy? All those battleships . . . .

GRANDPA. Last time we used battleships was in the Spanish-American War, and what did we get out of it? Cuba — and we gave that back. I wouldn't mind paying if it were something sensible.

HENDERSON (*beginning to get annoyed*). Well, what about Congress, and the Supreme Court, and the President? We've got to pay *them*, don't we?

GRANDPA (*ever so calmly*). Not with my money — no, sir.

HENDERSON (*furious*). Now wait a minute! I'm not here to argue with you. All I know is that you haven't paid an income tax and you've got to pay it!

GRANDPA. They've got to show me.

HENDERSON (*yelling*). We *don't* have to show you! I just told you! All those buildings down in Washington, and Interstate Commerce, and the Constitution!

GRANDPA. The Constitution was paid for long ago. And Interstate Commerce — what *is* Interstate Commerce, anyhow?

HENDERSON (*with murderous calm*). There are forty-eight states — see? And if there weren't Interstate Commerce, nothing could go from one state to another. See?

GRANDPA. Why not? They got fences?

HENDERSON. No, they haven't got fences! They've got *laws*! . . . My God, I never came across anything like this before!

GRANDPA. Well, I might pay about seventy-five dollars, but that's all it's worth.

HENDERSON. You'll pay every cent of it, like everybody else!

ED (*who has lost interest*). Listen, Essie — listen to this a minute.

[*The xylophone again; Essie goes into her dance.*]

HENDERSON (*going right ahead, battling against the music*). And let me tell you something else! You'll go to jail if you don't pay, do you hear that? There's a law, and if you think you're bigger than the law, you've got another think coming!

You'll hear from the United States Government, that's
all I can say! (*He is backing out of the room.*)
GRANDPA (*quietly*). Look out for those snakes.
HENDERSON (*jumping*). Jesus!

[*Out in the hall, and not more than a foot or two behind
Mr. Henderson, the firecracker boys are now ready to
test that little bomber. It goes off with a terrific detona-
tion, and Mr. Henderson jumps a full foot. He wastes
no time at all in getting out of there.*]

PAUL (*coming back into the room*). How did that sound to
you folks?
GRANDPA (*quite judicially*). I liked it.
PENNY. My goodness, he was mad, wasn't he?
GRANDPA. Oh, it wasn't his fault. It's just that the whole
thing is so silly.
PENNY (*suddenly finding herself with a perfectly good
Panama in her hand*). He forgot his hat.
GRANDPA. What size is it?
PENNY (*peering into its insides*). Seven and an eighth.
GRANDPA. Just right for me.
DE PINNA. Who was that fellow, anyhow?

[*Again the doorbell*]

PENNY. This *must* be Mr. Kirby.
PAUL. Better make sure this time.
PENNY. Yes, I will. (*She disappears.*)
ESSIE. I hope he's good-looking.
PENNY (*heard at the door*). How do you do?
A MAN'S VOICE. Good evening.
PENNY (*taking no chances*). Is this Mr. Anthony Kirby, Jr.?
TONY. Yes.
PENNY (*giving her all*). Well, Mr. Kirby, come right in! We've
been expecting you. Come right in! (*They come into sight;
Penny expansively addresses the family.*) This is *really*
Mr. Kirby! Now, I'm Alice's mother, and that's *Mr.* Syca-
more, and Alice's grandfather, and her sister Essie, and
Essie's husband. (*There are a few mumbled greetings.*)
There! Now you know *all* of us, Mr. Kirby. Give me your
hat and make yourself right at home.

[*Tony Kirby comes a few steps into the room. He is a personable young man, not long out of Yale, and, as we will presently learn, even more recently out of Cambridge. Although he fits all the physical requirements of a Boss's son, his face has something of the idealist in it. All in all, a very nice young man*]

TONY. How do you do?

[*Again the voice of the vigilant Alice floats down from upstairs. "Is that Mr. Kirby, Mother?"*]

PENNY (*shouting up the stairs*). Yes, Alice. He's *lovely!*
ALICE (*aware of storm signals*). I'll be right down.
PENNY. Do sit down, Mr. Kirby.
TONY. Thank you. (*A glance at the dinner table*) I hope I'm not keeping you from dinner?
GRANDPA. No, no. Have a tomato?
TONY. No, thank you.
PENNY (*producing the candy-filled skull*) How about a piece of candy?
TONY (*eyeing the container*). Ah — no, thanks.
PENNY. Oh, I forgot to introduce Mr. De Pinna. This is Mr. De Pinna, Mr. Kirby.

[*An exchange of "How do you do's?"*]

DE PINNA. Wasn't I reading about your father in the newspaper the other day? Didn't he get indicted or something?
TONY (*smiling*). Hardly that. He just testified before the Securities Commission.
DE PINNA. Oh.
PENNY (*sharply*). Yes, of course. I'm sure there was nothing crooked about it, Mr. De Pinna. As a matter of fact — (*she is now addressing Tony*) — Alice has often told us what a lovely man your father is.
TONY. Well, I know father couldn't get along without Alice. She knows more about the business than any of us.
ESSIE. You're awful young, Mr. Kirby, aren't you, to be vice-president of a big place like that?
TONY. Well, you know what that means, vice-president. All I have is a desk with my name on it.
PENNY. Is that all? Don't you get any salary?

TONY (*with a laugh*). Well, a little. More than I'm worth, I'm afraid.

PENNY. Now you're just being modest.

GRANDPA. Sounds kind of dull to me — Wall Street. Do you like it?

TONY. Well, the hours are short. And I haven't been there very long.

GRANDPA. Just out of college, huh?

TONY. Well, I knocked around for a while first. Just sort of had fun.

GRANDPA. What did you do? Travel?

TONY. For a while. Then I went to Cambridge for a year.

GRANDPA (*nodding*). England.

TONY. That's right.

GRANDPA. Say, what's an English commencement like? Did you see any?

TONY. Oh, very impressive.

GRANDPA. They are, huh?

TONY. Anyhow, now the fun's over, and — I'm facing the world.

PENNY. You've certainly got a good start, Mr. Kirby. Vice-president, and a rich father.

TONY. Well, that's hardly my fault.

PENNY (*brightly*). So now I suppose you're all ready to settle down and — get married.

PAUL. Come now, Penny, I'm sure Mr. Kirby knows his own mind.

PENNY. I wasn't making up his mind for him — was I, Mr. Kirby?

TONY. That's quite all right, Mrs. Sycamore.

PENNY (*to the others*). You see?

ESSIE. You mustn't rush him, Mother.

PENNY. Well, all I meant was he's bound to get married, and suppose the wrong girl gets him?

[*The descending Alice mercifully comes to Tony's rescue at this moment. Her voice is heard from the stairs.*]

ALICE. Well, here I am, a vision in white. (*She comes into the room — and very lovely indeed.*) Apparently you've had time to get acquainted.

PENNY. Oh, yes, indeed. We were just having a delightful talk about love and marriage.

ALICE. Oh, dear. (*She turns to Tony.*) I'm sorry. I came down as fast as I could.

RHEBA (*bringing a platter of sliced watermelon*). God damn those flies in the kitchen.... Oh, Miss Alice, you look beautiful. Where you going?

ALICE (*making the best of it*). I'm going out, Rheba.

RHEBA (*noticing Tony*). Stepping, huh?

[*The doorbell sounds.*]

ESSIE. That must be Kolenkhov.

ALICE (*uneasily*). I think we'd better go, Tony.

TONY. All right.

[*Before they can escape, however, Donald emerges from the kitchen, bearing a tray.*]

DONALD. Grandpa, you take cream on your cornflakes? I forget.

GRANDPA. Half and half, Donald.

[*The voice of Boris Kolenkhov looms from the outer door.*]

KOLENKHOV. Ah, my little Rhebishka!

RHEBA (*with a scream of laughter*). Yassuh, Mr. Kolenkhov!

KOLENKHOV. I am so hungry I could even eat my little Rhebishka! (*He appears in the archway, his great arm completely encircling the delighted Rheba. Mr. Kolenkhov is one of Rheba's pets, and if you like Russians he might be one of yours. He is enormous, hairy, loud, and very, very Russian. His appearance in the archway still further traps Alice and Tony.*) Grandpa, what do you think? I have had a letter from Russia! The Second Five-Year Plan is a failure![7] (*He lets out a laugh that shakes the rafters.*)

ESSIE. I practiced today, Mr. Kolenkhov!

KOLENKHOV (*with a deep Russian bow*). My Pavlowa![8]

---

[7] **I have had ... a failure:** Kolenkhov is a refugee from Russia's Communist government. Since he despises Stalin, he is elated to hear — and eager to believe — the rumor that the second phase of Stalin's attempt to industrialize Russia has failed.

[8] **Pavlowa:** Anna Pavlova (1885–1931), Russia's greatest ballerina. Her name is misspelled to signal Kolenkhov's heavy accent.

(*Another bow*) Madame Sycamore!... My little Alice!
(*He kisses her hand.*) Never have I seen you look so
magnificent.

ALICE. Thank you, Mr. Kolenkhov. Tony, this is Mr. Kolenkhov, Essie's dancing teacher. Mr. Kirby.

TONY. How do you do?

[*A click of the heels and a bow from Kolenkhov*]

ALICE (*determined, this time*). And now we really *must* go.
Excuse us, Mr. Kolenkhov — we're going to the Monte
Carlo ballet.

KOLENKHOV (*at the top of his tremendous voice*). The
Monte Carlo ballet! It *stinks!*

ALICE (*panicky now*). Yes. ... Well — good-bye, everybody.
Good-bye.

TONY. Good-bye. I'm so glad to have met you all.

[*A chorus of answering "Good-byes" from the family.
The young people are gone.*]

KOLENKHOV (*still furious*). The Monte Carlo ballet!

PENNY. Isn't Mr. Kirby lovely? ... Come on, everybody!
Dinner's ready!

ED (*pulling up a chair*). I thought he was a nice fellow,
didn't you?

ESSIE. Mm. And so good-looking.

PENNY. And he had such nice manners. Did you notice,
Paul? Did you notice his manners?

PAUL. I certainly did. You were getting pretty personal with
him.

PENNY. Oh, now, Paul. ... Anyhow, he's a very nice young
man.

DE PINNA (*as he seats himself*). He looks kind of like a cousin
of mine.

KOLENKHOV. Bakst! Diaghileff![9] *Then* you had the *ballet!*

PENNY. I think if they get married here I'll put the altar right
where the snakes are. You wouldn't mind, Grandpa, would
you?

---

[9] **Bakst** (bäkst)! **Diaghileff** (dē·äg'ə lef'): Leon Nikolaevich Bakst (1866?–
1924), a painter, and Sergei Pavlovich Diaghileff (1872–1929), a ballet
producer, were co-founders of Diaghileff's Russian Ballet. (Pavlova was
one of the renowned dancers who performed with this company.)

ESSIE. Oh, they'll want to get married in a church. His family and everything.

GRANDPA (*tapping on a plate for silence*). Quiet, everybody! Quiet! (*They are immediately silent — grace is about to be pronounced. Grandpa pauses a moment for heads to bow, then raises his eyes heavenward. He clears his throat and proceeds to say grace.*) Well, Sir, we've been getting along pretty good for quite a while now, and we're certainly much obliged. Remember, all we ask is just to go along and be happy in our own sort of way. Of course we want to keep our health, but as far as anything else is concerned, we'll leave it to You. Thank You. (*The heads come up as Rheba comes through the door with a steaming platter.*) So the Second Five-Year Plan is a failure, eh, Kolenkhov?

KOLENKHOV (*booming*). Catastrophic! (*He reaches across the table and spears a piece of bread. The family, too, is busily plunging in.*)

CURTAIN

SCENE 2

Late the same night. The house is in darkness save for a light in the hall.

Somewhere in the back regions an accordion is being played. Then quiet. Then the stillness of the night is suddenly broken again by a good loud BANG! from the cellar. Somewhere in the nether regions, one of the Sycamores is still at work.

Once more all is quiet, then the sound of a key in the outer door. The voices of Alice and Tony drift through.

ALICE. I could see them dance every night of the week. I think they're marvelous.

TONY. They are, aren't they? But of course just walking inside *any* theater gives *me* a thrill.

ALICE (*as they come into sight in the hallway*). It's been *so* lovely, Tony. I hate to have it over.

TONY. Oh, is it over? Do I have to go right away?

ALICE. Not if you don't want to.

TONY. I don't.

ALICE. Would you like a cold drink?

TONY. Wonderful.

ALICE (*pausing to switch on the light*). I'll see what's in the icebox. Want to come along?

TONY. I'd follow you to the ends of the earth.

ALICE. Oh, just the kitchen is enough. (*They go out. A pause, a ripple of gay laughter from the kitchen, then they return. Alice is carrying a couple of glasses, Tony brings two bottles of ginger ale and an opener.*) Lucky you're not hungry, Mr. K. An icebox full of cornflakes. That gives you a rough idea of the Sycamores.

TONY (*working away with the opener*). Of course, why they make these bottle openers for Singer midgets I never *was* able to — ah! (*As the bottle opens*) All over my coat.

ALICE. I'll take mine in a glass, if you don't mind.

TONY (*pouring*). There you are. A foaming beaker.

ALICE. Anyhow, it's cold.

TONY (*pouring his own*). Now if you'll please be seated, I'd like to offer a toast.

ALICE (*settling herself*). We are seated.

TONY. Miss Sycamore — (*he raises his glass on high*) — to you.

ALICE. Thank you, Mr. Kirby. (*Lifting her own glass*) To you. (*They both drink.*)

TONY (*happily*). I wouldn't trade one minute of this evening for — all the rice in China.

ALICE. Really?

TONY. Cross my heart.

ALICE (*a little sigh of contentment. Then shyly*). Is there much rice in China?

TONY. Terrific. Didn't you read *The Good Earth*? (*She laughs. They are silent for a moment.*) I suppose I ought to go.

ALICE. Is it very late?

TONY (*looks at his watch*). Very. (*Alice gives a little nod. Time doesn't matter.*) I don't want to go.

ALICE. I don't want you to.

TONY. All right, I won't. (*Silence again*) When do you get your vacation?

ALICE. Last two weeks in August.

TONY. I might take mine then, too.

ALICE. Really?

TONY. What are you going to do?

ALICE. I don't know. I hadn't thought much about it.

TONY. Going away, do you think?

ALICE. I might not. I like the city in the summertime.

TONY. I do too.

ALICE. But you always go up to Maine, don't you?

TONY. Why — yes, but I'm sure I *would* like the city in the summertime. That is, I'd like it if — Oh, you know what I mean, Alice. I'd love it if *you* were here.

ALICE. Well — it'd be nice if you were here, Tony.

TONY. You know what you're saying, don't you?

ALICE. What?

TONY. That you'd rather spend the summer with me than anybody else.

ALICE. It looks that way, doesn't it?

TONY. Well, if it's true about the summer, how would you feel about — the winter?

ALICE (*seeming to weigh the matter*). Yes. I'd — like that too.

TONY (*tremulous*). Then comes spring — and autumn. If you could — see your way clear about those, Miss Sycamore. . . .

ALICE (*again a little pause*). Yes.

TONY. I guess that's the whole year. We haven't forgotten anything, have we?

ALICE. No.

TONY. Well, then —

[*Another pause; their eyes meet. And at this moment, Penny is heard from the stairway.*]

PENNY. Is that you, Alice? What time is it? (*She comes into the room, wrapped in a bathrobe.*) Oh! (*In sudden embarrassment*) Excuse me, Mr. Kirby. I had no idea — that is, I — (*she senses the situation*) — I didn't mean to interrupt anything.

TONY. Not at all, Mrs. Sycamore.

ALICE (*quietly*). No, Mother.

PENNY. I just came down for a manuscript — (*fumbling at*

her table) — then you can go right ahead. Ah, here it is. "Sex Takes a Holiday." Well — good night, Mr. Kirby.

TONY. Good night, Mrs. Sycamore.

PENNY. Oh, I think you can call me Penny, don't you, Alice? At least I hope so.

[*With a little laugh she vanishes up the stairs. Before Penny's rippling laugh quite dies, BANG! from the cellar. Tony jumps.*]

ALICE (*quietly*). It's all right, Tony. That's Father.

TONY. This time of night?

ALICE (*ominously*). Any time of night. Any time of *day.*

[*She stands silent. In the pause, Tony gazes at her fondly.*]

TONY. You're more beautiful, more lovely, more adorable than anyone else in the whole world.

ALICE (*as he starts to embrace her*). Don't, Tony. I can't.

TONY. What?

ALICE. I can't, Tony.

TONY. My dear, just because your mother — all mothers are like that, Alice, and Penny's a darling. You see, I'm even calling her Penny.

ALICE. I don't mean that. (*She faces him squarely.*) Look, Tony. This is something I should have said a long time ago, but I didn't have the courage. I let myself be swept away because — because I loved you so.

TONY. Darling!

ALICE. No, wait, Tony. I want to make it clear to you. You're of a different world — a whole different kind of people. Oh, I don't mean money or socially — that's too silly. But your family and mine — it just wouldn't work, Tony. It just wouldn't work.

[*Again an interruption. This time it is Ed and Essie, returning from the neighborhood movie. We hear their voices at the door, deep in an argument. Ed: "All right, have it your way. She can't dance. That's why they pay her all that money — because she can't dance." And then Essie: "Well, I don't call that dancing, what she does."*]

[*They come into sight.*]

ESSIE. Oh, hello. (*There is an exchange of greetings, a note of constraint in Alice's voice. But Essie goes right ahead.*) Look! What do *you* think? Ed and I just saw Fred Astaire and Ginger Rogers. Do you think she can dance, Mr. Kirby?

TONY (*mildly taken aback by this*). Why, yes — I always thought so.

ESSIE. What does she do, anyhow? Now, look — you're Fred Astaire and I'm Ginger Rogers. (*She drapes herself against Tony, à la Ginger Rogers.*)

ALICE. Essie, please.

ESSIE. I just want to use him for a minute.... Look, Mr. Kirby — (*Her arms go round his neck, her cheek against his.*)

ALICE (*feeling that it's time to take action*). Essie, you're just as good as Ginger Rogers. We all agree.

ESSIE (*triumphantly*). You see, Ed?

ED. Yeh.... Come on, Essie — we're butting in here.

ESSIE. Oh, they've been together all evening.... Good night, Mr. Kirby.

[*An exchange of good nights — it looks as though the Carmichaels are really going upstairs before the whole thing gets too embarrassing. Then Ed turns casually to Essie in the doorway.*]

ED. Essie, did you ask Grandpa about us having a baby?

ESSIE (*as they ascend the stairs*). Yes — he said go right ahead. —

ALICE (*when they are gone*). You see? That's what it would be like, always.

TONY. But I didn't mind that. Besides, darling, we're not going to live with our families. It's just you and I.

ALICE. No, it isn't — it's never quite that. I love them, Tony — I love them deeply. Some people could cut away, but I couldn't. I know they do rather strange things — I never know what to expect next — but they're gay, and they're fun, and — I don't know — there's a kind of nobility about them. That may sound silly, but I mean — the way they just don't care about things that other people give their whole lives to. They're — really wonderful, Tony.

TONY. Alice, you talk as though only you could understand them. That's not true. Why, I fell in love with them tonight.

ALICE. But your family, Tony. I'd want *you*, and everything about you, everything about *me*, to be — one. I couldn't start out with a part of me that you didn't share, and part of you that I didn't share. Unless we were all one — you, and *your* mother and father — I'd be miserable. And they never can be, Tony — I know it. They couldn't be.

TONY. Alice, every family has got curious little traits. What of it? My father raises orchids at ten thousand dollars a bulb. Is that sensible? My mother believes in spiritualism. That's just as bad as your mother writing plays, isn't it?

ALICE. It goes deeper, Tony. Your mother believes in spiritualism because it's fashionable. And your father raises orchids because he can afford to. My mother writes plays because eight years ago a typewriter was delivered here by mistake.

TONY. Darling, what *of* it?

ALICE. And look at Grandpa. Thirty-five years ago he just quit business one day. He started up to his office in the elevator and came right down again. He just stopped. He could have been a rich man, but he said it took too much time. So for thirty-five years he's just collected snakes and gone to circuses and commencements. It never occurs to any of them —

[*As if to prove her point, they are suddenly interrupted at this moment by the entrance of Donald from the kitchen. It is a Donald who has plainly not expected to encounter midnight visitors, for he is simply dressed in a long white nightgown and a somewhat shorter bathrobe — a costume that permits a generous expanse of white nightshirt down around the legs, and, below that, a couple of very black shins. His appearance, incidentally, explains where all that music had been coming from, for an accordion is slung over his shoulder.*]

DONALD (*surprised, but not taken aback*). Oh, excuse me. I didn't know you folks was in here.

ALICE (*resigned*). It's all right, Donald.

DONALD. Rheba kind of fancied some candy, and — (*his

gaze is roaming the room) oh, there it is. (*He picks up Penny's skull, if you know what we mean.*) You-all don't want it, do you?

ALICE. No, Donald. Go right ahead.

DONALD. Thanks. (*He feels that the occasion calls for certain amenities.*) Have a nice evening?

ALICE. Yes, Donald.

DONALD. Nice dinner?

ALICE (*restraining herself*). Yes, Donald.

DONALD. The ballet nice?

ALICE (*entirely too quietly*). Yes, Donald.

DONALD (*summing it all up*). That's nice. (*He goes — and Alice bursts forth.*)

ALICE. Now! Now do you see what I mean? Could you explain Donald to your father? Could you explain Grandpa? You couldn't, Tony, you couldn't! I should have known! I did know! I love you, Tony, but I love them too! And it's no use, Tony! It's no use! (*She is weeping now in spite of herself.*)

TONY (*quietly*). There's only one thing you've said that matters — that makes any sense at all. You love me.

ALICE. But, Tony, I know so well. . . .

TONY. My darling, don't you think other people have had the same problem? Everybody's got a family.

ALICE (*through her tears*). But not like mine.

TONY. That doesn't stop people who love each other. . . . Darling! Darling, won't you trust me, and go on loving me, and forget everything else?

ALICE. How can I?

TONY. Because nothing can keep us apart. You know that. You must know it. Just as I know it. (*He takes her in his arms.*) They want you to be happy, don't they? They *must.*

ALICE. Of course they do. But they can't change, Tony. I wouldn't want them to change.

TONY. They won't have to change. They're charming, lovable people, just as they are. You're worrying about something that may never come up.

ALICE. Oh, Tony, am I?

TONY. All that matters right now is that we love each other.

That's right, isn't it?

ALICE (*whispering*). Yes.

TONY. Well, then!

ALICE (*in his arms*). Tony, Tony!

TONY. Now! I'd like to see a little gayety around here. Young gentleman calling, and getting engaged and everything.

ALICE (*smiling up into his face*). What do I say?

TONY. Well, first you thank the young man for getting engaged to you.

ALICE. Thank you, Mr. Kirby, for getting engaged to me.

TONY. And then you tell him what it was about him that first took your girlish heart.

ALICE. The back of your head.

TONY. Huh?

ALICE. Uh-huh. It wasn't your charm, and it wasn't your money — it was the back of your head. I just happened to like it.

TONY. What happened when I turned around?

ALICE. Oh, I got used to it after a while.

TONY. I see. . . . Oh, Alice, think of it. We're pretty lucky, aren't we?

ALICE. I know that *I* am. The luckiest girl in the world.

TONY. I'm not exactly unlucky myself.

ALICE. It's wonderful, isn't it?

TONY. Yes. . . . Lord, but I'm happy.

ALICE. Are you, Tony?

TONY. Terribly. . . . And now — good night, my dear. Until tomorrow.

ALICE. Good night.

TONY. Isn't it wonderful we work in the same office? Otherwise I'd be hanging around *here* all day.

ALICE. Won't it be funny in the office tomorrow — seeing each other and just going on as though nothing had happened?

TONY. Thank God I'm vice-president. I can dictate to you all day. "Dear Miss Sycamore: I love you, I love you, I love you."

ALICE. Oh, darling! You're such a fool.

TONY (*an arm about her as he starts toward the hallway*).

Why don't you meet me in the drugstore in the morning —
before you go up to the office? I'll have millions of things
to say to you by then.

ALICE. All right.

TONY. And then lunch, and then dinner tomorrow night.

ALICE. Oh, Tony! What will people say?

TONY. It's got to come out some time. In fact, if you know
a good housetop, I'd like to do a little shouting.

[*She laughs — a happy little ripple. They are out of
sight in the hallway by this time; their voices become
inaudible.*]

[*Paul, at this point, decides to call it a day down in the
cellar. He comes through the door, followed by Mr.
De Pinna. He is carrying a small metal container, filled
with powder.*]

PAUL. Yes, sir, Mr. De Pinna, we did a good day's work.

DE PINNA. That's what. Five hundred Black Panthers, three
hundred Willow Trees, and eight dozen Junior Kiddie
Bombers.

[*Alice comes back from the hallway, still under the
spell of her love.*]

PAUL. Why, hello, Alice. You just come in?

ALICE (*softly*). No. No, I've been home quite a while.

PAUL. Have a nice evening? Say, I'd like you to take a look
at this new red fire we've got.

ALICE (*almost singing it*). I had a beautiful evening, Father.

PAUL. Will you turn out the lights, Mr. De Pinna? I want
Alice to get the full effect.

ALICE (*who hasn't heard a word*). What, Father?

PAUL. Take a look at this new red fire. It's beautiful. (*Mr.
De Pinna switches the lights out; Paul touches a match
to the powder. The red fire blazes, shedding a soft glow
over the room.*) There! What do you think of it? Isn't it
beautiful?

ALICE (*radiant; her face aglow, her voice soft*). Yes, Father.
Everything is beautiful. It's the most beautiful red fire
in the world! (*She rushes to him and throws her arms
about him, almost unable to bear her own happiness.*)

CURTAIN

QUESTIONS

1. Grandpa describes college graduates as those who "get their diplomas, and then about forty years later suddenly say, 'Where am I?'" What is Grandpa saying about education and self-knowledge?

2. When Alice asks the assembled family what time it is, no one has any idea. Why is that significant? What does it say about the relevance of time to the daily life of the Vanderhof family? Why is time less important to the Vanderhofs than to the outside world?

3. How does Alice differ from the rest of her family? How does she feel about them? Does Alice see any future conflicts?

4. How does Tony's family differ from Alice's?

ACT TWO

A week later, and the family has just risen from the dinner table. Two or three of them have drifted out of the room, but Grandpa and Paul still sit over their coffee cups.

There is, however, a newcomer in the room. Her name is Gay Wellington, and, as we will presently guess, she is an actress, a nymphomaniac,[10] *and a terrible souse. At the moment she sits with a gin bottle in one hand and a glass in the other and is having a darned good time. Hovering over her, script in hand, is a slightly worried Penny. Ed is watching the proceedings from somewhere in the vicinity of the printing press, and Donald, leisurely clearing the table, has paused to see if Miss Wellington can really swallow that one more drink of gin that she is about to tackle. She does, and another besides.*

Penny finally decides to make a try.

PENNY. I'm ready to read the play now, Miss Wellington, if you are.

---

[10] *nymphomaniac:* a woman with an uncontrollable sex drive.

GAY WELLINGTON. Just a minute, dearie — just a minute.

[*The gin again.*]

PENNY. The only thing is — I hope you won't mind my mentioning this, but — you don't drink when you're acting, do you, Miss Wellington? I'm just asking, of course.

GAY. I'm glad you brought it up. Once a play opens, I never touch a drop. Minute I enter a stage door, this bottle gets put away till intermission.

GRANDPA (*who plainly has his doubts*). Have you been on the stage a long time, Miss Wellington?

GAY. All my life. I've played everything. Ever see *Peg o' My Heart?*

GRANDPA. Yes, indeed.

GAY (*with that fine logic for which the inebriated brain is celebrated*). I saw it too. Great show. (*She staggers backwards a bit, but recovers herself just in time.*) My! Hot night, ain't it?

DONALD (*ever helpful*). Want me to open a window, Miss Wellington?

GAY. No, the hell with the weather. (*She takes a second look at the dusky Donald.*) Say, he's cute.

[*Rheba, who has entered just in time to overhear this, gives Gay a look that tells her in no uncertain terms to keep out of Harlem on dark nights. Then she stalks back into the kitchen, Donald close on her heels.*]

DONALD (*trying to explain it all*). She's just acting, Rheba. She don't mean anything.

PENNY. Well, any time you're ready, we can go up to my room and start. I thought I'd read the play up in my room.

GAY. All right, dearie, just a minute. (*She starts to pour one more drink, then suddenly her gaze becomes transfixed. She shakes her head as though to dislodge the image, then looks again, receives verification, and starts to pour the gin back into the bottle.*) When I see snakes it's time to lay down. (*She makes for a couch in the corner, and passes right out — cold.*)

PENNY. Oh, but those are real, Miss Wellington. They're Grandpa's.... Oh, dear! I hope she's not going to — (*Shaking her*) Miss Wellington! Miss Wellington!

ED. She's out like a light.

PAUL. Better let her sleep it off.

DONALD (*carrying the news into the kitchen*). Rheba, Miss Wellington just passed out.

[*From the nether recesses we hear Rheba's reaction — an emphatic "Good!"*]

PENNY. Do you think she'll be all right?

GRANDPA. Yes, but I wouldn't cast her in the religious play.

PENNY. Well, I suppose I'll just have to wait. I wonder if I shouldn't cover her up.

GRANDPA. Next time you meet an actress on the top of a bus, Penny, I think I'd *send* her the play, instead of bringing her home to read it.

ESSIE (*as Ed starts in with the printing press*). Ed, I wish you'd stop printing and take those Love Dreams around. They're out in the kitchen.

ED. I will. I just want to finish up these circulars.

ESSIE. Well, do that later, can't you? You've got to get back in time to play for me when Kolenkhov comes.

GRANDPA. Kolenkhov coming tonight?

ESSIE. Yes, tomorrow night's his night, but I had to change it on account of Alice.

GRANDPA. Oh! . . . Big doings around here tomorrow night, huh?

PENNY. Isn't it exciting? You know, I'm so nervous — you'd think it was me he was engaged to, instead of Alice.

ESSIE. What do you think they'll *be* like — his mother and father? . . . Ed, what are you doing *now?*

ED. Penny, did you see the new mask I made last night? (*He reveals a new side of his character by suddenly holding a homemade mask before his face.*) Guess who it is.

PENNY. Don't tell me now, Ed. Wait a minute . . . Cleopatra.

ED (*furious*). It's Mrs. Roosevelt. (*He goes into the kitchen.*)

[*Paul, meanwhile, has gone to a table in the corner of the room, from which he now brings a steel-like boat model, two or three feet high, puts it down on the floor, and proceeds to sit down beside it. From a large cardboard box, which he has also brought with him, he proceeds to take out additional pieces of steel and fit them into the model.*]

PAUL. You know, the nice thing about these Erector Sets, you can make so many different things with them. Last week it was the Empire State Building.

GRANDPA. What is it this week?

PAUL. The Queen Mary.

PENNY (*looking it over*). Hasn't got the right hat on. (*Ed comes in from the kitchen, bringing a pile of about a dozen candy boxes, neatly wrapped, and tied together for purposes of delivery.*)

ED (*as Mr. De Pinna comes in from the hall*). Look. Mr. De Pinna, would you open the door and see if there's a man standing in front of the house?

ESSIE. Why, what for?

ED. Well, the last two days, when I've been out delivering, I think a man's been following me.

ESSIE. Ed, you're crazy.

ED. No, I'm not. He follows me, and he stands and watches the house.

DE PINNA. Really? (*Striding out*) I'll take a look and see.

GRANDPA. I don't see what anybody would follow *you* for, Ed.

PENNY. Well, there's a lot of kidnapping going on, Grandpa.

GRANDPA. Yes, but not of Ed.

ED (*as Mr. De Pinna returns from the hall*). Well? Did you see him?

DE PINNA. There's nobody out there at all.

ED. You're sure?

DE PINNA. Positive. I just saw him walk away.

ED. You see? I told you.

ESSIE. Oh, it might have been anybody, walking along the street. Ed, will you hurry and get back?

ED (*picking up his boxes*). Oh, all right.

DE PINNA. Want to go down now, Mr. Sycamore, and finish packing up the fireworks?

PAUL (*putting the Queen Mary back on the table*). Yeh, we've got to take the stuff up to Mt. Vernon in the morning.

[*They go into the cellar. Simultaneously the voice of Alice, happily singing, is heard as she descends the stairs.*]

ALICE. Mother, may I borrow some paper? I'm making out a list for Rheba tomorrow night.

PENNY. Yes, dear. Here's some.

ALICE (*as she sights Miss Wellington*). Why, what happened to your actress friend? Is she giving a performance?

PENNY. No, she's not acting, Alice. She's really drunk.

ALICE. Essie, you're going to give Rheba the kitchen all day tomorrow, aren't you? Because she'll need it.

ESSIE. Of course, Alice. I'm going to start some Love Dreams now, so I'll be 'way ahead. (*She goes into the kitchen.*)

ALICE. Thanks, dear. . . . Look, Mother, I'm coming home at three o'clock tomorrow. Will you have everything down in the cellar by that time? The typewriter, and the snakes, and the xylophone, and the printing press : . . .

GRANDPA. And Miss Wellington.

ALICE. And Miss Wellington. That'll give me time to arrange the table and fix the flowers.

GRANDPA. The Kirbys are certainly going to get the wrong impression of this house.

ALICE. You'll *do* all that, won't you, Mother?

PENNY. Of course, dear.

ALICE. And I think we'd better have cocktails ready by seven-fifteen, in case they happen to come a little early. . . . I wonder if I ought to let Rheba cook the dinner. What do you think, Grandpa?

GRANDPA. Now, Alice, I wouldn't worry. From what I've seen of the boy I'm sure the Kirbys are very nice people, and if everything isn't so elaborate tomorrow night, it's all right too.

ALICE. Darling, I'm not trying to impress them, or pretend we're anything that we aren't. I just want everything to — go off well.

GRANDPA. No reason why it shouldn't, Alice.

PENNY. We're all going to do everything we can to make it a nice party.

ALICE. Oh, my darlings, I love you. You're the most wonderful family in the world, and I'm the happiest girl in the world. I didn't know anyone could *be* so happy. He's so wonderful, Grandpa. Why, just seeing him — you don't know what it does to me.

GRANDPA. Just seeing him. Just seeing him for lunch, and dinner, and until four o'clock in the morning, and at nine o'clock *next* morning you're at the office again and there he is. You just see him, huh?

ALICE. I don't care! I'm in love! (*She swings open the kitchen door.*) Rheba! Rheba! (*She goes into the kitchen.*)

GRANDPA. Nice, isn't it? Nice to see her so happy.

PENNY. I remember when I was engaged to Paul — how happy I was. And you know, I still feel that way.

GRANDPA. I know.... Nice the way Ed and Essie get along too, isn't it?

PENNY. And Donald and Rheba, even though they're *not* married.... Do you suppose Mr. De Pinna will ever marry anyone, Grandpa?

GRANDPA (*a gesture toward the couch*). Well, there's Miss Wellington.

PENNY. Oh, dear, I *wish* she'd wake up. If we're going to read the play tonight —

[*Mr. De Pinna comes up from the cellar, bringing along a rather large-sized unframed painting.*]

DE PINNA. Mrs. Sycamore, look what I found! (*He turns the canvas around, revealing a portrait of a somewhat lumpy discus thrower, in Roman costume — or was it Greek?*) Remember?

PENNY. Why, of course. It's my painting of you as the Discus Thrower. Look, Grandpa.

GRANDPA. I remember it. Say, you've gotten a little bald, haven't you, Mr. De Pinna?

DE PINNA (*running a hand over his completely hairless head*). Is it very noticeable?

PENNY. Well, it was a long time ago — just before I stopped painting. Let me see — that's eight years.

DE PINNA. Too bad you never finished it, Mrs. Sycamore.

PENNY. I always meant to finish it, Mr. De Pinna, but I just started to write a play one day and that was that. I never painted again.

GRANDPA. Just as well, too. *I* was going to have to strip next.

DE PINNA (*meditatively*). Who would have thought, that

day I came to deliver the ice, that I was going to stay here
for eight years?

GRANDPA. The milkman was here for five, just ahead of you.

DE PINNA. Why did he leave, anyhow? I forget.

GRANDPA. He didn't leave. He died.

PENNY. He was such a nice man. Remember the funeral,
Grandpa? We never knew his name and it was kind of
hard to get a certificate.

GRANDPA. What was the name we finally made up for him?

PENNY. Martin Vanderhof. We gave him *your* name.

GRANDPA. Oh, yes, I remember.

PENNY. It was a lovely thought, because otherwise he never
would have got all those flowers.

GRANDPA. Certainly was. And it didn't hurt *me* any. Not
bothered with mail any more, and I haven't had a telephone
call from that day to this. (*He catches an unwary fly and
drops it casually into the snake solarium.*)

PENNY. Yes, it was really a wonderful idea.

DE PINNA (*with the picture*). I wish you'd finish this sometime, Mrs. Sycamore. I'd kind of like to have it.

PENNY. You know what, Mr. De Pinna? I think I'll do some
work on it. Right tonight.

DE PINNA. Say! Will you?

[*The doorbell rings.*]

PENNY (*peering at the prostrate Gay*). I don't think she's
going to wake up anyhow. . . . Look, Mr. De Pinna! You
go down in the cellar and bring up the easel and get into
your costume. Is it still down there?

DE PINNA (*excited*). I think so! (*He darts into the cellar.*)

PENNY. Now, where did I put my palette and brushes?

[*She dashes up the stairs as the voice of Kolenkhov is
heard at the door, booming, of course.*]

KOLENKHOV. Rhebishka! My little Rhebishka!

RHEBA (*delighted, as usual*). Yassuh, Mr. Kolenkhov!

PENNY (*as she goes up the stairs*). Hello, Mr. Kolenkhov.
Essie's in the kitchen.

KOLENKHOV. Madame Sycamore, I greet you! (*His great arm
again encircling Rheba, he drags her protestingly into the*

room.) Tell me, Grandpa — what should I do about Rhebishka! I keep telling her she would make a great toe dancer, but she laughs only!

RHEBA (*breaking away*). No, suh! I couldn't get up on my toes, Mr. Kolenkhov! I got corns! (*She goes into the kitchen.*)

KOLENKHOV (*calling after her*). Rhebishka, you could wear diamonds! (*Suddenly he sights the portrait of Mr. De Pinna.*) What is that?

GRANDPA (*who has taken up his stamp album again*). It's a picture of Mr. De Pinna. Penny painted it.

KOLENKHOV (*summing it up*). It stinks.

GRANDPA. I know. (*He indicates the figure on the couch.*) How do you like that?

KOLENKHOV (*peering over*). What is *that?*

GRANDPA. She's an actress. Friend of Penny's.

KOLENKHOV. She is drunk — no?

GRANDPA. She is drunk — yes. . . . How are *you,* Kolenkhov?

KOLENKHOV. Magnificent! Life is chasing around inside of me, like a squirrel.

GRANDPA. 'Tis, huh? . . . What's new in Russia? Any more letters from your friend in Moscow?

KOLENKHOV. I have just heard from him. I saved for you the stamps. (*He hands it over.*)

GRANDPA (*receiving it with delight*). Thanks, Kolenkhov.

KOLENKHOV. They have sent him to Siberia.

GRANDPA. That so? How's he like it?

KOLENKHOV. He has escaped. He has escaped and gone back to Moscow. He will get them yet, if they do not get him. The Soviet Government! I could take the whole Soviet Government and — grrah! (*He crushes Stalin and all in one great paw, just as Essie comes in from the kitchen.*)

ESSIE. I'm sorry I'm late, Mr. Kolenkhov. I'll get into my dancing clothes right away.

KOLENKHOV. Tonight you will really work, Pavlowa. (*As Essie goes up the stairs*) Tonight we will take something new.

GRANDPA. Essie making any progress, Kolenkhov?

KOLENKHOV (*first making elaborately sure that Essie is gone*). Confidentially, she stinks.

GRANDPA. Well, as long as she's having fun. . . .

[*Donald ambles in from the kitchen, chuckling.*]

DONALD. You sure do tickle Rheba, Mr. Kolenkhov. She's laughing her head off out there.

KOLENKHOV. She is a great woman. . . . Donald, what do you think of the Soviet Government?

DONALD. The what, Mr. Kolenkhov?

KOLENKHOV. I withdraw the question. What do you think of *this* Government?

DONALD. Oh, I like it fine. I'm on relief, you know.

KOLENKHOV. Oh, yes. And you like it?

DONALD. Yassuh, it's fine. Only thing is you got to go round to the place every week and collect it, and sometimes you got to stand in line pretty near half an hour. Government ought to be run better than that — don't you think, Grandpa?

GRANDPA (*as he fishes an envelope out of his pocket*). Government ought to stop sending me letters. Want me to be at the United States Marshal's office Tuesday morning at ten o'clock.

KOLENKHOV (*peering at the letter*). Ah! Income tax! They have got you, Grandpa.

GRANDPA. Mm. I'm supposed to give 'em a lot of money so as to keep Donald on relief.

DONALD. You don't say, Grandpa? You going to pay it now?

GRANDPA. That's what they want.

DONALD. You mean I can come right *here* and get it instead of standing in that line?

GRANDPA. No, Donald. You will have to waste a full half hour of your time every week.

DONALD. Well, I don't like it. It breaks up my week. (*He goes into the kitchen.*)

KOLENKHOV. He should have been in Russia when the Revolution came. Then he would have stood in line — a bread line. (*He turns to Grandpa.*) Ah, Grandpa, what they have done to Russia. Think of it! The Grand Duchess Olga Katrina, a cousin of the Czar, she is a waitress in Childs' restaurant! I ordered baked beans from her only yesterday. It broke my heart. A crazy world, Grandpa.

GRANDPA. Oh, the world's not so crazy, Kolenkhov. It's the people *in* it. Life's pretty simple if you just relax.

KOLENKHOV. How can you relax in times like these?

GRANDPA. Well, if they'd relaxed there wouldn't *be* times like these. That's just my point. Life is simple and kind of beautiful if you let it come to you. But the trouble is, people forget that. I know I did. I was right in the thick of it — fighting, and scratching, and clawing. Regular jungle. One day it just kind of struck me. I wasn't having any fun.

KOLENKHOV. So you did what?

GRANDPA. Just relaxed. Thirty-five years ago, that was. And I've been a happy man ever since.

[*From somewhere or other Grandpa has brought one of those colored targets that one buys at Schwartz's. He now hangs it up on the cellar door, picks up a handful of feathered darts, and carefully throws one at the target.*]

[*At the same time Alice passes through the room, en route from kitchen to the upstairs region.*]

ALICE. Good evening, Mr. Kolenkhov.

KOLENKHOV (*bowing low over her head*). Ah, Miss Alice! I have not seen you to present my congratulations. May you be very happy and have many children. That is my prayer for you.

ALICE. Thank you, Mr. Kolenkhov. That's quite a thought. (*Singing gayly, she goes up the stairs.*)

KOLENKHOV (*looking after her*). Ah, love! That is all that is left in the world, Grandpa.

GRANDPA. Yes, but there's plenty of that.

KOLENKHOV. And soon Stalin will take that away, too. I tell you, Grandpa —

[*He stops as Penny comes down the stairs — a living example of what the well-dressed artist should wear. She has on an artist's smock over her dress, a flowing black tie, and a large black velvet tam-o'-shanter, worn at a rakish angle. She carries a palette and an assortment of paints and brushes.*]

PENNY. Seems so nice to get into my art things again. They still look all right, don't they, Grandpa?

GRANDPA. Yes, indeed.

KOLENKHOV. You are a breath of Paris, Madame Sycamore.

PENNY. Oh, thank you, Mr. Kolenkhov.

DONALD (*coming in from the kitchen*). I didn't know you was working for the WPA.[11]

PENNY. Oh, no, Donald. You see, I used to paint all the time, and then one day —

[*The outer door slams and Ed comes in.*]

ED (*in considerable excitement*). It happened again! There was a fellow following me every place I went!

PENNY. Nonsense, Ed. It's your imagination.

ED. No, it isn't. It happens every time I go out to deliver candy.

GRANDPA. Maybe he wants a piece of candy.

ED. It's all right for you to laugh, Grandpa, but he keeps following me.

KOLENKHOV (*somberly*). You do not know what following is. In Russia *everybody* is followed. I was followed right out of Russia.

PENNY. Of course. You see, Ed — the whole thing is just imagination. (*Mr. De Pinna comes up from the cellar, ready for posing. He wears the traditional Roman costume, and he certainly cuts a figure. He is carrying Penny's easel, a discus, and a small platform for posing purposes.*) Ah, here we are! . . . Right here, Mr. De Pinna.

DONALD (*suddenly getting it*). Oh, is that picture supposed to be Mr. De Pinna?

PENNY (*sharply*). Of course it is, Donald. What's it look like — me?

DONALD (*studying the portrait*). Yes, it does — a little bit.

PENNY. Nonsense! What would I be doing with a discus?

KOLENKHOV. Ed, for tonight's lesson we use the first movement of *Scheherazade*.

ED. Okay.

---

[11] **WPA:** Works Progress Administration, a depression-born federal agency that created jobs — even for artists, who were commissioned to paint murals on the walls of federal buildings like post offices.

DE PINNA (*about to mount the platform*). I hope I haven't forgotten how to pose. (*He takes up the discus and strikes the classic pose of the Discus Thrower. Somehow, it is not quite convincing.*)

DONALD. What's he going to do with that thing? Throw it?

PENNY. No, no, Donald. He's just posing. . . . Mr. De Pinna, has something happened to your figure during these eight years?

DE PINNA (*pulling in his stomach*). No, I don't think it's any different.

[*With a sudden snort, Gay Wellington comes to.*]

PENNY (*immediately alert*). Yes, Miss Wellington?

[*For answer, Gay peers first at Penny, then at Mr. De Pinna. Then, with a strange snort, she just passes right out again.*]

PENNY. Oh, dear.

[*Essie comes tripping down the stairs — very much the ballet dancer. She is in full costume — ballet skirt, tight white satin bodice, a garland of roses in her hair.*]

ESSIE. Sorry, Mr. Kolenkhov, I couldn't find my slippers.

KOLENKHOV (*having previously removed his coat, he now takes off his shirt, displaying an enormous hairy chest beneath his undershirt*). We have a hot night for it, my Pavlowa, but art is only achieved through perspiration.

PENNY. Why, that's wonderful, Mr. Kolenkhov. Did you hear that, Grandpa — art is only achieved through perspiration.

GRANDPA. Yes, but it helps if you've got a little talent with it. (*He returns to his dart throwing.*) Only made two bull's-eyes last night. Got to do better than that. (*He hurls a dart at the board, then his eye travels to Miss Wellington, whose posterior offers an even easier target.*) Mind if I use Miss Wellington, Penny?

PENNY. What, Grandpa?

GRANDPA (*shakes his head*). Never mind. . . . Too easy.

[*Grandpa throws another dart at the target.*]

KOLENKHOV. You are ready? We begin! (*With a gesture he orders the music started; under Kolenkhov's critical eye Essie begins the mazes of the dance.*) Fouettée, temps, élevée. (*Essie obliges with her own idea of fouettée, temps, élevée.*) Pirouette! . . . Come, come! You can do that! It's eight years now. Pirouette! . . . At last! . . . Entrechat! . . . Entrechat! (*Essie leaps into the air, her feet twirling.*) No, Grandpa, you cannot relax with Stalin in Russia. The Czar relaxed, and what happened to *him*?

GRANDPA. He was too late.

ESSIE (*still leaping away*). Mr. Kolenkhov! Mr. Kolenkhov!

KOLENKHOV. If he had not relaxed, the Grand Duchess Olga Katrina would not be selling baked beans today.

ESSIE (*imploringly*). Mr. Kolenkhov!

KOLENKHOV. I am sorry. (*The doorbell rings.*) We go back to the pirouette.

PENNY. Could you pull in your stomach, Mr. De Pinna? . . . That's right.

KOLENKHOV. A little freer. A little freer with the hands. The whole body must work. Ed, help us with the music. The music must be free, too.

[*By way of guiding Ed, Kolenkhov hums the music at the pace that it should go. He is even pirouetting a bit himself.*]

[*From the front door comes the murmur of voices, not quite audible over the music. Then the stunned figure of Rheba comes into the archway, her eyes popping.*]

RHEBA. Mrs. Sycamore. . . . Mrs. Sycamore. (*With a gesture that has a grim foreboding in it, she motions toward the still invisible reason for her panic.*)

[*There is a second's pause, and then the reason is revealed in all its horror. The Kirbys, in full evening dress, stand in the archway. All three of them: Mr. and Mrs. Kirby, and Tony*]

[*Penny utters a stifled gasp; the others are too stunned even to do that. Their surprise at seeing the Kirbys, however, is no greater than that of the Kirbys at the sight that is spread before them.*]

[*Grandpa, alone of them all, rises to the situation. With a kind of old-world grace, he puts away his darts and makes the guests welcome.*]

GRANDPA. How do you do?

KIRBY (*uncertainly*). How do you do?

[*Not that it helps any, but Mr. De Pinna is squirming into his bathrobe, Kolenkhov is thrusting his shirt into his trousers, and Ed is hastily getting into his coat.*]

TONY. Are we too early?

GRANDPA. No, no. It's perfectly all right—we're glad to see you.

PENNY (*getting rid of the smock and tam*). Why—yes. Only— we thought it was to be tomorrow night.

MRS. KIRBY. Tomorrow night!

KIRBY. What!

GRANDPA. Now, it's perfectly all right. Please sit right down and make yourselves at home. (*His eyes still on the Kirbys,*

300

The Kirbys' arrival, from the Virginia
Museum Theatre's production, 1966.

*he gives Donald a good push toward the kitchen, by way
of a hint. Donald goes, promptly, with a quick little
stunned whistle that sums up HIS feelings.)*
KIRBY. Tony, how could you possibly—
TONY. I—I don't know. I thought—
MRS. KIRBY. Really, Tony! This is most embarrassing.
GRANDPA. Not at all. Why, we weren't doing a thing.
PENNY. Just spending the evening at home.
GRANDPA. That's all. . . . Now, don't let it bother you. This
is Alice's mother, Mrs. Sycamore . . . Alice's sister, Mrs.
Carmichael. . . . *Mr.* Carmichael. . . . Mr. Kolenkhov. . . .
*(At this point Mr. De Pinna takes an anticipatory step for-
ward, and Grandpa is practically compelled to perform the
introduction.)* And — Mr. De Pinna. Mr. De Pinna, would
you tell Mr. Sycamore to come right up? Tell him that Mr.
and Mrs. Kirby are here.

301

PENNY (*her voice a heavy whisper*). And be sure to put his pants on.

DE PINNA (*whispering right back*). All right. . . . Excuse me. (*He vanishes — discus and all.*)

GRANDPA. Won't you sit down?

PENNY (*first frantically trying to cover the prostrate Gay Wellington*). I'll tell Alice that you're — (*she is at the foot of the stairs*) — Alice! Alice, dear! (*The voice of Alice from above, "What is it?"*) Alice, will you come down, dear? We've got a surprise for you. (*She comes back into the room, summoning all her charm.*) Well!

GRANDPA. Mrs. Kirby, may I take your wrap?

MRS. KIRBY. Well — thank you. If you're perfectly sure that we're not— (*Suddenly she sees the snakes and lets out a scream.*)

GRANDPA. Oh, don't be alarmed, Mrs. Kirby. They're perfectly harmless.

MRS. KIRBY (*edging away from the solarium*). Thank you. (*She sinks into a chair, weakly.*)

GRANDPA. Ed. Take 'em into the kitchen.

[*Ed at once obeys.*]

PENNY. Of course we're so used to them around the house —

MRS. KIRBY. I'm sorry to trouble you, but snakes happen to be the one thing —

KIRBY. I feel very uncomfortable about this. Tony, how could you have done such a thing?

TONY. I'm sorry, Dad. I thought it was tonight.

KIRBY. It was very careless of you. *Very!*

GRANDPA. Now, now, Mr. Kirby — we're delighted.

PENNY. Oh, now, anybody can get mixed up, Mr. Kirby.

GRANDPA. Penny, how about some dinner for these folks? They've come for dinner, you know.

MRS. KIRBY. Oh, please don't bother. We're really not hungry at all.

PENNY. But it's not a bother. Ed!— (*Her voice drops to a loud whisper.*) Ed, tell Donald to run down to the A. and P. and get half a dozen bottles of beer, and — ah — some canned salmon — (*her voice comes up again*) — do you like canned salmon, Mr. Kirby?

KIRBY. Please don't trouble, Mrs. Sycamore. I have a little indigestion, anyway.

PENNY. Oh, I'm sorry. . . . How about you, Mrs. Kirby? Do you like canned salmon?

MRS. KIRBY (*you just know that she hates it*). Oh, I'm very fond of it.

PENNY. You can have frankfurters if you'd rather.

MRS. KIRBY (*regally*). Either one will do.

PENNY (*to Ed again*). Well, make it frankfurters, and some canned corn, and Campbell's Soup.

ED (*going out the kitchen door*). Okay!

PENNY (*calling after him*). And tell him to hurry! (*Penny again addresses the Kirbys.*) The A. and P. is just at the corner, and frankfurters don't take *any* time to boil.

GRANDPA (*as Paul comes through the cellar door*). And this is Alice's father, *Mr.* Sycamore. Mr. and Mrs. Kirby.

THE KIRBYS. How do you do?

PAUL. I hope you'll forgive my appearance.

PENNY. This is Mr. Sycamore's busiest time of the year. Just before the Fourth of July —

[*And then Alice comes down. She is a step into the room before she realizes what has happened; then she fairly freezes in her tracks.*]

ALICE. Oh!

TONY. Darling, will you ever forgive me? I'm the most dull-witted person in the world. I thought it was tonight.

ALICE (*staggered*). Why, Tony, I thought you — (*To the Kirbys*)— I'm so sorry — I can't imagine — why, I wasn't — have you all met each other?

KIRBY. Yes, indeed.

MRS. KIRBY. How do you do, Alice?

ALICE (*not even yet in control of herself*). How do you do, Mrs. Kirby? I'm afraid I'm not very — presentable.

TONY. Darling, you look lovely.

KIRBY. Of course she does. Don't let this upset you, my dear — we've all just met each other a night sooner, that's all.

MRS. KIRBY. Of course.

ALICE. But I was planning such a nice party tomorrow night . . . .

KIRBY (*being the good fellow*). Well, we'll come again to-morrow night.

TONY. There you are, Alice. Am I forgiven?

ALICE. I guess so. It's just that I — we'd better see about getting you some dinner.

PENNY. Oh, that's all done, Alice. That's all been attended to.

[*Donald, hat in hand, comes through the kitchen door; hurries across the room and out the front way. The Kirbys graciously pretend not to see.*]

ALICE. But mother — what are you — what did you send out for? Because Mr. Kirby suffers from indigestion — he can only eat certain things.

KIRBY. Now, it's quite all right.

TONY. Of course it is, darling.

PENNY. I asked him what he wanted, Alice.

ALICE (*doubtfully*). Yes, but —

KIRBY. Now, it's not as serious as all that. Just because I have a little indigestion.

KOLENKHOV (*helping things along*). Perhaps it is not indigestion at all, Mr. Kirby. Perhaps you have stomach ulcers.

ALICE. Don't be absurd, Mr. Kolenkhov!

GRANDPA. You mustn't mind Mr. Kolenkhov, Mr. Kirby. He's a Russian, and Russians are inclined to look on the dark side.

KOLENKHOV. All right, I am a Russian. But a friend of mine, a Russian, *died* from stomach ulcers.

KIRBY. Really, I —

ALICE (*desperately*). Please, Mr. Kolenkhov! Mr. Kirby has indigestion and that's all.

KOLENKHOV (*with a Russian shrug of the shoulders*). All right. Let him wait.

GRANDPA (*leaping into the breach*). Tell me, Mr. Kirby, how do you find business conditions? Are we pretty well out of the depression?

KIRBY. What? . . . Yes, yes, I think so. Of course, it all depends.

GRANDPA. But you figure that things are going to keep on improving?

KIRBY. Broadly speaking, yes. As a matter of fact, industry is now operating at sixty-four per cent of full capacity, as against eighty-two per cent in 1925. Of course in 1929, a peak year —

[*Peak year or no peak year, Gay Wellington chooses this moment to come to life. With a series of assorted snorts, she throws the cover back and pulls herself to a sitting position, blinking uncertainly at the assemblage. Then she rises, and weaves unsteadily across the room. The imposing figure of Mr. Kirby intrigues her.*]

GAY (*playfully rumpling Mr. Kirby's hair as she passes him*). Hello, Cutie. (*And with that she lunges on her way — up the stairs.*)

[*The Kirbys, of course, are considerably astounded by this exhibition; the Sycamores have watched it with varying degrees of frozen horror. Alice, in particular, is speechless; it is Grandpa who comes to her rescue.*]

GRANDPA. That may seem a little strange to you, but she's not quite accountable for her actions. A friend of Mrs. Sycamore's. She came to dinner and was overcome by the heat.

PENNY. Yes, some people feel it, you know, more than others. Perhaps I'd better see if she's all right. Excuse me, please. (*She goes hastily up the stairs.*)

ALICE. It *is* awfully hot. (*A fractional pause*) You usually escape all this hot weather, don't you, Mrs. Kirby? Up in Maine?

MRS. KIRBY (*on the frigid side*). As a rule. I had to come down this week, however, for the Flower Show.

TONY. Mother wouldn't miss that for the world. That blue ribbon is the high spot of her year.

ESSIE. I won a ribbon at a Flower Show once. For raising onions. Remember?

ALICE (*quickly*). That was a Garden Show, Essie.

ESSIE. Oh, yes.

[*Penny comes bustling down the stairs again.*

PENNY. I'm so sorry, but I think she'll be all right now. . . . Has Donald come back yet?

ALICE. No, he hasn't.

PENNY. Well, he'll be right back, and it won't take any time at all. I'm afraid you must be starved.

KIRBY. Oh, no. Quite all right. (*Pacing the room, he suddenly comes upon Paul's Erector Set.*) Hello! What's this? I didn't know there were little children in the house.

PAUL. Oh, no. That's mine.

KIRBY. Really? Well, I suppose every man has his hobby. Or do you use this as a model of some kind?

PAUL. No, I just play with it.

KIRBY. I see.

TONY. Maybe you'd be better off if *you* had a hobby like that, Dad. Instead of raising orchids.

KIRBY (*indulgently*). Yes, I wouldn't be surprised.

ALICE (*leaping on this as a safe topic*). Oh, *do* tell us about your orchids, Mr. Kirby. (*She addresses the others.*) You know, they take six years before they blossom. Think of that!

KIRBY (*warming to his subject*). Oh, some of them take longer than that. I've got one coming along now that I've waited ten years for.

PENNY (*making a joke*). Believe it or not, I was waiting for an orchid.

KIRBY. Ah — yes. Of course during that time they require the most scrupulous care. I remember a bulb that I was very fond of —

[*Donald suddenly bulges through the archway, his arms full. The tops of beer bottles and two or three large cucumbers peep over the edge of the huge paper bags.*]

PENNY. Ah, here we are! Did you get everything, Donald?

DONALD. Yes'm. Only the frankfurters didn't look very good, so I got pickled pigs' feet.

[*Mr. Kirby blanches at the very idea.*]

ALICE (*taking command*) Never mind, Donald — just bring everything into the kitchen. (*She turns at the kitchen door.*) Mr. Kirby, please tell them *all* about the orchids — I know they'd love to hear it. And — excuse me. (*She goes.*)

GRANDPA. Kind of an expensive hobby, isn't it, Mr. Kirby — raising orchids?

KIRBY. Yes, it is, but I feel that if a hobby gives one sufficient pleasure, it's never expensive.

GRANDPA. That's very true.

KIRBY. You see, I need something to relieve the daily nerve strain. After a week in Wall Street I'd go crazy if I didn't have something like that. Lot of men I know have yachts — just for that very reason.

GRANDPA (*mildly*). Why don't they give up Wall Street?

KIRBY. How's that?

GRANDPA. I was just joking.

MRS. KIRBY. I think it's necessary for everyone to have a hobby. Of course it's more to me than a hobby, but my great solace is — spiritualism.

PENNY. Now, Mrs. Kirby, don't tell me you fell for that. Why, everybody knows it's a fake.

MRS. KIRBY (*freezing*). To me, Mrs. Sycamore, spiritualism is — I would rather not discuss it, Mrs. Sycamore.

PAUL. Remember, Penny, you've got one or two hobbies of your own.

PENNY. Yes, but not silly ones.

GRANDPA (*with a little cough*). I don't think it matters what the hobby is — the important thing is to have one.

KOLENKHOV. To be ideal, a hobby should improve the body as well as the mind. The Romans were a great people! Why! What was their hobby? Wrestling. In wrestling you have to think quick with the mind and act quick with the body.

KIRBY. Yes, but I'm afraid wrestling is not very practical for most of us. (*He gives a deprecating little laugh.*) I wouldn't make a very good showing as a wrestler.

KOLENKHOV. You could be a *great* wrestler. You are built for it. Look!

[*With a startlingly quick movement Kolenkhov grabs Mr. Kirby's arms, knocks his legs from under him with a quick movement of a foot, and presto! Mr. Kirby is flat on his whatsis. Not only that, but instantaneously Kolenkhov is on top of him.*]

[*Just at this moment Alice re-enters the room — naturally, she stands petrified. Several people, of course,*

*rush immediately to the rescue, Tony and Paul arriving
at the scene of battle first. Amidst the general confusion
they help Mr. Kirby to his feet.*]

ALICE. Mr. Kirby! Are you — hurt?

TONY. Are you all right, Father?

KIRBY (*pulling himself together*). I — I — uh — (*he blinks,
uncertainly*) — where are my glasses?

ALICE. Here they are, Mr. Kirby. . . . Oh, Mr. Kirby, they're
broken.

KOLENKHOV (*full of apology*). Oh, I am sorry. But when you
wrestle again, Mr. Kirby, you will of course not wear glasses.

KIRBY (*coldly furious*). I do not intend to wrestle again,
Mr. Kolenkhov. (*He draws himself up, stiffly, and in
return gets a sharp pain in the back. He gives a little gasp.*)

TONY. Better sit down, father.

ALICE. Mr. Kolenkhov, how could you do such a thing? Why
didn't somebody stop him?

MRS. KIRBY. I think, if you don't mind, perhaps we had better
be going.

TONY. Mother!

ALICE (*close to tears*). Oh, Mrs. Kirby — please! Please don't
go! Mr. Kirby — please! I — I've ordered some scrambled
eggs for you, and — plain salad — Oh, please don't go!

KOLENKHOV. I am sorry if I did something wrong. And I
apologize.

ALICE. I can't tell you how sorry I am, Mr. Kirby. If I'd been
here —

KIRBY (*from a great height*). That's quite all right.

TONY. Of course it is. It's all right, Alice. We're not going.

[*The Kirbys reluctantly sit down again.*]
[*A moment's silence — no one knows quite what to say.*]

PENNY (*brightly*). Well! That was exciting for a minute,
wasn't it?

GRANDPA (*quickly*). You were talking about your orchids,
Mr. Kirby. Do you raise many different varieties?

KIRBY (*still unbending*). I'm afraid I've quite forgotten
about my orchids.

[*More silence, and everyone very uncomfortable*]

ALICE. I'm — awfully sorry, Mr. Kirby.

KOLENKHOV (*exploding*). What did I do that was so terrible? I threw him on the floor! Did it kill him?

ALICE. Please, Mr. Kolenkhov.

[*An annoyed gesture from Kolenkhov; another general pause*]

PENNY. I'm sure dinner won't be any time at all now.

[*A pained smile from Mrs. Kirby*]

ESSIE. Would you like some candy while you're waiting? I've got some freshly made.

KIRBY. My doctor does not permit me to eat candy. Thank you.

ESSIE. But these are nothing, Mr. Kirby. Just cocoanut and marshmallow fudge.

ALICE. Don't, Essie.

[*Rheba appears in the kitchen doorway, beckoning violently to Alice.*]

RHEBA (*in a loud whisper*). Miss Alice! Miss Alice! (*Alice quickly flies to Rheba's side.*) The eggs fell down the sink.

ALICE (*desperately*). Make some more! Quick!

RHEBA. I ain't got any.

ALICE. Send Donald out for some!

RHEBA (*disappearing*). All right.

ALICE (*calling after her*). Tell him to run! (*She turns back to the Kirbys.*) I'm so sorry. There'll be a little delay, but everything will be ready in just a minute.

[*At this moment Donald fairly shoots out of the kitchen door and across the living room, beating the Olympic record for all time.*]
[*Penny tries to ease the situation with a gay little laugh. It doesn't quite come off, however.*]

TONY. I've certainly put you people to a lot of trouble, with my stupidity.

GRANDPA. Not at all, Tony.

PENNY. Look! Why don't we all play a game of some sort while we're waiting?

TONY. Oh, that'd be fine.

ALICE. Mother, I don't think Mr. and Mrs. Kirby —

KOLENKHOV. *I* have an idea. I know a wonderful trick with a glass of water. (*He reaches for a full glass that stands on the table.*)

ALICE (*quickly*). No, Mr. Kolenkhov.

GRANDPA (*shaking his head*). No-o.

PENNY. But I'm sure Mr. and Mrs. Kirby would love this game. It's perfectly harmless.

ALICE. Please, Mother. . . .

KIRBY. I'm not very good at games, Mrs. Sycamore.

PENNY. Oh, but *any* fool could play this game, Mr. Kirby. (*She is bustling around, getting paper and pencil.*) All you do is write your name on a piece of paper —

ALICE. But Mother, Mr. Kirby doesn't want —

PENNY. Oh, he'll love it! (*Going right on*) Here you are, Mr. Kirby. Write your name on this piece of paper. And Mrs. Kirby, you do the same on this one.

ALICE. Mother, what *is* this game?

PENNY. I used to play it at school. It's called Forget-Me-Not. Now, I'm going to call out five words — just anything at all — and as I say each word, you're to put down the first thing that comes into your mind. Is that clear? For instance, if I say "grass," you might put down "green" — just whatever you think of, see? Or if I call out "chair," you might put down "table." It shows the reactions people have to different things. You see how simple it is, Mr. Kirby?

TONY. Come on, father! Be a sport!

KIRBY (*stiffly*). Very well. I shall be happy to play it.

PENNY. You see, Alice? He *does* want to play.

ALICE (*uneasily*). Well —

PENNY. Now, then? Are we ready?

KOLENKHOV. Ready!

PENNY. Now, remember — you must play fair. Put down the first thing that comes into your mind.

KIRBY (*pencil poised*). I understand.

PENNY. Everybody ready? . . . The first word is "potatoes." (*She repeats it.*) "Potatoes." . . . Ready for the next one? . . . "Bathroom." (*Alice shifts rather uneasily, but seeing that no one else seems to mind, she relaxes again.*) Got that?

KOLENKHOV. Go ahead.

PENNY. All ready? . . . "Lust."

ALICE. Mother, this is not exactly what you —

PENNY. Nonsense, Alice — that word's all right.

ALICE. Mother, it's *not* all right.

MRS. KIRBY (*unexpectedly*). Oh, I don't know. It seems to me that's a perfectly fair word.

PENNY (*to Alice*). You see? Now, you mustn't interrupt the game.

KIRBY. May I have that last word again, please?

PENNY. "Lust," Mr. Kirby.

KIRBY (*writing*). I've got it.

GRANDPA. This is quite a game.

PENNY. Sssh, Grandpa. . . . All ready? . . . "Honeymoon." (*Essie snickers a little, which is all it takes to start Penny off. Then she suddenly remembers herself.*) Now, Essie! . . . All right. The last word is "sex."

ALICE (*under her breath*). Mother!

PENNY. Everybody got "sex"? . . . All right — now give me all the papers.

GRANDPA. What happens now?

PENNY. Oh, this is the best part. Now I read out your reactions.

KIRBY. I see. It's really quite an interesting game.

PENNY. I knew you'd like it. I'll ready your paper first, Mr. Kirby. (*To the others*) I'm going to read Mr. Kirby's paper first. Listen, everybody! This is Mr. Kirby's. . . . "Potatoes — steak." That's very good. See how they go together? Steak and potatoes?

KIRBY (*modestly, but obviously pleased with himself*). I just happened to think of it.

PENNY. It's *very* good. . . . "Bathroom — toothpaste." Uh-huh. "Lust — unlawful." Isn't that nice? "Honeymoon — trip." Yes. And "sex — male." Yes, of course . . . That's really a wonderful paper, Mr. Kirby.

KIRBY (*taking a curtain call*). Thank you. . . . It's more than just a game, you know. It's sort of an experiment in psychology, isn't it?

PENNY. Yes, it is — it shows just how your *mind* works. Now we'll see how *Mrs.* Kirby's mind works. . . . Ready? . . . This is *Mrs.* Kirby. . . . "Potatoes — starch." I know just what you mean, Mrs. Kirby. . . . "Bathroom — Mr. Kirby."

KIRBY. What's that?

PENNY. "Bathroom — Mr. Kirby."

KIRBY (*turning to his wife*). I don't quite follow that, my dear.

MRS. KIRBY. I don't know — I just thought of you in connection with it. After all, you *are* in there a good deal, Anthony. Bathing, and shaving — well, you *do* take a long time.

KIRBY. Indeed? I hadn't realized that I was being selfish in the matter. . . . Go on, Mrs. Sycamore.

ALICE (*worried*). I think it's a very silly game and we ought to stop it.

KIRBY. No, no. Please go on, Mrs. Sycamore.

PENNY. Where was I . . . Oh, yes. . . . "Lust — human."

KIRBY. Human? (*Thin-lipped*) Really!

MRS. KIRBY. I just meant, Anthony, that lust is after all a — human emotion.

KIRBY. I don't agree with you, Miriam. Lust is not a human emotion. It is depraved.

MRS. KIRBY. Very well, Anthony. I'm wrong.

ALICE. Really, it's the most pointless game. Suppose we play Twenty Questions?

KIRBY. No, I find this game rather interesting. Will you go on, Mrs. Sycamore? What was the next word?

PENNY (*reluctantly*). Honeymoon.

KIRBY. Oh, yes. And what was Mrs. Kirby's answer.

PENNY. Ah — "Honeymoon — dull."

KIRBY (*murderously calm*). Did you say — dull?

MRS. KIRBY. What I meant, Anthony, was that Hot Springs was not very gay that season. All those old people sitting on the porch all afternoon, and — nothing to do at night.

KIRBY. That was not your reaction at the time, as I recall it.

TONY. Father, this is only a *game*.

KIRBY. A very illuminating game. Go on, Mrs. Sycamore!

PENNY (*brightly, having taken a look ahead*). This one's all right, Mr. Kirby. "Sex — Wall Street."

KIRBY. Wall Street? What do you mean by that, Miriam?

MRS. KIRBY (*nervously*). I don't know what I meant, Anthony. Nothing.

KIRBY. But you must have meant something, Miriam, or you wouldn't have put it down.

MRS. KIRBY. It was just the first thing that came into my head, that's all.

KIRBY. But what does it mean? Sex — Wall Street.

MRS. KIRBY (*annoyed*). Oh, I don't know what it means, Anthony. It's just that you're always talking about Wall Street, even when — (*She catches herself.*) I don't know what I meant. . . . Would you mind terribly, Alice, if we didn't stay for dinner? I'm afraid this game has given me a headache.

ALICE (*quietly*). I understand, Mrs. Kirby.

KIRBY (*clearing his throat*). Yes, possibly we'd better postpone the dinner, if you don't mind.

PENNY. But you're coming tomorrow night, aren't you?

MRS. KIRBY (*quickly*). I'm afraid we have an engagement tomorrow night.

KIRBY. Perhaps we'd better postpone the whole affair a little while. This hot weather, and — ah —

TONY (*smouldering*). I think we're being very ungracious, Father. Of *course* we'll stay to dinner — tonight.

MRS. KIRBY (*unyielding*). I have a very bad headache, Tony.

KIRBY. Come, come, Tony, I'm sure everyone understands.

TONY (*flaring*). Well, *I* don't. I think we ought to stay to dinner.

ALICE (*very low*). No, Tony.

TONY. What?

ALICE. We were fools, Tony, ever to think it would work. It won't. Mr. Kirby, I won't be at the office tomorrow. I — won't be there at all any more.

TONY. Alice, what are you talking about?

KIRBY (*to Alice*), I'm sorry, my dear — very sorry. . . . Are you ready, Miriam?

MRS. KIRBY (*with enormous dignity*). Yes, Anthony.

KIRBY. It's been very nice to have met you all. . . . Are you coming, Anthony?

TONY. No, Father. I'm not.

KIRBY. I see. . . . Your mother and I will be waiting for you at home. . . . Good night. (*With Mrs. Kirby on his arm, he sweeps toward the outer door.*)

[*Before the Kirbys can take more than a step toward the door, however, a new figure looms up in the archway. It is a quiet and competent-looking individual with a steely eye, and two more just like him loom up behind him.*]

THE MAN (*very quietly*). Stay right where you are, everybody. (*There is a little scream from Mrs. Kirby, an exclamation from Penny.*) Don't move.

PENNY. Oh, good heavens!

KIRBY. How dare you? Why, what does this mean?

GRANDPA. What *is* all this?

KIRBY. I demand an explanation!

THE MAN. Keep your mouth shut, you! (*He advances slowly into the room, looking the group over. Then he turns to one of his men.*) Which one is it?

ANOTHER MAN (*goes over and puts a hand on Ed's shoulder*). This is him.

ESSIE. Ed!

ED (*terrified*). Why, what do you mean?

ALICE. Grandpa, what is it?

KIRBY. This is an outrage!

THE MAN. Shut up! (*He turns to Ed.*) What's your name?

ED. Edward — Carmichael. I haven't done anything.

THE MAN. You haven't, huh?

GRANDPA (*not at all scared*). This seems rather high-handed to me. What's it all about?

THE MAN. Department of Justice.

PENNY. Oh, my goodness! J-men!

ESSIE. Ed, what have you done?

ED. I haven't done anything.

GRANDPA. What's the boy done, Officer?

ALICE. What is it? What's it all about?

THE MAN (*taking his time, and surveying the room*). That door lead to the cellar?

PENNY. Yes, it does.

PAUL. Yes.

THE MAN (*ordering a man to investigate*). Mac . . . (*Mac goes into the cellar*) . . . Jim!

JIM. Yes, sir.

THE MAN. Take a look upstairs and see what you find.

JIM. Okay. (*Jim goes upstairs.*)

ED (*panicky*). I haven't done anything!

THE MAN. Come here, you! (*He takes some slips of paper out of his pocket.*) Ever see these before?

ED (*gulping*). They're my — circulars.

THE MAN. You print this stuff, huh?

ED. Yes, sir.

THE MAN. And you put 'em into boxes of candy to get 'em into people's homes.

ESSIE. The Love Dreams!

ED. But I didn't mean anything!

THE MAN. You didn't huh? (*He reads the circulars.*) "Dynamite the Capitol!" "Dynamite the White House!" "Dynamite the Supreme Court!" "God is the State; the State is God!"

ED. But I didn't mean that. I just like to print. Don't I, Grandpa?

[*Donald returns with the eggs at this point, and stands quietly watching the proceedings.*]

GRANDPA. Now, Officer, the Government's in no danger from Ed. Printing is just his hobby, that's all. He prints anything.

THE MAN. He does, eh?

PENNY. I never heard of such nonsense.

KIRBY. I refuse to stay here and —

[*Mr. De Pinna, at this point, is shoved through the cellar door by Mac, protesting as he comes.*]

DE PINNA. Hey, let me get my pipe, will you? Let me get my pipe!

MAC. Shut up, you! . . . We were right, Chief. They've got enough gunpowder down there to blow up the whole city.

PAUL. But we only use that —

THE MAN. Keep still! . . . Everybody in this house is under arrest.

KIRBY. What's that?

MRS. KIRBY. Oh, good heavens!

GRANDPA. Now look here, Officer — this is all nonsense.

DE PINNA. You'd better let me get my pipe. I left it —

THE MAN. Shut up, all of you!

KOLENKHOV. It seems to me, Officer —

THE MAN. Shut up!

[*From the stairs comes the sound of drunken singing — "There was a young lady," etc. Gay Wellington, wrapped in Penny's negligee, is being carried down the stairway by a somewhat bewildered G-man.*]

THE G-MAN. Keep still, you! Stop that! Stop it!

THE LEADER (*after Gay has been persuaded to quiet down*). Who's that?

GRANDPA (*pretty tired of the whole business*). That — is my mother.

[*And then, suddenly, we hear from the cellar. Mr. De Pinna seems to have been right about his pipe, to judge from the sounds below. It is a whole year's supply of fireworks — bombs, big crackers, little crackers, sky-rockets, pinwheels, everything. The house is fairly rocked by the explosion.*]

[*In the room, of course, pandemonium reigns. Mrs. Kirby screams; the G-man drops Gay right where he stands and dashes for the cellar, closely followed by Mr. De Pinna and Paul; Penny dashes for her manuscripts and Ed rushes to save his xylophone. Kolenkhov waves his arms wildly and dashes in all directions at once; everyone is rushing this way and that.*]

[*All except one. The exception, of course, is Grandpa, who takes all things as they come. Grandpa just says "Well, well, well!" — and sits down. If a lot of people weren't in the way, in fact, you feel he'd like to throw a few darts.*]

CURTAIN

QUESTIONS

1. How do you account for the fact that people like the milkman and Mr. De Pinna have come to the Vanderhofs' — and stayed?

2. Describe the scene in the Vanderhof living room when the Kirbys walk in. How are the Kirbys dressed? How is Mr. De Pinna dressed? What is the effect of seeing them side by side? Why is the Kirbys' entrance dramatically effective?

3. How is Penny characterized by her offer of A. and P. frankfurters, canned salmon, and beer to the Kirbys? What makes her offer inappropriate? Does Penny realize the effect of the offer on the Kirbys? Is Tony like his parents?

4. What do Mr. Kirby's feelings about Paul's Erector Set — that it's either for little children or for building industrial models — reveal about Mr. Kirby's attitude toward play?

5. The word game Penny suggests is a form of psychological free association that is supposed to reveal one's true, uninhibited feelings toward the subject mentioned. What do Mr. Kirby's responses reveal about his attitude toward life? What do Mrs. Kirby's responses reveal about her attitude toward her husband? How open with each other have they been in the past? What's wrong with their life as it is presented?

6. As the curtain descends on the climactic second act, Grandpa's calm makes the surrounding chaos even more amusing. Why? What does that calm reveal about Grandpa's attitude toward life?

ACT THREE

The following day.
Rheba is in the midst of setting the table for dinner, pausing occasionally in her labors to listen to the Edwin C. Hill[12] of the moment — Donald. With intense interest and concentration, he is reading aloud from a newspaper.

DONALD. ". . . for appearance in the West Side Court this morning. After spending the night in jail, the defendants, thirteen in all, were brought before Judge Callahan and given suspended sentences for manufacturing fireworks without a permit."

RHEBA. Yah. Kept me in the same cell with a stripteaser from a burlesque show.

DONALD. I was in the cell with Mr. Kirby. My, he was mad!

RHEBA. Mrs. Kirby and the stripteaser — they were fighting all night.

DONALD. Whole lot about *Mr.* Kirby here. (*Reading again*) "Anthony W. Kirby, head of Kirby & Co., 62 Wall Street, who was among those apprehended, declared he was in no way interested in the manufacture of fireworks, but refused to state why he was on the premises at the time of the raid. Mr. Kirby is a member of the Union Club, the Racquet Club,

[12] *Edwin C. Hill* (1884–1957): famous radio commentator.

the Harvard Club, and the National Geographic Society."
My, he certainly is a joiner!

RHEBA. All those rich men are Elks or something.

DONALD (*looking up from his paper*). I suppose, after all this,
Mr. Tony ain't ever going to marry Miss Alice, huh?

RHEBA. No, suh, and it's too bad, too. Miss Alice sure loves
that boy.

DONALD. Ever notice how white folks always getting themselves in trouble?

RHEBA. Yassuh, I'm glad I'm colored. (*She sighs, heavily.*)
I don't know what I'm going to do with all that food out in
the kitchen. Ain't going to be no party tonight, that's sure.

DONALD. Ain't we going to eat it anyhow?

RHEBA. Well, I'm cooking it, but I don't think anybody going
to have an appetite.

DONALD. *I'm* hungry.

RHEBA. Well, *they* ain't. They're all so broke up about Miss
Alice.

DONALD. What's she want to go 'way for? Where's she going?

RHEBA. I don't know — mountains someplace. And she's
going, all right, no matter what they say. I know Miss Alice
when she gets that look in her eye.

DONALD. Too bad, ain't it?

RHEBA. Sure is.

[*Mr. De Pinna comes up from the cellar, bearing the ear-
marks of the previous day's catastrophe. There is a small
bandage around his head and over one eye, and another
around his right hand. He also limps slightly.*]

DE PINNA. Not even a balloon left. (*He exhibits a handful of
exploded firecrackers.*) Look.

RHEBA. How's your hand, Mr. De Pinna? Better?

DE PINNA. Yes, it's better. (*A step toward the kitchen*) Is
there some more olive oil[13] out there?

RHEBA (*nods*). It's in the salad bowl.

DE PINNA. Thanks. (*He goes out the kitchen door as Penny
comes down the stairs. It is a new and rather subdued
Penny.*)

---

[13] **olive oil:** to heal burns.

PENNY (*with a sigh*). Well, she's going. Nothing anybody said could change her.

RHEBA. She ain't going to stay away long, is she, Mrs. Sycamore?

PENNY. I don't know, Rheba. She won't say.

RHEBA. My, going to be lonesome around here without her. (*She goes into the kitchen.*)

DONALD. How *you* feel, Mrs. Sycamore?

PENNY. Oh, I'm all right, Donald. Just kind of upset. (*She is at her desk.*) Perhaps if I do some work, maybe I'll feel better.

DONALD. Well, I won't bother you then, Mrs. Sycamore. (*He goes into the kitchen.*)

[*Penny puts a sheet of paper into the typewriter; stares at it blankly for a moment; types in desultory fashion, gives it up. She leans back and sits staring straight ahead.*]

[*Paul comes slowly down the stairs; stands surveying the room a moment; sighs. He goes over to the Erector Set; absentmindedly pulls out the flag. Then, with another sigh, he drops into a chair.*]

PAUL. She's going, Penny.

PENNY. Yes. (*She is quiet for a moment; then she starts to weep, softly.*)

PAUL (*going to her*). Now, now, Penny.

PENNY. I can't help it, Paul. Somehow I feel it's our fault.

PAUL. It's mine more than yours, Penny. All these years I've just been — going along, enjoying myself, when maybe I should have been thinking more about Alice.

PENNY. Don't say that, Paul. You've been a wonderful father. And husband, too.

PAUL. No, I haven't. Maybe if I'd gone ahead and been an architect — I don't know — something Alice could have been proud of. I felt that all last night, looking at Mr. Kirby.

PENNY. But we've been so happy, Paul.

PAUL. I know, but maybe that's not enough. I used to think it was, but — I'm kind of all mixed up now.

PENNY (*after a pause*). What time is she going?

PAUL. Pretty soon. Train leaves at half past seven.

PENNY. Oh, if only she'd see Tony. I'm sure he could persuade her.

PAUL. But she won't, Penny. He's been trying all day.

PENNY. Where is he now?

PAUL. I don't know — I suppose walking around the block again. Anyhow, she won't talk to him.

PENNY. Maybe Tony can catch her as she's leaving.

PAUL. It won't help, Penny.

PENNY. No, I don't suppose so. . . . I feel so sorry for Tony, too. (*Grandpa comes down the stairs — unsmiling, but not too depressed by the situation. Anxiously*) Well?

GRANDPA. Now, Penny, let the girl alone.

PENNY. But, Grandpa —

GRANDPA. Suppose she *goes* to the Adirondacks? She'll be back. You can take just so much Adirondacks, and then you come home.

PENNY. Oh, but it's all so terrible, Grandpa.

GRANDPA. In a way, but it has its bright side, too.

PAUL. How do you mean?

GRANDPA. Well, Mr. Kirby getting into the patrol wagon, for one thing, and the expression on his face when he and Donald had to take a bath together. I'll never forget that if I live to be a hundred, and I warn you people I intend to. If I can have things like that going on.

PENNY. Oh, it was even worse with Mrs. Kirby. When the matron stripped her. There was a burlesque dancer there and she kept singing a strip song while Mrs. Kirby undressed.

GRANDPA. I'll bet you Bar Harbor is going to seem pretty dull to the Kirbys for the rest of the summer.

[*With a determined step, Alice comes swiftly down the stairs. Over her arm she carries a couple of dresses. Looking neither to right nor left, she heads for the kitchen.*]

GRANDPA. Need any help, Alice?

ALICE (*in a strained voice*). No, thanks, Grandpa. Ed is helping with the bags. I'm just going to press these.

PENNY. Alice, dear —

GRANDPA. Now, Penny.

[*Ed has appeared in the hallway with a couple of hat-boxes, Essie behind him.*]

ED. I'll bring the big bag down as soon as you're ready, Alice.

ESSIE. Do you want to take some candy along for the train, Alice?

ALICE. No, thanks, Essie.

PENNY. Really, Alice, you could be just as alone here as you could in the mountains. You could stay right in your room all the time.

ALICE (*quietly*). No, Mother, I want to be by myself — away from everybody. I love you all — you know that. But I just have to go away for a while. I'll be all right. . . . Father, did you 'phone for a cab?

PAUL. No, I didn't know you wanted one.

PENNY. Oh, I told Mr. De Pinna to tell you, Paul. Didn't he tell you?

ED. Oh, he told *me*, but I forgot.

ALICE (*the final straw*). Oh, I wish I lived in a family that didn't always forget *every*thing. That — that behaved the way *other* people's families do. I'm sick of cornflakes, and — Donald, and — (*unconsciously, in her impatience, she has picked up one of Grandpa's darts; is surprised to find it suddenly in her hand*) — everything! (*She dashes the dart to the floor.*) Why can't we be like other people? Roast beef, and two green vegetables, and — doilies on the table, and — a place you could bring your friends to — without — (*Unable to control herself further, she bursts out of the room, into the kitchen.*)

ESSIE. I'll — see if I can do anything. (*She goes into the kitchen.*)

[*The others look at each other for a moment, helplessly. Penny, with a sigh, drops into her chair again. Paul also sits. Grandpa mechanically picks up the dart from the floor; smooths out the feathers. Ed, with a futile gesture, runs his fingers idly over the xylophone keys. He stops quickly as every head turns to look at him.*]

[*The sound of the door opening, and Tony appears in the archway. A worried and disheveled Tony*]

PENNY (*quickly*). Tony, talk to her! She's in the kitchen!

TONY. Thanks. (*He goes immediately into the kitchen. The family, galvanized, listen intently. Almost immediately, Alice emerges from the kitchen again, followed by Tony. She crosses the living room and starts quickly up the stairs.*) Alice, won't you listen to me? Please!

ALICE (*not stopping*). Tony, it's no use.

TONY (*following her*). Alice, you're not being fair. At least let me talk to you.

[*They are both gone — up the stairs.*]

PENNY. Perhaps if I went upstairs with them. . . .

GRANDPA. Now, Penny. Let them alone.

[*Essie comes out of the kitchen.*]

ESSIE, Where'd they go? (*Ed, with a gesture, indicates the upstairs region.*) She walked right out the minute he came in.

[*Mr. De Pinna also emerges from the kitchen.*]

MR. DE PINNA. Knocked the olive oil right out of my hand. I'm going to smell kind of fishy.

GRANDPA. How're you feeling, Mr. De Pinna? Hand still hurting you?

DE PINNA. No, it's better.

PAUL. Everything burnt up, huh? Downstairs?

DE PINNA (*nodding, sadly*). Everything. And my Roman costume, too.

GRANDPA (*to Penny*). I told you there was a bright side to everything. All except my twenty-two years back income tax. (*He pulls an envelope out of his pocket.*) I get another letter every day.

DE PINNA. Say, what are you going to do about that, Grandpa?

GRANDPA. Well, I had a kind of idea yesterday. It may not work, but I'm trying it, anyhow.

DE PINNA (*eagerly*). What is it?

[*Suddenly Kolenkhov appears in the doorway.*]

KOLENKHOV (*even he is subdued*). Good evening, everybody!

PENNY. Why, Mr. Kolenkhov!

GRANDPA. Hello, Kolenkhov.

KOLENKHOV. Forgive me. The door was open.

GRANDPA. Come on in.

KOLENKHOV. You will excuse my coming today. I realize
you are — upset.

PENNY. That's all right, Mr. Kolenkhov.

ESSIE. I don't think I can take a lesson, Mr. Kolenkhov. I
don't feel up to it.

KOLENKHOV (*uncertainly*). Well, I — ah —

PENNY. Oh, but do stay to dinner, Mr. Kolenkhov. We've
got all that food out there, and somebody's got to eat it.

KOLENKHOV. I will be happy to, Madame Sycamore.

PENNY. Fine.

KOLENKHOV. Thank you. . . . Now, I wonder if I know you
well enough to ask of you a great favor.

PENNY. Why, of course, Mr. Kolenkhov. What is it?

KOLENKHOV. You have heard me talk about my friend the
Grand Duchess Olga Katrina.

PENNY. Yes?

KOLENKHOV. She is a great woman, the Grand Duchess.
Her cousin was the Czar of Russia, and today she is waitress
in Childs' Restaurant. Columbus Circle.

PENNY. Yes, I know. If there's anything at all that we can do,
Mr. Kolenkhov. . . .

KOLENKHOV. I tell you. The Grand Duchess Olga Katrina
has not had a good meal since before the revolution.

GRANDPA. She must be hungry.

KOLENKHOV. And today the Grand Duchess not only has her
day off — Thursday — but it is also the anniversary of Peter
the Great. A remarkable man!

PENNY. Mr. Kolenkhov, if you mean you'd like the Grand
Duchess to come to dinner, why, we'd be honored.

ESSIE. Oh, yes!

KOLENKHOV (*with a bow*). In the name of the Grand Duchess,
I thank you.

PENNY. I can hardly wait to meet her. When will she be here?

KOLENKHOV. She is outside in the street, waiting. I bring
her in. (*And he goes out.*)

GRANDPA. You know, if this keeps on I want to live to be a
hundred and *fifty*.

PENNY (*feverishly*). Ed, straighten your tie. Essie, look at your dress. How do *I* look? All right?

[*Kolenkhov appears in the hallway and stands at rigid attention.*]

KOLENKHOV (*his voice booming*). The Grand Duchess Olga Katrina! (*And the Grand Duchess Olga Katrina, wheat cakes and maple syrup out of her life for a few hours, sweeps into the room. She wears a dinner gown that has seen better days, and the whole is surmounted by an extremely tacky-looking evening wrap, trimmed with bits of ancient and moth-eaten fur. But once a Grand Duchess, always a Grand Duchess. She rises above everything — Childs, evening wrap, and all.*) Your Highness, permit me to present Madame Sycamore — (*Penny, having seen a movie or two in her time, knows just what to do. She curtsies right to the floor and catches hold of a chair just in time.*) Madame Carmichael — (*Essie does a curtsey that begins where all others leave off. Starting on her toes, she merges The Dying Swan with an extremely elaborate genuflection.*) Grandpa —

GRANDPA (*with a little bow*). Madame.

KOLENKHOV. Mr. Sycamore, Mr. Carmichael, and Mr. De Pinna.

[*Paul and Ed content themselves with courteous little bows, but not so the social-minded Mr. De Pinna. He bows to the floor — and stays there for a moment.*]

GRANDPA. All right now, Mr. De Pinna.

[*Mr. De Pinna gets to his feet again.*]

PENNY. Will you be seated, Your Highness?

THE GRAND DUCHESS. Thank you. You are most kind.

PENNY. We are honored to receive you, Your Highness.

THE GRAND DUCHESS. I am most happy to be here. What time is dinner?

PENNY (*a little startled*). Oh, it'll be quite soon, Your Highness — very soon.

THE GRAND DUCHESS. I do not mean to be rude, but I must be back at the restaurant by eight o'clock. I am substituting for another waitress.

KOLENKHOV. I will make sure you are on time, Your Highness.

DE PINNA. You know, Highness, I think you waited on me
in Childs' once. The Seventy-Second Street place?

THE GRAND DUCHESS. No, no. That was my sister.

KOLENKHOV. The Grand Duchess Natasha.

THE GRAND DUCHESS. *I* work in Columbus Circle.

GRANDPA. Quite a lot of your family living over here now,
aren't there?

THE GRAND DUCHESS. Oh, yes — many. My uncle, the Grand
Duke Sergei — he is an elevator man at Macy's. A very nice
man. Then there is my cousin, Prince Alexis. He will not
speak to the rest of us because he works at Hattie Carnegie's. He has cards printed — Prince Alexis of Hattie Carnegie. Bah!

KOLENKHOV. When he was selling Eskimo Pies at Luna Park
he was willing to talk to you.

THE GRAND DUCHESS. Ah, Kolenkhov, our time is coming.
My sister Natasha is studying to be a manicure, Uncle Sergei
they have promised to make floorwalker, and next month I
get transferred to the Fifth Avenue Childs'. From there it
is only a step to Schraffts', and *then* we will see what Prince
Alexis says!

GRANDPA (*nodding*). I think you've got him.

THE GRAND DUCHESS. You are telling *me?* (*She laughs a
triumphant Russian laugh, in which Kolenkhov joins.*)

PENNY. Your Highness — did you know the Czar? Personally,
I mean.

THE GRAND DUCHESS. Of course — he was my cousin. It was
terrible, what happened, but perhaps it was for the best.
Where could he get a job now?

KOLENKHOV. That is true.

THE GRAND DUCHESS (*philosophically*). Yes. And poor relations are poor relations. It is the same in every family. My
cousin, the King of Sweden — he was very nice to us for
about ten years, but then he said, I just cannot go on. I am
not doing so well, either. . . . I do not blame him.

PENNY. No, of course not. . . . Would you excuse me for just
a moment? (*She goes to the foot of the stairs and stands
peering up anxiously, hoping for news of Alice.*)

DE PINNA (*the historian at heart*). Tell me, Grand Duchess, is it true what they say about Rasputin?[14]

THE GRAND DUCHESS. Everyone wants to know about Rasputin. . . . Yes, my dear sir, it is true. In spades.

DE PINNA. You don't say?

KOLENKHOV. Your Highness, we have to watch the time.

THE GRAND DUCHESS. Yes, I must not be late. The manager does not like me. He is a Communist.

PENNY. We'll hurry things up. Essie, why don't you go out in the kitchen and give Rheba a hand?

THE GRAND DUCHESS (*rising*). I will help, too. I am a very good cook.

PENNY. Oh, but Your Highness! Not on your day off!

THE GRAND DUCHESS. I do not mind. Where is your kitchen?

ESSIE. Right through here, but you're the guest of honor, Your Highness.

THE GRAND DUCHESS. But I love to cook! Come, Kolenkhov! If they have got sour cream and pot cheese I will make you some blintzes!

KOLENKHOV. Ah! Blintzes! . . . Come, Pavlowa! We show you something! (*With Essie, he goes into the kitchen.*)

DE PINNA. Say! The Duchess is all right, isn't she? Hey, Duchess! Can I help? (*And into the kitchen*)

PENNY. Really, she's a very nice woman, you know. Considering she's a Grand Duchess.

GRANDPA. Wonderful what people go through, isn't it? And still keep kind of gay, too.

PENNY. Mm. She made me forget about everything for a minute. (*She returns to the stairs and stands listening.*)

PAUL. I'd better call that cab, I suppose.

PENNY. No, wait, Paul. I think I hear them. Maybe Tony has — (*She stops as Alice's step is heard on the stair. She enters — dressed for traveling. Tony looms up behind her.*)

ALICE. Ed, will you go up and bring my bag down?

TONY (*quickly*). Don't you do it, Ed!

[*Ed hesitates, uncertain.*]

[14] **Rasputin** (ra·spüt′ən): Grigori Efimovich Rasputin (1871?–1916), a Russian monk who gained control over Czar Nicholas II and his wife and whose harmful influence contributed to the collapse of the Russian empire. He was finally assassinated by a group of noblemen.

ALICE. Ed, please!

TONY (*a moment's pause; then he gives up*). All right, Ed. Bring it down. (*Ed goes up the stairs as Tony disconsolately stalks across the room. Then he faces the Sycamores.*) Do you know that you've got the stubbornest daughter in all forty-eight states?

[*The doorbell rings.*]

ALICE. That must be the cab. (*She goes to the door.*)

GRANDPA. If it is, it's certainly wonderful service.

[*To the considerable surprise of everyone, the voice of Mr. Kirby is heard at the front door.*]

KIRBY. Is Tony here, Alice?

ALICE. Yes. Yes, he is.

[*Mr. Kirby comes in.*]

KIRBY (*uncomfortably*). Ah — good afternoon. Forgive my intruding. . . . Tony, I want you to come home with me. Your mother is very upset.

TONY (*he looks at Alice*). Very well, Father. . . . Good-bye, Alice.

ALICE (*very low*). Good-bye, Tony.

KIRBY (*trying to ease the situation*). I need hardly say that this is as painful to Mrs. Kirby and myself as it is to you people. I — I'm sorry, but I'm sure you understand.

GRANDPA. Well, yes — and in a way, no. Now, I'm not the kind of person tries to run other people's lives, but the fact is, Mr. Kirby, I don't think these two young people have got as much sense as — ah — you and I have.

ALICE (*tense*). Grandpa, will you please not do this?

GRANDPA (*disarmingly*). I'm just talking to Mr. Kirby. A cat can look at a king, can't he?

[*Alice, with no further words, takes up the telephone and dials a number. There is finality in her every movement.*]

PENNY. You — you want me to do that for you, Alice?

ALICE. No, thanks, Mother.

PAUL. You've got quite a while before the train goes, Alice.

ALICE (*into the phone*). Will you send a cab to 761 Claremont, right away, please? . . . That's right, thank you. (*She hangs up.*)

KIRBY. And now if you'll excuse us . . . are you ready, Tony?

GRANDPA. Mr. Kirby, I suppose after last night you think this family is crazy, don't you?

KIRBY. No, I would not say that, although I am not accustomed to going out to dinner and spending the night in jail.

GRANDPA. Well, you've got to remember, Mr. Kirby, you came on the wrong night. Now tonight, I'll bet you, nothing'll happen at all. (*There is a great burst of Russian laughter from the kitchen — the mingled voices of Kolenkhov and the Grand Duchess. Grandpa looks off in the direction of the laughter, then decides to play safe.*) Maybe.

KIRBY. Mr. Vanderhof, it was not merely last night that convinced Mrs. Kirby and myself that this engagement would be unwise.

TONY. Father, I can handle my own affairs. (*He turns to Alice.*) Alice, for the last time, will you marry me?

ALICE. No, Tony. I know exactly what your father means, and he's right.

TONY. No, he's *not*, Alice.

GRANDPA. Alice, you're in love with this boy, and you're not marrying him because we're the kind of people we are.

ALICE. Grandpa —

GRANDPA. I know. You think the two families wouldn't get along. Well, maybe they wouldn't — but who says they're right and we're wrong?

ALICE. I didn't say that, Grandpa. I only feel —

GRANDPA. Well, what *I* feel is that Tony's too nice a boy to wake up twenty years from now with nothing in his life but stocks and bonds.

KIRBY. How's that?

GRANDPA (*turning to Mr. Kirby*). Yes. Mixed up and unhappy, the way you are.

KIRBY (*outraged*). I beg your pardon, Mr. Vanderhof, I am a very happy man.

GRANDPA. Are you?

KIRBY. Certainly I am.

GRANDPA. I don't think so. What do you think you get your indigestion from? Happiness? No, sir. You get it because most of your time is spent in doing things you don't want to do.

KIRBY. I don't do anything I don't want to do.

GRANDPA. Yes, you do. You said last night that at the end of a week in Wall Street you're pretty near crazy. Why do you keep on doing it?

KIRBY. Why do I keep on — why, that's my *business*. A man can't give up his business.

GRANDPA. Why not? You've got all the money you need. You can't take it with you.

KIRBY. That's a very easy thing to say, Mr. Vanderhof. But I have spent my entire life building up my business.

GRANDPA. And what's it got you? Same kind of mail every morning, same kind of deals, same kind of meetings, same dinners at night, same indigestion. Where does the fun come in? Don't you think there ought to be something *more*, Mr. Kirby? You must have wanted more than that when you started out. We haven't got too much time, you know — any of us.

KIRBY. What do you expect me to do? Live the way *you* do? Do nothing?

GRANDPA. Well, I have a lot of fun. Time enough for every-thing — read, talk, visit the zoo now and then, practice my darts, even have time to notice when spring comes around. Don't see anybody I don't want to, don't have six hours of things I *have* to do every day before I get *one* hour to do what I like in — and I haven't taken bicarbonate of soda in thirty-five years. What's the matter with that?

KIRBY. The matter with that? But suppose we *all* did it? A fine world we'd have, everybody going to zoos. Don't be ridiculous, Mr. Vanderhof. Who would do the work?

GRANDPA. There's always people that like to work — you can't *stop* them. Inventions, and they fly the ocean. There're always people to go down to Wall Street, too — because they *like* it. But from what I've seen of you, I don't think you're one of them. I think you're missing something.

KIRBY. I am not aware of missing anything.

GRANDPA. I wasn't either, till I quit. I used to get down to that office nine o'clock sharp, no matter how I felt. Lay awake nights for fear I wouldn't get that contract. Used to worry about the world, too. Got *all* worked up about whether Cleveland or Blaine was going to be elected President —

seemed awful important at the time, but who cares now?
What I'm trying to say, Mr. Kirby, is that I've had thirty-five
years that nobody can take away from me, no matter what
they do to the world. See?

KIRBY. Yes, I do see. And it's a very dangerous philosophy,
Mr. Vanderhof. It's — it's un-American. And it's exactly why
I'm opposed to this marriage. I don't want Tony to come
under its influence.

TONY (*a gleam in his eye*). What's the matter with it, Father?

KIRBY. Matter with it? Why, it's — it's downright Commu-
nism, that's what it is.

TONY. You didn't always think so.

KIRBY. I most certainly did. What are you talking about?

TONY. I'll tell you what I'm talking about. You didn't always
think so, because there was a time when you wanted to be a
trapeze artist.

KIRBY. Why — why, don't be an idiot, Tony.

TONY. Oh, yes, you did. I came across those letters you wrote
to Grandfather. Do you remember those?

KIRBY. NO! . . . How dared you read those letters? How dared
you?

PENNY. Why, isn't that wonderful? Did you wear tights, Mr.
Kirby?

KIRBY. Certainly not! The whole thing is absurd. I was fourteen years old at the time.

TONY. Yes, but at *eighteen* you wanted to be a saxophone
player, didn't you?

KIRBY. Tony!

TONY. And at twenty-one you ran away from home because
Grandfather wanted you to go into the business. It's all
down there in black and white. You didn't *always* think so.

GRANDPA. Well, well, well!

KIRBY. I may have had silly notions in my youth, but thank
God my father knocked them out of me. I went into the
business and forgot about them.

TONY. Not altogether, Father. There's still a saxophone in the
back of your clothes closet.

GRANDPA. There is?

KIRBY (*quietly*). That's enough, Tony. We'll discuss this later.

TONY. No, I want to talk about it *now*. I think Mr. Vanderhof

is right — dead right. I'm never going back to that office.
I've always hated it, and I'm not going on with it. And I'll
tell you something else. I didn't make a mistake last night.
I knew it was the wrong night. I brought you here on purpose.

ALICE. Tony!

PENNY. Well, for heaven's —

TONY. Because I wanted you to wake up. I wanted you to see
a real family — as they really *were*. A family that loved and
understood each other. You don't understand *me*. You've
never had time. Well, I'm not going to make *your* mistake.
I'm clearing out.

KIRBY. Clearing out? What do you mean?

TONY. I mean I'm not going to be pushed into the business
just because I'm your son. I'm getting out while there's still
time.

KIRBY (*stunned*). Tony, what are you going to do?

TONY. I don't know. Maybe I'll be a bricklayer, but at least
I'll be doing something I want to do.

[*Whereupon the doorbell rings.*]

PENNY. That must be the cab.

GRANDPA. Ask him to wait a minute, Ed.

ALICE. Grandpa!

GRANDPA. Do you mind, Alice? . . . You know, Mr. Kirby,
Tony is going through just what you and I did when we
were his age. I think, if you listen hard enough, you can
hear yourself saying the same things to *your* father twenty-
five years ago. We all did it. And we were right. How many
of us would be willing to settle when we're young for what
we eventually get? All those plans we make . . . what happens to them? It's only a handful of the lucky ones that can
look back and say that they even came close. (*Grandpa has
hit home. Mr. Kirby turns slowly and looks at his son, as
though seeing him for the first time. Grandpa continues.*)
So . . . before they clean out that closet, Mr. Kirby, I think
I'd get in a few good hours on that saxophone.

[*A slight pause, then the Grand Duchess, an apron over
her evening dress, comes in from the kitchen.*]

THE GRAND DUCHESS. I beg your pardon, but before I make
the blintzes, how many will there be for dinner?

PENNY. Why, I don't know — ah —

GRANDPA. Your Highness, may I present Mr. Anthony Kirby,
and Mr. Kirby, Junior? The Grand Duchess Olga Katrina.

KIRBY. How's that?

THE GRAND DUCHESS. How do you do? Before I make the
blintzes, how many will there be to dinner?

GRANDPA. Oh, I'd make quite a stack of them, Your Highness.
Can't ever tell.

THE GRAND DUCHESS. Good! The Czar always said to me,
Olga, do not be stingy with the blintzes. (*She returns to the
kitchen, leaving a somewhat stunned Mr. Kirby behind her.*)

KIRBY. Ah — who did you say that was, Mr. Vanderhof?

GRANDPA (*very offhand*). The Grand Duchess Olga Katrina,
of Russia. She's cooking the dinner.

KIRBY. Oh!

GRANDPA. And speaking of dinner, Mr. Kirby, why don't you
and Tony both stay?

PENNY. Oh, please do, Mr. Kirby. We've got all that stuff
we were going to have last night. I mean tonight.

GRANDPA. Looks like a pretty good dinner, Mr. Kirby, and'll
kind of give us a chance to get acquainted. Why not stay?

KIRBY. Why — I'd like to very much. (*He turns to Tony, with
some trepidation.*) What do you say, Tony? Shall we stay
to dinner?

TONY. Yes, father. I think that would be fine. If — (*his eyes go
to Alice*) — if Alice will send away that cab.

GRANDPA. How about it, Alice? Going to be a nice crowd.
Don't you think you ought to stay for dinner?

ALICE. Mr. Kirby — Tony — oh, Tony! (*And she is in his arms.*)

TONY. Darling!

ALICE. Grandpa, you're wonderful!

GRANDPA. I've been telling you that for years. (*He kisses her.*)

[*Essie enters from the kitchen, laden with dishes.*]

ESSIE. Grandpa, here's a letter for you. It was in the icebox.

GRANDPA (*looks at the envelope*). The government again.

TONY (*happily*). Won't you step into the office, Miss Sycamore? I'd like to do a little dictating.

GRANDPA (*with his letter*). Well, well, well!

PENNY. What is it, Grandpa?

GRANDPA. The United States Government apologizes. I don't owe 'em a nickel. It seems I died eight years ago.

ESSIE. Why, what do they mean, Grandpa?

GRANDPA. Remember Charlie, the milkman? Buried under my name?

PENNY. Yes.

GRANDPA. Well, I just told them they made a mistake and I was Martin Vanderhof, Jr. So they're very sorry and I may even get a refund.

ALICE. Why, Grandpa, you're an old crook.

GRANDPA. Sure!

KIRBY (*interested*). Pardon me, how did you say you escaped the income tax, Mr. Vanderhof?

KOLENKHOV (*bursting through the kitchen door, bringing a chair with him*). Tonight, my friends, you are going to eat.... (*He stops short as he catches sight of Kirby.*)

KIRBY (*heartily*). Hello, there!

KOLENKHOV (*stunned*). How do you do?

KIRBY. Fine! Fine! Never was better.

KOLENKHOV (*to Grandpa*). What has happened?

GRANDPA. He's relaxing. (*Ed strikes the keys of the xylophone.*) That's right. Play something, Ed.

[*He starts to play. Essie is immediately up on her toes.*]

THE GRAND DUCHESS (*entering from the kitchen*). Everything will be ready in a minute. You can sit down.

PENNY. Come on, everybody. Dinner! (*They start to pull up chairs.*) Come on, Mr. Kirby!

KIRBY (*still interested in the xylophone*). Yes, yes, I'm coming.

PENNY. Essie, stop dancing and come to dinner.

KOLENKHOV. You will like Russian food, Mr. Kirby.

PENNY. But you must be careful of your indigestion.

KIRBY. Nonsense! I haven't any indigestion.

TONY. Well, Miss Sycamore, how was your trip to the Adirondacks?

ALICE. Shut your face, Mr. Kirby!

KOLENKHOV. In Russia, when they sit down to dinner....

GRANDPA (*tapping on his plate*). Quiet! Everybody! Quiet!

(*Immediately the talk ceases. All heads are lowered as Grandpa starts to say grace.*) Well, Sir, here we are again. We want to say thanks once more for everything You've done for us. Things seem to be going along fine. Alice is going to marry Tony, and it looks as if they're going to be very happy. Of course the fireworks blew up, but that was Mr. De Pinna's fault, not Yours. We've all got our health and as far as anything else is concerned, we'll leave it to You. Thank You.

[*The heads come up again. Rheba and Donald come through the kitchen door with stacks and stacks of blintzes. Even the Czar would have thought there were enough.*]

CURTAIN

QUESTIONS

1. The Grand Duchess and Mr. Kirby both represent the wealthy aristocracy of their two countries. How do their social stations differ now? Which of the two is richer in human warmth and experience? What does the Grand Duchess' willingness to cook on her day off reveal about her? Would Mrs. Kirby offer to cook?

2. Mr. Kirby accuses Grandpa Vanderhof of doing "nothing." In what ways is this accusation true? In what ways is it not? How would each define "nothing"?

3. Mr. Kirby feels Grandpa Vanderhof's philosophy of withdrawing from the problems of the world is "dangerous." Is he wholly wrong in feeling this? How do you think an audience might have responded to this in 1936?

4. While the Grand Duchess is cooking blintzes, she enters, according to the stage directions, with "an apron over her evening dress." How does this costume reflect her life and personality?

5. What causes Mr. Kirby to change his mind about Tony's marrying Alice? What kind of person was Mr. Kirby as a young man? What had he become? How will he change?

6. Define the "it" that you "can't take with you."

AFTER THE CURTAIN

Comic Contrasts and Paradoxes

Extremes placed side by side seem comic: the elongated Mutt or the squat Jeff alone are not nearly as funny. Side by side they are funnier because each emphasizes the grotesqueness of the other. So it is with Laurel and Hardy — a fat balloon bound to a skinny beanpole. Can you think of other comic strips or movie teams where contrast creates comedy?

The same principle — when placed side by side, extremes create laughter — holds for the play. There is nothing inherently comic about being rich — or about being poor. But when the very rich and the very poor are measured against each other, and when the rich are found to be repressed, lacking in humor and humanity, while the poor are relaxed, warm and open, then our expectations are upset and laughter results. Add to this an American audience's inclination to side with the underdog, and our delight increases as the rich and pompous Mr. Kirby is undercut and finally converted to Martin Vanderhof's philosophy. How would you define that philosophy?

Behind this contrast of rich with poor lies the paradox — the seeming contradiction — that upsets our expectations about people: the rich are really poor; the poor are really rich. In terms of the play, explain how that is possible. What do the poor possess? What do the rich own? Why does Mr. Kirby raise orchids? What would he do with an Erector Set? How would his millionaire friends feel about the first hobby? About the second?

But Grandpa Vanderhof is only one foil[1] to Mr. Kirby. The Grand Duchess Olga Katrina is the second. An ex-aristocrat, once wealthy, now poor, she carries on her life with verve and dignity. Which of the two — the Grand Duchess or Mr. Kirby — is actually the more democratic? What is ironic about this? What was the Grand Duchess's political background? What hope does she hold for Mr. Kirby? Must the rich always be rigid snobs?

[1] foil: See page 248.

Underlying the comic paradoxes of *You Can't Take It With You* is a romantic view of life and human nature: poverty enriches because it forces people to develop themselves rather than their stock portfolios. A social critic might well term the play socially dangerous because it romanticizes poverty. For poverty, a critic might argue, removes choice and forces people into an iron schedule, working — or seeking work — eating and sleeping so as to be able to go on working. Martin Vanderhof's poverty, however, was self-chosen rather than imposed: for him it was a way of clearing his life of the trivialities of business and money-making so he would have time to enjoy the profundities of zoos and walking. He chose what was right for *him*. Did Mr. Kirby choose what was right for him? How do we know? What will Mr. Kirby probably choose to do in the future?

Social and Racial Stereotyping

To gain its effect rapidly, comedy must simplify character so as to point out the inconsistencies of human behavior. Mr. Kirby is a stereotyped businessman: he fits the popular image of a pompous snob making more money than he could ever possibly have time to spend while wishing he didn't have to spend five days a week on Wall Street. He is not complex and, until almost the close of the play, remains a top-hatted millionaire designed for Hart and Kaufman to throw eggs at. His distorted oversimplification is comic and inoffensive.

The same cannot be said for the stereotyped "stage Negro" characters — Rheba and Donald — as seen by a society, like ours today, suddenly conscious of its racism. Donald fits the mold of the shiftless, out-of-work Negro, prompt only in receiving his welfare check. And he and Rheba live together as if the thought of marriage never occurred to them. About all that can be said for the condescension towards them in the play and in the stage directions is that white American society was less conscious at the time of the depth of its paternalism toward the Negro: white society is now acutely aware of it. In the thirties discrimination against Jews was a more central concern, and one of the play's authors, George S. Kaufman — himself a Jew — would probably have been made to feel less than welcome at clubs of the type Mr. Kirby belonged to. Indeed, that even such a compassionate human being as George S. Kaufman was largely blind to the racial condescension in his play suggests the insensitivity of its era rather than the moral failure of the playwright.

Can you detect other examples of national or occupational stereotyping? How does the play treat exiled Russians? Internal Revenue agents?

For all these defects — and while slight, they *are* present — the play has had an astounding stage career, having been revived on Broadway (Helen Hayes played the Grand Duchess), showcased at an international exposition, and above all, reenacted thousands of times as the Junior or Senior play in high school auditoriums for the last three decades. Why, in your opinion, has *You Can't Take It With You* lasted so long? What is its appeal? Which parts of it did you especially like? Dislike? How do you explain its special appeal to high school audiences? Is it connected with the play's glorification of individualism, unconcern with convention, idealism?

Writing and Thinking

1. For a group of your classmates who have not read the play, write a two- or three-page paper describing, defining, and illustrating Grandpa Vanderhof's philosophy of living. Is it "dangerous" and "un-American," as Mr. Kirby said? (Was it in 1936?)

2. By giving examples from both the play and from your own life, write a three- to four-page paper defining and illustrating what the "it" is you "can't take with you."

3. Write a letter such as Mrs. Kirby might have written to a bridge friend describing her evening at the Vanderhofs'; or write the scene as Grandpa Vanderhof would have.

4. Write a paper describing a day in your life ten years from today. Begin it by waking up and close it with going to sleep. What will you do? Where will you be? Who will you be? Do you feel now you will be doing what you want to do or what you have to do? Or will these be the same?

Our Town

BEFORE THE CURTAIN

To this point, all the playwrights in this book have attempted to *create* an illusion of real life: Ibsen placed actual lamps and bookcases on his stage so that the audience would recognize his world of heroes and hypocrites as their own; even the romantic Rostand tries to make his sets authentic, filling Ragueneau's bakery with glowing ovens and rolling pins. But as soon as every play was presented as though it were taking place in the "real world" that laps at the walls of every theater, the impact of realism declined. Indeed, by the early part of the twentieth century, settings became so elaborate and so ingeniously "real" they threatened to smother the plays they were meant to clothe. David Belasco, an early twentieth-century producer, once designed such an exact replica of Delmonico's restaurant on stage — with each table and chair exactly placed as in the real restaurant, and with real food being cooked and served on stage — that all most of the audience ever remembered about the play was its restaurant setting. The cycle had come full circle: the theatergoer's imagination was beginning to choke amid the clutter. Far from creating a sense of actuality — as Ibsen intended they should — realistic sets and staging had become a distraction from the central issues and concerns of the plays themselves. Instead of simulating reality, set designers were duplicating it.

In an introduction to *Our Town,* Thornton Wilder describes his feeling that due to the limitations of the "box-set stage" a certain magic had left the theater: "Toward the end of the twenties I began to lose pleasure in going to the theater. I ceased to believe the stories I saw presented there. . . . I didn't believe a word of them." Linking the decline in theatrical excitement to the rise of a newly middle-class audience who "distrusted the passions and tried to deny them" and flocked instead to melodrama or sentimental drama (as exemplified in the TV espionage shows and situation comedies), Wilder feels that the middle-class audience tried to destroy the power of drama by insisting that it be too localized, too concrete. But for Wilder, theater tells two kinds of truth: "It has one foot planted firmly in the particular . . . yet it tends and strains to exhibit . . . general truth." Since the middle class objected to the power of theater to generalize — to probe and explore and reveal their own ambitions and weaknesses and fears — "they tamed it and drew its teeth; squeezed it into that removed showcase. They loaded the stage with specific objects because every concrete object on the stage fixes and narrows the action to one moment in time and place."

With its naked stage, *Our Town* is an attempt to escape from strict localization — though it takes place in a staunchly New England small town — by focusing on the small yet momentous events that go to make of the fabric of all our lives: doing homework despite the moonlight flooding through our window; pausing to walk a girl home before shagging flies at the sandlot; deciding where — or whether — to go to college; getting married although full of fears, qualms, and misgivings. What the townspeople of Grover's Corners live through is what all of us fortunate enough to be born can look forward to. Wilder himself writes about the play:

> *Our Town.* . . . is an attempt to find a value above all price for the smallest events in our daily life. . . . I have set the village against the largest dimensions of time and place. The recurrent words in this play . . . are "hundreds," "thousands," and "millions." Emily's joys and griefs, her algebra lessons and her birthday presents — what are they when we consider all the billions of girls who have lived, who are living, and who will live? . . . Our claim, our hope, our despair are in the mind — not

in things, not in "scenery." Molière said that for the theater all he needed was a platform and a passion or two. The climax of this play needs only five square feet of boarding and the passion to know what life means to us.

Our Town, then, is the local set amid the eternal, a hymn to the commonplace. Its stage is bare but not barren, since the play takes place mostly within ourselves. To read it, all we need are eyes—and "the passion to know what life means to us."

Our Town

THORNTON WILDER

Characters

STAGE MANAGER[1]	MR. WEBB
DR. GIBBS	WOMAN IN BALCONY
JOE CROWELL	MAN IN AUDITORIUM
HOWIE NEWSOME	LADY IN THE BOX
MRS. GIBBS	SIMON STIMSON
MRS. WEBB	MRS. SOAMES
GEORGE GIBBS	CONSTABLE WARREN
REBECCA GIBBS	SI CROWELL
WALLY WEBB	BASEBALL PLAYERS
EMILY WEBB	SAM CRAIG
PROFESSOR WILLARD	JOE STODDARD

The entire play takes place
in Grover's Corners, New Hampshire.

ACT ONE

No curtain.
No scenery.
The audience, arriving, sees an empty stage in half-light.
Presently the Stage Manager, hat on and pipe in mouth,
enters and begins placing a table and three chairs down-
stage left, and a table and three chairs downstage right.

[1] **Stage Manager:** person who is responsible for the technical aspects of a stage production: the set, lighting, costumes, and other details. During a performance he is in complete charge of the stage.

He also places a low bench at the corner of what will be the Webb house, left.

"Left" and "right" are from the point of view of the actor facing the audience. "Up" is toward the back wall.

As the house lights go down he has finished setting the stage and leaning against the right proscenium pillar[2] watches the late arrivals in the audience.

When the auditorium is in complete darkness, he speaks:

STAGE MANAGER:

This play is called "Our Town." It was written by Thornton Wilder; produced and directed by A. . . . (or: produced by A. . . .; directed by B. . . .). In it you will see Miss C. . . .; Miss D. . . .; Miss E. . . .; and Mr. F. . . .; Mr. G. . . .; Mr. H. . . .; and many others. The name of the town is Grover's Corners, New Hampshire — just across the Massachusetts line: latitude 42 degrees 40 minutes; longitude 70 degrees 37 minutes. The First Act shows a day in our town. The day is May 7, 1901. The time is just before dawn.

A rooster crows.

The sky is beginning to show some streaks of light over in the East there, behind our mount'in.

The morning star always gets wonderful bright the minute before it has to go, — doesn't it?

He stares at it for a moment, then goes upstage.

Well, I'd better show you how our town lies. Up here —

That is: parallel with the back wall.

is Main Street. Way back there is the railway station; tracks go that way. Polish Town's across the tracks, and some Canuck[3] families.

Toward the left.

Over there is the Congregational Church; across the street's the Presbyterian.

Methodist and Unitarian are over there.

Baptist is down in the holla' by the river.

Catholic Church is over beyond the tracks.

[2] *proscenium pillar:* one of the columns forming the sides of the arch which frames the forward part of the stage.

[3] **Canuck:** French-Canadian.

Here's the Town Hall and Post Office combined; jail's in the basement.

Bryan[4] once made a speech from these very steps here.

Along here's a row of stores. Hitching posts and horse blocks in front of them. First automobile's going to come along in about five years — belonged to Banker Cartwright, our richest citizen . . . lives in the big white house up on the hill.

Here's the grocery store and here's Mr. Morgan's drugstore. Most everybody in town manages to look into those two stores once a day.

Public School's over yonder. High School's still farther over. Quarter of nine mornings, noontimes, and three o'clock afternoons, the hull town can hear the yelling and screaming from those schoolyards.

> *He approaches the table and chairs downstage right.*

This is our doctor's house, — Doc Gibbs'. This is the back door.

> *Two arched trellises, covered with vines and flowers, are pushed out, one by each proscenium pillar.*

There's some scenery for those who think they have to have scenery.

This is Mrs. Gibbs' garden. Corn . . . peas . . . beans . . . hollyhocks . . . heliotrope . . . and a lot of burdock.

> *Crosses the stage.*

In those days our newspaper come out twice a week — the Grover's Corners *Sentinel* — and this is Editor Webb's house. And this is Mrs. Webb's garden.

Just like Mrs. Gibbs', only it's got a lot of sunflowers, too.

> *He looks upward, center stage.*

Right here . . .'s a big butternut tree.

> *He returns to his place by the right proscenium pillar and looks at the audience for a minute.*

Nice town, y'know what I mean?

Nobody very remarkable ever come out of it, s'far as we know. The earliest tombstones in the cemetery up there on the mountain say 1670–1680 — they're Grovers and Cartwrights and Gibbses and Herseys — same names as are around here now.

---

[4] **Bryan**: William Jennings Bryan (1860–1925), fiery orator and Democratic candidate for the Presidency in 1896, 1900, and 1908.

Well, as I said: it's about dawn.

The only lights on in town are in a cottage over by the tracks where a Polish mother's just had twins. And in the Joe Crowell house, where Joe Junior's getting up so as to deliver the paper. And in the depot, where Shorty Hawkins is gettin' ready to flag the 5:45 for Boston.

> *A train whistle is heard. The Stage Manager takes out his watch and nods.*

Naturally, out in the country — all around — there've been lights on for some time, what with milkin's and so on. But town people sleep late.

So — another day's begun.

There's Doc Gibbs comin' down Main Street now, comin' back from that baby case. And here's his wife comin' downstairs to get breakfast.

> *Mrs. Gibbs, a plump, pleasant woman in the middle thirties, comes "downstairs" right. She pulls up an imaginary window shade in her kitchen and starts to make a fire in her stove.*

Doc Gibbs died in 1930. The new hospital's named after him. Mrs. Gibbs died first — long time ago, in fact. She went out to visit her daughter, Rebecca, who married an insurance man in Canton, Ohio, and died there — pneumonia — but her body was brought back here. She's up in the cemetery there now — in with a whole mess of Gibbses and Herseys — she was Julia Hersey 'fore she married Doc Gibbs in the Congregational Church over there.

In our town we like to know the facts about everybody.

There's Mrs. Webb, coming downstairs to get her breakfast, too.

— That's Doc Gibbs. Got that call at half past one this morning.

And there comes Joe Crowell, Jr., delivering Mr. Webb's *Sentinel.*

> *Dr. Gibbs has been coming along Main Street from the left. At the point where he would turn to approach his house, he stops, sets down his — imaginary — black bag, takes off his hat, and rubs his face with fatigue, using an enormous handkerchief.*

Mrs. Webb, a thin, serious, crisp woman, has entered her kitchen, left, tying on an apron. She goes through the motions of putting wood into a stove, lighting it, and preparing breakfast.
Suddenly, Joe Crowell, Jr., eleven, starts down Main Street from the right, hurling imaginary newspapers into doorways.

JOE CROWELL, JR.:
Morning, Doc Gibbs.

DR. GIBBS:
Morning, Joe.

JOE CROWELL, JR.:
Somebody been sick, Doc?

DR. GIBBS:
No. Just some twins born over in Polish Town.

JOE CROWELL, JR.:
Do you want your paper now?

DR. GIBBS:
Yes, I'll take it. — Anything serious goin' on in the world since Wednesday?

JOE CROWELL, JR.:
Yessir. My schoolteacher, Miss Foster, 's getting married to a fella over in Concord.

DR. GIBBS:
I declare. — How do you boys feel about that?

JOE CROWELL, JR.:
Well, of course, it's none of my business — but I think if a person starts out to be a teacher, she ought to stay one.

DR. GIBBS:
How's your knee, Joe?

JOE CROWELL, JR.:

Fine, Doc, I never think about it at all. Only like you said, it always tells me when it's going to rain.

DR. GIBBS:

What's it telling you today? Goin' to rain?

JOE CROWELL, JR.:

No, sir.

DR. GIBBS:

Sure?

JOE CROWELL, JR.:

Yessir.

DR. GIBBS:

Knee ever make a mistake?

JOE CROWELL, JR.:

No, sir.

> *Joe goes off. Dr. Gibbs stands reading his paper.*

STAGE MANAGER:

Want to tell you something about that boy Joe Crowell there. Joe was awful bright — graduated from high school here, head of his class. So he got a scholarship to Massachusetts Tech. Graduated head of his class there, too. It was all wrote up in the Boston paper at the time. Goin' to be a great engineer, Joe was. But the war broke out and he died in France. — All that education for nothing.

HOWIE NEWSOME:

> *Off left.*

Giddap, Bessie! What's the matter with you today?

STAGE MANAGER:

Here comes Howie Newsome, deliverin' the milk.

> *Howie Newsome, about thirty, in overalls, comes along Main Street from the left, walking beside an invisible horse and wagon and carrying an imaginary rack with milk bottles. The sound of clinking milk bottles is heard. He leaves some bottles at Mrs.*

Webb's trellis, then, crossing the stage to Mrs. Gibbs',
he stops center to talk to Dr. Gibbs.

HOWIE NEWSOME:

Morning, Doc.

DR. GIBBS:

Morning, Howie.

HOWIE NEWSOME:

Somebody sick?

DR. GIBBS:

Pair of twins over to Mrs. Goruslawski's.

HOWIE NEWSOME:

Twins, eh? This town's gettin' bigger every year.

DR. GIBBS:

Goin' to rain, Howie?

HOWIE NEWSOME:

No, no. Fine day — that'll burn through. Come on, Bessie.

DR. GIBBS:

Hello, Bessie.
          He strokes the horse, which has remained up center.
How old is she, Howie?

HOWIE NEWSOME:

Going on seventeen. Bessie's all mixed up about the route
ever since the Lockharts stopped takin' their quart of milk
every day. She wants to leave 'em a quart just the same —
keeps scolding me the hull trip.
          He reaches Mrs. Gibbs' back door. She is waiting for
          him.

MRS. GIBBS:

Good morning, Howie.

HOWIE NEWSOME:

Morning, Mrs. Gibbs. Doc's just comin' down the street.

MRS. GIBBS:

Is he? Seems like you're late today.

HOWIE NEWSOME:

Yes. Somep'n went wrong with the separator. Don't know what 'twas.
> *He passes Dr. Gibbs up center.*

Doc!

DR. GIBBS:

Howie!

MRS. GIBBS:
> *Calling upstairs.*

Children! Children! Time to get up.

HOWIE NEWSOME:

Come on, Bessie!
> *He goes off right.*

MRS. GIBBS:

George! Rebecca!
> *Dr. Gibbs arrives at his back door and passes through the trellis into his house.*

MRS. GIBBS:

Everything all right, Frank?

DR. GIBBS:

Yes. I declare — easy as kittens.

MRS. GIBBS:

Bacon'll be ready in a minute. Set down and drink your coffee. You can catch a couple hours' sleep this morning, can't you?

DR. GIBBS:

Hm! . . . Mrs. Wentworth's coming at eleven. Guess I know what it's about, too. Her stummick ain't what it ought to be.

MRS. GIBBS:

All told, you won't get more'n three hours' sleep. Frank Gibbs, I don't know what's goin' to become of you. I do wish

I could get you to go away someplace and take a rest. I think
it would do you good.

MRS. WEBB:

Emileeee! Time to get up! Wally! Seven o'clock!

MRS. GIBBS:

I declare, you got to speak to George. Seems like something's
come over him lately. He's no help to me at all. I can't even
get him to cut me some wood.

DR. GIBBS:

> *Washing and drying his hands at the sink. Mrs. Gibbs
> is busy at the stove.*

Is he sassy to you?

MRS. GIBBS:

No. He just whines! All he thinks about is that baseball —
George! Rebecca! You'll be late for school.

DR. GIBBS:

M-m-m . . .

MRS. GIBBS:

George!

DR. GIBBS:

George, look sharp!

GEORGE'S VOICE:

Yes, Pa!

DR. GIBBS:

> *As he goes off the stage.*

Don't you hear your mother calling you? I guess I'll go upstairs and get forty winks.

MRS. WEBB:

Walleee! Emileee! You'll be late for school! Walleee! You
wash yourself good or I'll come up and do it myself.

REBECCA GIBBS' VOICE:

Ma! What dress shall I wear?

MRS. GIBBS:

Don't make a noise. Your father's been out all night and needs his sleep. I washed and ironed the blue gingham for you special.

REBECCA:

Ma, I hate that dress.

MRS. GIBBS:

Oh, hush-up-with-you.

REBECCA:

Every day I go to school dressed like a sick turkey.

MRS. GIBBS:

Now, Rebecca, you always look *very* nice.

REBECCA:

Mama, George's throwing soap at me.

MRS. GIBBS:

I'll come and slap the both of you, — that's what I'll do.

> *A factory whistle sounds.*
> *The children dash in and take their places at the tables. Right, George, about sixteen, and Rebecca, eleven. Left, Emily and Wally, same ages. They carry strapped schoolbooks.*

STAGE MANAGER:

We've got a factory in our town too — hear it? Makes blankets. Cartwrights own it and it brung 'em a fortune.

MRS. WEBB:

Children! Now I won't have it. Breakfast is just as good as any other meal, and I won't have you gobbling like wolves. It'll stunt your growth, — that's a fact. Put away your book, Wally.

WALLY:

Aw, Ma! By ten o'clock I got to know all about Canada.

MRS. WEBB:

You know the rule's well as I do — no books at table. As for me, I'd rather have my children healthy than bright.

EMILY:

I'm both, Mama: you know I am. I'm the brightest girl in school for my age. I have a wonderful memory.

MRS. WEBB:

Eat your breakfast.

WALLY:

I'm bright, too, when I'm looking at my stamp collection.

MRS. GIBBS:

I'll speak to your father about it when he's rested. Seems to me twenty-five cents a week's enough for a boy your age. I declare I don't know how you spend it all.

GEORGE:

Aw, Ma, — I gotta lotta things to buy.

MRS. GIBBS:

Strawberry phosphates — that's what you spend it on.

GEORGE:

I don't see how Rebecca comes to have so much money. She has more'n a dollar.

REBECCA:

> *Spoon in mouth, dreamily.*

I've been saving it up gradual.

MRS. GIBBS:

Well, dear, I think it's a good thing to spend some every now and then.

REBECCA:

Mama, do you know what I love most in the world — do you? — Money.

MRS. GIBBS:

Eat your breakfast.

THE CHILDREN:

Mama, there's first bell. — I gotta hurry. — I don't want any more. — I gotta hurry.

> *The children rise, seize their books, and dash out through the trellises. They meet, down center, and chattering, walk to Main Street, then turn left.*
>
> *The Stage Manager goes off, unobtrusively, right.*

MRS. WEBB:

Walk fast, but you don't have to run. Wally, pull up your pants at the knee. Stand up straight, Emily.

MRS. GIBBS:

Tell Miss Foster I send her my best congratulations — can you remember that?

REBECCA:

Yes, Ma.

MRS. GIBBS:

You look real nice, Rebecca. Pick up your feet.

ALL:

Good-bye.

> *Mrs. Gibbs fills her apron with food for the chickens and comes down to the footlights.*

MRS. GIBBS:

Here, chick, chick, chick.
No, go away, you. Go away.
Here, chick, chick, chick.
What's the matter with *you?* Fight, fight, fight, — that's all you do. Hm . . . *you* don't belong to me. Where'd you come from?

> *She shakes her apron.*

Oh, don't be so scared. Nobody's going to hurt you.

> *Mrs. Webb is sitting on the bench by her trellis, stringing beans.*

Good morning, Myrtle. How's your cold?

MRS. WEBB:

Well, I still get that tickling feeling in my throat. I told

Charles I didn't know as I'd go to choir practice tonight.
Wouldn't be any use.

MRS. GIBBS:

Have you tried singing over your voice?

MRS. WEBB:

Yes, but somehow I can't do that and stay on the key. While
I'm resting myself I thought I'd string some of these beans.

MRS. GIBBS:

> *Rolling up her sleeves as she crosses the stage for a
> chat.*

Let me help you. Beans have been good this year.

MRS. WEBB:

I've decided to put up forty quarts if it kills me. The children
say they hate 'em, but I notice they're able to get 'em down
all winter.

> *Pause. Brief sound of chickens cackling.*

MRS. GIBBS:

Now, Myrtle. I've got to tell you something, because if I
don't tell somebody I'll burst.

MRS. WEBB:

Why, Julia Gibbs!

MRS. GIBBS:

Here, give me some more of those beans. Myrtle, did one of
those secondhand-furniture men from Boston come to see
you last Friday?

MRS. WEBB:

No-o.

MRS. GIBBS:

Well, he called on me. First I thought he was a patient
wantin' to see Dr. Gibbs. 'N he wormed his way into my
parlor, and, Myrtle Webb, he offered me three hundred and
fifty dollars for Grandmother Wentworth's highboy, as I'm
sitting here!

MRS. WEBB:

Why, Julia Gibbs!

MRS. GIBBS:

He did! That old thing! Why, it was so big I didn't know where to put it and I almost give it to Cousin Hester Wilcox.

MRS. WEBB:

Well, you're going to take it, aren't you?

MRS. GIBBS:

I don't know.

MRS. WEBB:

You don't know — three hundred and fifty dollars! What's come over you?

MRS. GIBBS:

Well, if I could get the Doctor to take the money and go away someplace on a real trip, I'd sell it like that. — Y'know, Myrtle, it's been the dream of my life to see Paris, France. — Oh, I don't know. It sounds crazy, I suppose, but for years I've been promising myself that if we ever had the chance —

MRS. WEBB:

How does the Doctor feel about it?

MRS. GIBBS:

Well, I did beat about the bush a little and said that if I got a legacy — that's the way I put it — I'd make him take me somewhere.

MRS. WEBB:

M-m-m . . . What did he say?

MRS. GIBBS:

You know how he is. I haven't heard a serious word out of him since I've known him. No, he said, it might make him discontented with Grover's Corners to go traipsin' about Europe; better let well enough alone, he says. Every two years he makes a trip to the battlefields of the Civil War, and that's enough treat for anybody, he says.

MRS. WEBB:

Well, Mr. Webb just *admires* the way Dr. Gibbs knows everything about the Civil War. Mr. Webb's a good mind to give up Napoleon and move over to the Civil War, only Dr. Gibbs being one of the greatest experts in the country just makes him despair.

MRS. GIBBS:

It's a fact! Dr. Gibbs is never so happy as when he's at Antietam or Gettysburg. The times I've walked over those hills, Myrtle, stopping at every bush and pacing it all out, like we were going to buy it.

MRS. WEBB:

Well, if that secondhand man's really serious about buyin' it, Julia, you sell it. And then you'll get to see Paris, all right. Just keep droppin' hints from time to time — that's how I got to see the Atlantic Ocean, y'know.

MRS. GIBBS:

Oh, I'm sorry I mentioned it. Only it seems to me that once in your life before you die you ought to see a country where they don't talk in English and don't even want to.

The Stage Manager enters briskly from the right.
He tips his hat to the ladies, who nod their heads.

STAGE MANAGER:

Thank you, ladies. Thank you very much.

Mrs. Gibbs and Mrs. Webb gather up their things,
return into their homes, and disappear.

Now we're going to skip a few hours.

But first we want a little more information about the town, kind of a scientific account, you might say.

So I've asked Professor Willard of our State University to sketch in a few details of our past history here.

Is Professor Willard here?

Professor Willard, a rural savant,[5] pince-nez[6] on a
wide satin ribbon, enters from the right with some
notes in his hand.

---

[5] *savant:* scholar.

[6] *pince-nez* (pans'nā): eyeglasses held on the nose by a spring.

May I introduce Professor Willard of our State University. A few brief notes, thank you, Professor, — unfortunately our time is limited.

PROFESSOR WILLARD:

Grover's Corners . . . let me see . . . Grover's Corners lies on the old Pleistocene[7] granite of the Appalachian range. I may say it's some of the oldest land in the world. We're very proud of that. A shelf of Devonian[8] basalt crosses it with vestiges of Mesozoic[9] shale, and some sandstone outcroppings; but that's all more recent: two hundred, three hundred million years old.

Some highly interesting fossils have been found . . . I may say: unique fossils . . . two miles out of town, in Silas Peckham's cow pasture. They can be seen at the museum in our University at any time — that is, at any reasonable time. Shall I read some of Professor Gruber's notes on the meteorological situation — mean precipitation, et cetera?

STAGE MANAGER:

Afraid we won't have time for that, Professor. We might have a few words on the history of man here.

PROFESSOR WILLARD:

Yes . . . anthropological data: Early Amerindian stock. Cotahatchee tribes . . . no evidence before the tenth century of this era . . . hm . . . now entirely disappeared . . . possible traces in three families. Migration toward the end of the seventeenth century of English brachiocephalic[10] blue-eyed stock . . . for the most part. Since then some Slav and Mediterranean —

STAGE MANAGER:

And the population, Professor Willard?

[7] **Pleistocene:** period of geologic time when man first appeared on earth (about 500,000 years ago).

[8] **Devonian:** period in which fish, amphibians, and forests appeared (about 385,000,000 years ago).

[9] **Mesozoic:** era in which dinosaurs and other reptiles inhabited the earth (230,000,000 to 90,000,000 years ago).

[10] **brachiocephalic:** short headed. (Proper spelling is *brachycephalic*.)

PROFESSOR WILLARD:

Within the town limits: 2,640.

STAGE MANAGER:

Just a moment, Professor.
> *He whispers into the professor's ear.*

PROFESSOR WILLARD:

Oh, yes, indeed? — The population, *at the moment,* is 2,642. The Postal District brings in 507 more, making a total of 3,149. — Mortality and birth rates: constant. — By MacPherson's gauge: 6.032.

STAGE MANAGER:

Thank you very much, Professor. We're all very much obliged to you, I'm sure.

PROFESSOR WILLARD:

Not at all, sir; not at all.

STAGE MANAGER:

This way, Professor, and thank you again.
> *Exit* PROFESSOR WILLARD.

Now the political and social report: Editor Webb. — Oh, Mr. Webb?
> *Mrs. Webb appears at her back door.*

MRS. WEBB:

He'll be here in a minute. . . . He just cut his hand while he was eatin' an apple.

STAGE MANAGER:

Thank you, Mrs. Webb.

MRS. WEBB:

Charles! Everybody's waitin'.
> *Exit Mrs. Webb.*

STAGE MANAGER:

Mr. Webb is Publisher and Editor of the Grover's Corners *Sentinel.* That's our local paper, y'know.

*Mr. Webb enters from his house, pulling on his coat.
His finger is bound in a handkerchief.*

MR. WEBB:

Well . . . I don't have to tell you that we're run here by a
Board of Selectmen. — All males vote at the age of twenty-
one. Women vote indirect. We're lower middle class:
sprinkling of professional men . . . ten per cent illiterate
laborers. Politically, we're eighty-six per cent Republicans;
six per cent Democrats; four per cent Socialists; rest, indifferent.
Religiously, we're eighty-five per cent Protestants; twelve
per cent Catholics; rest, indifferent.

STAGE MANAGER:

Have you any comments, Mr. Webb?

MR. WEBB:

Very ordinary town, if you ask me. Little better behaved than
most. Probably a lot duller.
But our young people here seem to like it well enough.
Ninety per cent of 'em graduating from high school settle
down right here to live — even when they've been away to
college.

STAGE MANAGER:

Now, is there anyone in the audience who would like to ask
Editor Webb anything about the town?

WOMAN IN THE BALCONY:

Is there much drinking in Grover's Corners?

MR. WEBB:

Well, ma'am, I wouldn't know what you'd call *much*. Satiddy
nights the farmhands meet down in Ellery Greenough's
stable and holler some. We've got one or two town drunks,
but they're always having remorses every time an evangelist
comes to town. No, ma'am, I'd say likker ain't a regular
thing in the home here, except in the medicine chest. Right
good for snake bite, y'know — always was.

BELLIGERENT MAN AT BACK OF AUDITORIUM:

Is there no one in town aware of —

STAGE MANAGER:

Come forward, will you, where we can all hear you — What were you saying?

BELLIGERENT MAN:

Is there no one in town aware of social injustice and industrial inequality?

MR. WEBB:

Oh, yes, everybody is — somethin' terrible. Seems like they spend most of their time talking about who's rich and who's poor.

BELLIGERENT MAN:

Then why don't they do something about it?
He withdraws without waiting for an answer.

MR. WEBB:

Well, I dunno. . . . I guess we're all hunting like everybody else for a way the diligent and sensible can rise to the top and the lazy and quarrelsome can sink to the bottom. But it ain't easy to find. Meanwhile, we do all we can to help those that can't help themselves and those that can we leave alone. — Are there any other questions?

LADY IN A BOX:

Oh, Mr. Webb? Mr. Webb, is there any culture or love of beauty in Grover's Corners?

MR. WEBB:

Well, ma'am, there ain't much — not in the sense you mean. Come to think of it, there's some girls that play the piano at High School Commencement; but they ain't happy about it. No, ma'am, there isn't much culture; but maybe this is the place to tell you that we've got a lot of pleasures of a kind here: we like the sun comin' up over the mountain in the morning, and we all notice a good deal about the birds. We pay a lot of attention to them. And we watch the change of the seasons; yes, everybody knows about them. But those other things — you're right, ma'am, — there ain't much. — *Robinson Crusoe* and the Bible; and Handel's "Largo," we all know that; and Whistler's "Mother" — those are just about as far as we go.

LADY IN A BOX:

So I thought. Thank you, Mr. Webb.

STAGE MANAGER:

Thank you, Mr. Webb.
> *Mr. Webb retires.*

Now, we'll go back to the town. It's early afternoon. All 2,642 have had their dinners and all the dishes have been washed.
> *Mr. Webb, having removed his coat, returns and starts pushing a lawn mower to and fro beside his house.*

There's an early-afternoon calm in our town: a buzzin' and a hummin' from the school buildings; only a few buggies on Main Street — the horses dozing at the hitching posts; you all remember what it's like. Doc Gibbs is in his office, tapping people and making them say "ah." Mr. Webb's cuttin' his lawn over there; one man in ten thinks it's a privilege to push his own lawn mower.

No, sir. It's later than I thought. There are the children coming home from school already.
> *Shrill girls' voices are heard, off left. Emily comes along Main Street, carrying some books. There are some signs that she is imagining herself to be a lady of startling elegance.*

EMILY:

I *can't*, Lois. I've got to go home and help my mother. I *promised.*

MR. WEBB:

Emily, walk simply. Who do you think you are today?

EMILY:

Papa, you're terrible. One minute you tell me to stand up straight, and the next minute you call me names. I just don't listen to you.
> *She gives him an abrupt kiss.*

MR. WEBB:

Golly, I never got a kiss from such a great lady before.

> *He goes out of sight. Emily leans over and picks some flowers by the gate of her house.*
>
> *George Gibbs comes careening down Main Street. He is throwing a ball up to dizzying heights and waiting to catch it again. This sometimes requires his taking six steps backward. He bumps into an old lady invisible to us.*

GEORGE:

Excuse me, Mrs. Forrest.

STAGE MANAGER:

> *As Mrs. Forrest.*

Go out and play in the fields, young man. You got no business playing baseball on Main Street.

GEORGE:

Awfully sorry, Mrs. Forrest. — Hello, Emily.

EMILY:

H'lo.

GEORGE:

You made a fine speech in class.

EMILY:

Well ... I was really ready to make a speech about the Monroe Doctrine, but at the last minute Miss Corcoran made me talk about the Louisiana Purchase instead. I worked an awful long time on both of them.

GEORGE:

Gee, it's funny, Emily. From my window up there I can just see your head nights when you're doing your homework over in your room.

EMILY:

Why, can you?

GEORGE:

You certainly do stick to it, Emily. I don't see how you can sit still that long. I guess you like school.

EMILY:

Well, I always feel it's something you have to go through.

GEORGE:

Yeah.

EMILY:

I don't mind it really. It passes the time.

GEORGE:

Yeah. — Emily, what do you think? We might work out a kinda telegraph from your window to mine; and once in a while you could give me a kinda hint or two about one of those algebra problems. I don't mean the answers, Emily, of course not . . . just some little hint. . . .

EMILY:

Oh, I think *hints* are allowed. — So — ah — if you get stuck, George, you whistle to me; and I'll give you some hints.

GEORGE:

Emily, you're just naturally bright, I guess.

EMILY:

I figure that it's just the way a person's born.

GEORGE:

Yeah. But, you see, I want to be a farmer, and my Uncle Luke says whenever I'm ready I can come over and work on his farm, and if I'm any good I can just gradually have it.

EMILY:

You mean the house and everything?
> *Enter Mrs. Webb with a large bowl and sits on the bench by her trellis.*

GEORGE:

Yeah. Well, thanks . . . I better be getting out to the baseball field. Thanks for the talk, Emily. — Good afternoon, Mrs. Webb.

MRS. WEBB:

Good afternoon, George.

GEORGE:

So long, Emily.

EMILY:

So long, George.

MRS. WEBB:

Emily, come and help me string these beans for the winter. George Gibbs let himself have a real conversation, didn't he? Why, he's growing up. How old would George be?

EMILY:

I don't know.

MRS. WEBB:

Let's see. He must be almost sixteen.

EMILY:

Mama, I made a speech in class today and I was very good.

MRS. WEBB:

You must recite it to your father at supper. What was it about?

EMILY:

The Louisiana Purchase. It was like silk off a spool. I'm going to make speeches all my life. — Mama, are these big enough?

MRS. WEBB:

Try and get them a little bigger if you can.

EMILY:

Mama, will you answer me a question, serious?

MRS. WEBB:

Seriously, dear — not serious.

EMILY:

Seriously, — will you?

MRS. WEBB:

Of course, I will.

EMILY:

Mama, am I good looking?

MRS. WEBB:

Yes, of course you are. All my children have got good features; I'd be ashamed if they hadn't.

EMILY:

Oh, Mama, that's not what I mean. What I mean is: am I *pretty?*

MRS. WEBB:

I've already told you, yes. Now that's enough of that. You have a nice young pretty face. I never heard of such foolishness.

EMILY:

Oh, Mama, you never tell us the truth about anything.

MRS. WEBB:

I *am* telling you the truth.

EMILY:

Mama, were *you* pretty?

MRS. WEBB:

Yes, I was, if I do say it. I was the prettiest girl in town next to Mamie Cartwright.

EMILY:

But, Mama, you've got to say *some*thing about me. Am I pretty enough . . . to get anybody . . . to get people interested in me?

MRS. WEBB:

Emily, you make me tired. Now stop it. You're pretty enough

for all normal purposes. — Come along now and bring that bowl with you.

STAGE MANAGER:

Thank you. Thank you! That'll do. We'll have to interrupt

EMILY:

Oh, Mama, you're no help at all.

STAGE MANAGER:

Thank you. Thank you! That'll do. We'll have to interrupt again here. Thank you, Mrs. Webb; thank you, Emily.
Mrs. Webb and Emily withdraw.
There are some more things we want to explore about this town.
> *He comes to the center of the stage. During the following speech the lights gradually dim to darkness, leaving only a spot on him.*

I think this is a good time to tell you that the Cartwright interests have just begun building a new bank in Grover's Corners — had to go to Vermont for the marble, sorry to say. And they've asked a friend of mine what they should put in the cornerstone for people to dig up . . . a thousand years from now. . . . Of course, they've put in a copy of the *New York Times* and a copy of Mr. Webb's *Sentinel*. . . . We're kind of interested in this because some scientific fellas have found a way of painting all that reading matter with a glue — a silicate glue — that'll make it keep a thousand — two thousand years.
We're putting in a Bible . . . and the Constitution of the United States — and a copy of William Shakespeare's plays. What do you say, folks? What do you think?
Y'know — Babylon once had two million people in it, and all we know about 'em is the names of the kings and some copies of wheat contracts . . . and contracts for the sale of slaves. Yet every night all those families sat down to supper, and the father came home from his work, and the smoke went up the chimney, — same as here. And even in Greece and Rome, all we know about the *real* life of the people is what we can piece together out of the joking poems and the comedies they wrote for the theater back then.
So I'm going to have a copy of this play put in the cornerstone and the people a thousand years from now'll know a few

simple facts about us — more than the Treaty of Versailles
and the Lindbergh flight.

See what I mean?

So — people a thousand years from now — this is the way we
were in the provinces north of New York at the beginning of
the twentieth century. — This is the way we were: in our
growing up and in our marrying and in our living and in our
dying.

> *A choir partially concealed in the orchestra pit has
> begun singing "Blessed Be the Tie That Binds."*
> *Simon Stimpson stands directing them.*
> *Two ladders have been pushed onto the stage; they
> serve as indication of the second story in the Gibbs
> and Webb houses. George and Emily mount them
> and apply themselves to their schoolwork.*
> *Dr. Gibbs has entered and is seated in his kitchen
> reading.*

Well! — good deal of time's gone by. It's evening.

You can hear choir practice going on in the Congregational
Church.

The children are at home doing their schoolwork.

The day's running down like a tired clock.

SIMON STIMSON:

Now look here, everybody. Music come into the world to give
pleasure. — Softer! Softer! Get it out of your heads that
music's only good when it's loud. You leave loudness to the
Methodists. You couldn't beat 'em, even if you wanted to.
Now again. Tenors!

GEORGE:

Hssst! Emily!

EMILY:

Hello.

GEORGE:

Hello!

EMILY:

I can't work at all. The moonlight's so *terrible*.

GEORGE:
Emily, did you get the third problem?

EMILY:
Which?

GEORGE:
The *third?*

EMILY:
Why, yes, George — that's the easiest of them all.

GEORGE:
I don't see it. Emily, can you give me a hint?

EMILY:
I'll tell you one thing: the answer's in yards.

GEORGE:
!!! In yards? How do you mean?

EMILY:
In *square* yards.

GEORGE:
Oh . . . in square yards.

EMILY:
Yes, George, don't you see?

GEORGE:
Yeah.

EMILY:
In square yards of *wallpaper.*

GEORGE:
Wallpaper, — oh, I see. Thanks a lot, Emily.

EMILY:
You're welcome. My, isn't the moonlight *terrible?* And choir practice going on. — I think if you hold your breath you can hear the train all the way to Contoocook. Hear it?

GEORGE:

M-m-m — What do you know!

EMILY:

Well, I guess I better go back and try to work.

GEORGE:

Good night, Emily. And thanks.

EMILY:

Good night, George.

SIMON STIMSON:

Before I forget it: how many of you will be able to come in Tuesday afternoon and sing at Fred Hersey's wedding? — show your hands. That'll be fine; that'll be right nice. We'll do the same music we did for Jane Trowbridge's last month. — Now we'll do: "Art Thou Weary; Art Thou Languid?" It's a question, ladies and gentlemen, make it talk. Ready.

DR. GIBBS:

Oh, George, can you come down a minute?

GEORGE:

Yes, Pa.

He descends the ladder.

DR. GIBBS:

Make yourself comfortable, George; I'll only keep you a minute. George, how old are you?

GEORGE:

I? I'm sixteen, almost seventeen.

DR. GIBBS:

What do you want to do after school's over?

GEORGE:

Why, you know, Pa. I want to be a farmer on Uncle Luke's farm.

DR. GIBBS:

You'll be willing, will you, to get up early and milk and feed the stock . . . and you'll be able to hoe and hay all day?

GEORGE:

Sure, I will. What are you . . . what do you mean, Pa?

DR. GIBBS:

Well, George, while I was in my office today I heard a funny sound . . . and what do you think it was? It was your mother chopping wood. There you see your mother — getting up early; cooking meals all day long; washing and ironing; — and still she has to go out in the back yard and chop wood. I suppose she just got tired of asking you. She just gave up and decided it was easier to do it herself. And you eat her meals, and put on the clothes she keeps nice for you, and you run off and play baseball, — like she's some hired girl we keep around the house but that we don't like very much. Well, I knew all I had to do was call your attention to it. Here's a handkerchief, son. George, I've decided to raise your spending money twenty-five cents a week. Not, of course, for chopping wood for your mother, because that's a present you give her, but because you're getting older — and I imagine there are lots of things you must find to do with it.

GEORGE:

Thanks, Pa.

DR. GIBBS:

Let's see — tomorrow's your payday. You can count on it — Hmm. Probably Rebecca'll feel she ought to have some more too. Wonder what could have happened to your mother. Choir practice never was as late as this before.

GEORGE:

It's only half past eight, Pa.

DR. GIBBS:

I don't know why she's in that old choir. She hasn't any more voice than an old crow. . . . Traipsin' around the streets at this hour of the night . . . Just about time you retired, don't you think?

GEORGE:

Yes, Pa.

George mounts to his place on the ladder.
Laughter and good nights can be heard on stage left
and presently Mrs. Gibbs, Mrs. Soames, and Mrs.
Webb come down Main Street. When they arrive
at the corner of the stage, they stop.

MRS. SOAMES:

Good night, Martha. Good night, Mr. Foster.

MRS. WEBB:

I'll tell Mr. Webb; I *know* he'll want to put it in the paper.

MRS. GIBBS:

My, it's late!

MRS. SOAMES:

Good night, Irma.

MRS. GIBBS:

Real nice choir practice, wa'n't it? Myrtle Webb! Look at that moon, will you! Tsk-tsk-tsk. Potato weather, for sure.
They are silent a moment, gazing up at the moon.

MRS. SOAMES:

Naturally I didn't want to say a word about it in front of those others, but now we're alone — really, it's the worst scandal that ever was in this town!

MRS. GIBBS:

What?

MRS. SOAMES:

Simon Stimson!

MRS. GIBBS:

Now, Louella!

MRS. SOAMES:

But, Julia! To have the organist of a church *drink* and *drunk* year after year. You know he was drunk tonight.

MRS. GIBBS:

Now, Louella! We all know about Mr. Stimson, and we all

know about the troubles he's been through, and Dr. Ferguson
knows too, and if Dr. Ferguson keeps him on there in his job,
the only thing the rest of us can do is just not to notice it.

MRS. SOAMES:

Not to notice it! But it's getting worse.

MRS. WEBB:

No, it isn't, Louella. It's getting better. I've been in that choir
twice as long as you have. It doesn't happen anywhere near so
often. . . . My, I hate to go to bed on a night like this. — I
better hurry. Those children'll be sitting up till all hours.
Good night, Louella.
> *They all exchange good nights. She hurries down-*
> *stage, enters her house and disappears.*

MRS. GIBBS:

Can you get home safe, Louella?

MRS. SOAMES:

It's as bright as day. I can see Mr. Soames scowling at the
window now. You'd think we'd been to a dance the way the
menfolk carry on.
> *More good nights. Mrs. Gibbs arrives at her home and*
> *passes through the trellis into the kitchen.*

MRS. GIBBS:

Well, we had a real good time.

DR. GIBBS:

You're late enough.

MRS. GIBBS:

Why, Frank, it ain't any later 'n usual.

DR. GIBBS:

And you stopping at the corner to gossip with a lot of hens.

MRS. GIBBS:

Now, Frank, don't be grouchy. Come out and smell the
heliotrope in the moonlight.
> *They stroll out arm in arm along the footlights.*
Isn't that wonderful? What did you do all the time I was away?

DR. GIBBS:

Oh, I read — as usual. What were the girls gossiping about tonight?

MRS. GIBBS:

Well, believe me, Frank — there is something to gossip about.

DR. GIBBS:

Hmm! Simon Stimson far gone, was he?

MRS. GIBBS:

Worst I've ever seen him. How'll that end, Frank? Dr. Ferguson can't forgive him forever.

DR. GIBBS:

I guess I know more about Simon Stimson's affairs than anybody in this town. Some people ain't made for small-town life. I don't know how that'll end; but there's nothing we can do but just leave it alone. Come, get in.

MRS. GIBBS:

No, not yet . . . Frank, I'm worried about you.

DR. GIBBS:

What are you worried about?

MRS. GIBBS:

I think it's my duty to make plans for you to get a real rest and change. And if I get that legacy, well, I'm going to insist on it.

DR. GIBBS:

Now, Julia, there's no sense in going over that again.

MRS. GIBBS:

Frank, you're just *unreasonable!*

DR. GIBBS:

> *Starting into the house.*

Come on, Julia, it's getting late. First thing you know you'll catch cold. I gave George a piece of my mind tonight. I reckon you'll have your wood chopped for a while anyway. No, no, start getting upstairs.

MRS. GIBBS:

Oh, dear. There's always so many things to pick up, seems like. You know, Frank, Mrs. Fairchild always locks her front door every night. All those people up that part of town do.

DR. GIBBS:

Blowing out the lamp.

They're all getting citified, that's the trouble with them. They haven't got nothing fit to burgle and everybody knows it.

They disappear.

Rebecca climbs up the ladder beside George.

GEORGE:

Get out, Rebecca. There's only room for one at this window. You're always spoiling everything.

REBECCA:

Well, let me look just a minute.

GEORGE:

Use your own window.

REBECCA:

I did, but there's no moon there. . . . George, do you know what I think, do you? I think maybe the moon's getting nearer and nearer and there'll be a big 'splosion.

GEORGE:

Rebecca, you don't know anything. If the moon were getting nearer, the guys that sit up all night with telescopes would see it first and they'd tell about it, and it'd be in all the newspapers.

REBECCA:

George, is the moon shining on South America, Canada, and half the whole world?

GEORGE:

Well — prob'ly is.

The Stage Manager strolls on.

Pause. The sound of crickets is heard.

STAGE MANAGER:

Nine thirty. Most of the lights are out. No, there's Constable Warren trying a few doors on Main Street. And here comes Editor Webb, after putting his newspaper to bed.

> *Mr. Warren, an elderly policeman, comes along Main Street from the right, Mr. Webb from the left.*

MR. WEBB:

Good evening, Bill.

CONSTABLE WARREN:

Evenin', Mr. Webb.

MR. WEBB:

Quite a moon!

CONSTABLE WARREN:

Yepp.

MR. WEBB:

All quiet tonight?

CONSTABLE WARREN:

Simon Stimson is rollin' around a little. Just saw his wife movin' out to hunt for him so I looked the other way — there he is now.

> *Simon Stimson comes down Main Street from the left, only a trace of unsteadiness in his walk.*

MR. WEBB:

Good evening, Simon . . . Town seems to have settled down for the night pretty well. . . .

> *Simon Stimson comes up to him and pauses a moment and stares at him, swaying slightly.*

Good evening . . . Yes, most of the town's settled down for the night, Simon. . . . I guess we better do the same. Can I walk along a ways with you?

> *Simon Stimson continues on his way without a word and disappears at the right.*

Good night.

CONSTABLE WARREN:

I don't know how that's goin' to end, Mr. Webb.

MR. WEBB:

Well, he's seen a peck of trouble, one thing after another. . . .
Oh, Bill . . . if you see my boy smoking cigarettes, just give
him a word, will you? He thinks a lot of you, Bill.

CONSTABLE WARREN:

I don't think he smokes no cigarettes, Mr. Webb. Leastways,
not more'n two or three a year.

MR. WEBB:

Hm . . . I hope not. — Well, good night, Bill.

CONSTABLE WARREN:

Good night, Mr. Webb.
        Exit.

MR. WEBB:

Who's that up there? Is that you, Myrtle?

EMILY:

No, it's me, Papa.

MR. WEBB:

Why aren't you in bed?

EMILY:

I don't know. I just can't sleep yet, Papa. The moonlight's
so *won*-derful. And the smell of Mrs. Gibbs' heliotrope. Can
you smell it?

MR. WEBB:

Hm . . . Yes. Haven't any troubles on your mind, have you,
Emily?

EMILY:

Troubles, Papa? *No.*

MR. WEBB:

Well, enjoy yourself, but don't let your mother catch you.
Good night, Emily.

EMILY:

Good night, Papa.

> *Mr. Webb crosses into the house, whistling "Blessed Be the Tie That Binds" and disappears.*

REBECCA:

I never told you about that letter Jane Crofut got from her minister when she was sick. He wrote Jane a letter and on the envelope the address was like this: It said: Jane Crofut; The Crofut Farm; Grover's Corners; Sutton County; New Hampshire; United States of America.

GEORGE:

What's funny about that?

REBECCA:

But listen, it's not finished: the United States of America; Continent of North America; Western Hemisphere; the Earth; the Solar System; the Universe; the Mind of God — that's what it said on the envelope.

GEORGE:

What do you know!

REBECCA:

And the postman brought it just the same.

GEORGE:

What do you know!

STAGE MANAGER:

That's the end of the First Act, friends. You can go and smoke now, those that smoke.

CURTAIN

QUESTIONS

1. *Our Town* takes place in a small New England town between 1901 and 1938 — the year of the play's first production. Yet there are references to Napoleon, Babylon, Gettysburg, the Western Hemisphere, the Solar

System, and the mind of God in the first act. What is the purpose of these references? Is Grover's Corners meant to be "more than" a small, neglected New England town? What is that "more than"?

2. How important are the facts about rock formations, temperature, and rainfall that Professor Willard tells us about Grover's Corners? What are the really important things about Grover's Corners?

3. What happens to our understanding about Grover's Corners when we realize a fossil several million years old was found in "Silas Peckham's cow pasture"?

4. Is *Our Town* a wholly happy place? Is Emily totally good? How does she feel about herself at the breakfast table? What does Rebecca want most? What does Simon Stimson's behavior tell us about life in Grover's Corners? (While we can never really know what happened to him, we can speculate from the tone of his comments to the choir why he took to drinking.) How sensitive a musician does he seem to be? What does Grover's Corners lack?

5. Who might the Stage Manager be? How does he feel about life in Grover's Corners? Does he intend for us to share his feelings? Would you like to live in Grover's Corners? Explain why or why not.

ACT TWO

The tables and chairs of the two kitchens are still on the stage.
The ladders and the small bench have been withdrawn.
The Stage Manager has been at his accustomed place watching the audience return to its seats.

STAGE MANAGER:
Three years have gone by.
Yes, the sun's come up over a thousand times.
Summers and winters have cracked the mountains a little bit more and the rains have brought down some of the dirt.
Some babies that weren't even born before have begun talking regular sentences already; and a number of people who thought they were right young and spry have noticed that they can't bound up a flight of stairs like they used to, without their heart fluttering a little.
All that can happen in a thousand days.

Nature's been pushing and contriving in other ways, too: a number of young people fell in love and got married.

Yes, the mountain got bit away a few fractions of an inch; millions of gallons of water went by the mill; and here and there a new home was set up under a roof.

Almost everybody in the world gets married, — you know what I mean? In our town there aren't hardly any exceptions. Most everybody in the world climbs into their graves married.

The First Act was called the Daily Life. This act is called Love and Marriage. There's another act coming after this: I reckon you can guess what that's about.

So:

It's three years later. It's 1904.

It's July 7th, just after High School Commencement.

That's the time most of our young people jump up and get married.

Soon as they've passed their last examinations in solid geometry and Cicero's Orations, looks like they suddenly feel themselves fit to be married.

It's early morning. Only this time it's been raining. It's been pouring and thundering.

Mrs. Gibbs' garden, and Mrs. Webb's here: drenched.

All those bean poles and pea vines: drenched.

All yesterday over there on Main Street, the rain looked like curtains being blown along.

Hm . . . it may begin again any minute.

There! You can hear the 5:45 for Boston.

> *Mrs. Gibbs and Mrs. Webb enter their kitchens and start the day as in the First Act.*

And there's Mrs. Gibbs and Mrs. Webb come down to make breakfast, just as though it were an ordinary day. I don't have to point out to the women in my audience that those ladies they see before them, both of those ladies cooked three meals a day — one of 'em for twenty years, the other for forty — and no summer vacation. They brought up two children apiece, washed, cleaned the house, — and *never a nervous breakdown.*

It's like what one of those Middle West poets said: You've got to love life to have life, and you've got to have life to love life. . . .

It's what they call a vicious circle.

HOWIE NEWSOME:
>   *Off stage left.*

Giddap, Bessie!

STAGE MANAGER:

Here comes Howie Newsome delivering the milk. And there's Si Crowell delivering the papers like his brother before him.
>   *Si Crowell has entered hurling imaginary newspapers into doorways; Howie Newsome has come along Main Street with Bessie.*

SI CROWELL:

Morning, Howie.

HOWIE NEWSOME:

Morning, Si. — Anything in the papers I ought to know?

SI CROWELL:

Nothing much, except we're losing about the best baseball pitcher Grover's Corners ever had — George Gibbs.

HOWIE NEWSOME:

Reckon he is.

SI CROWELL:

He could hit and run bases, too.

HOWIE NEWSOME:

Yep. Mighty fine ball player. — Whoa! Bessie! I guess I can stop and talk if I've a mind to!

SI CROWELL:

I don't see how he could give up a thing like that just to get married. Would you, Howie?

HOWIE NEWSOME:

Can't tell, Si. Never had no talent that way.
>   *Constable Warren enters. They exchange good mornings.*

You're up early, Bill.

CONSTABLE WARREN:

Seein' if there's anything I can do to prevent a flood. River's been risin' all night.

HOWIE NEWSOME:

Si Crowell's all worked up here about George Gibbs' retiring from baseball.

CONSTABLE WARREN:

Yes, sir; that's the way it goes. Back in '84 we had a player, Si — even George Gibbs couldn't touch him. Name of Hank Todd. Went down to Maine and become a parson. Wonderful ball player. — Howie, how does the weather look to you?

HOWIE NEWSOME:

Oh, 'tain't bad. Think maybe it'll clear up for good.
> *Constable Warren and Si Crowell continue on their way.*
> *Howie Newsome brings the milk first to Mrs. Gibbs' house. She meets him by the trellis.*

MRS. GIBBS:

Good morning, Howie. Do you think it's going to rain again?

HOWIE NEWSOME:

Morning, Mrs. Gibbs. It rained so heavy, I think maybe it'll clear up.

MRS. GIBBS:

Certainly hope it will.

HOWIE NEWSOME:

How much did you want today?

MRS. GIBBS:

I'm going to have a houseful of relations, Howie. Looks to me like I'll need three-a-milk and two-a-cream.

HOWIE NEWSOME:

My wife says to tell you we both hope they'll be very happy, Mrs. Gibbs. Know they *will*.

MRS. GIBBS:

Thanks a lot, Howie. Tell your wife I hope she gits there to the wedding.

HOWIE NEWSOME:

Yes, she'll be there; she'll be there if she kin.
Howie Newsome crosses to Mrs. Webb's house.
Morning, Mrs. Webb.

MRS. WEBB:

Oh, good morning, Mr. Newsome. I told you four quarts of milk, but I hope you can spare me another.

HOWIE NEWSOME:

Yes'm . . . and the two of cream.

MRS. WEBB:

Will it start raining again, Mr. Newsome?

HOWIE NEWSOME:

Well. Just sayin' to Mrs. Gibbs as how it may lighten up. Mrs. Newsome told me to tell you as how we hope they'll both be very happy, Mrs. Webb. Know they *will*.

MRS. WEBB:

Thank you, and thank Mrs. Newsome, and we're counting on seeing you at the wedding.

HOWIE NEWSOME:

Yes, Mrs. Webb. We hope to git there. Couldn't miss that. Come on, Bessie.
Exit Howie Newsome.
Dr. Gibbs descends in shirt sleeves and sits down at his breakfast table.

DR. GIBBS:

Well, Ma, the day has come. You're losin' one of your chicks.

MRS. GIBBS:

Frank Gibbs, don't you say another word. I feel like crying every minute. Sit down and drink your coffee.

·DR. GIBBS:

The groom's up shaving himself — only there ain't an awful lot to shave. Whistling and singing, like he's glad to leave us. — Every now and then he says "I do" to the mirror, but it don't sound convincing to me.

MRS. GIBBS:

I declare, Frank, I don't know how he'll get along. I've arranged his clothes and seen to it he's put warm things on, — Frank! they're too *young*. Emily won't think of such things. He'll catch his death of cold within a week.

DR. GIBBS:

I was remembering my wedding morning, Julia.

MRS. GIBBS:

Now don't start that, Frank Gibbs.

DR. GIBBS:

I was the scaredest young fella in the State of New Hampshire. I thought I'd make a mistake for sure. And when I saw you comin' down that aisle, I thought you were the prettiest girl I'd ever seen, but the only trouble was that I'd never seen you before. There I was in the Congregational Church marryin' a total stranger.

MRS. GIBBS:

And how do you think I felt! — Frank, weddings are perfectly awful things. Farces — that's what they are!
She puts a plate before him.
Here, I've made something for you.

DR. GIBBS:

Why, Julia Hersey — French toast!

MRS. GIBBS:

'Tain't hard to make and I had to do *some*thing.
Pause. Dr. Gibbs pours on the syrup.

DR. GIBBS:

How'd you sleep last night, Julia?

MRS. GIBBS:

Well, I heard a lot of the hours struck off.

DR. GIBBS:

Ye-e-s! I get a shock every time I think of George setting out to be a family man — that great gangling thing! — I tell you Julia, there's nothing so terrifying in the world as a *son*. The relation of father and son is the darndest, awkwardest —

MRS. GIBBS:

Well, mother and daughter's no picnic, let me tell you.

DR. GIBBS:

They'll have a lot of troubles, I suppose, but that's none of our business. Everybody has a right to their own troubles.

MRS. GIBBS:

> *At the table, drinking her coffee, meditatively.*

Yes . . . people are meant to go through life two by two. 'Tain't natural to be lonesome.

> *Pause. Dr. Gibbs starts laughing.*

DR. GIBBS:

Julia, do you know one of the things I was scared of when I married you?

MRS. GIBBS:

Oh, go along with you!

DR. GIBBS:

I was afraid we wouldn't have material for conversation more'n'd last us a few weeks.

> *Both laugh.*

I was afraid we'd run out and eat our meals in silence, that's a fact. — Well, you and I been conversing for twenty years now without any noticeable barren spells.

MRS. GIBBS:

Well, — good weather, bad weather — 'tain't very choice, but I always find something to say.

> *She goes to the foot of the stairs.*

Did you hear Rebecca stirring around upstairs?

DR. GIBBS:

No. Only day of the year Rebecca hasn't been managing everybody's business up there. She's hiding in her room. — I got the impression she's crying.

MRS. GIBBS:

Lord's sakes! — This has got to stop. — Rebecca! Rebecca! Come and get your breakfast.
> *George comes rattling down the stairs, very brisk.*

GEORGE:

Good morning, everybody. Only five more hours to live.
> *Makes the gesture of cutting his throat, and a loud "k-k-k," and starts through the trellis.*

MRS. GIBBS:

George Gibbs, where are you going?

GEORGE:

Just stepping across the grass to see my girl.

MRS. GIBBS:

Now, George! You put on your overshoes. It's raining torrents. You don't go out of this house without you're prepared for it.

GEORGE:

Aw, Ma. It's just a *step!*

MRS. GIBBS:

George! You'll catch your death of cold and cough all through the service.

DR. GIBBS:

George, do as your mother tells you!
> *Dr. Gibbs goes upstairs.*
> *George returns reluctantly to the kitchen and panto-mimes putting on overshoes.*

MRS. GIBBS:

From tomorrow on you can kill yourself in all weathers, but while you're in my house you'll live wisely, thank you. —

Maybe Mrs. Webb isn't used to callers at seven in the morning.
— Here, take a cup of coffee first.

GEORGE:

Be back in a minute.
   He crosses the stage, leaping over the puddles.
Good morning, Mother Webb.

MRS. WEBB:

Goodness! You frightened me! — Now, George, you can come
in a minute out of the wet, but you know I can't ask you in.

GEORGE:

Why not — ?

MRS. WEBB:

George, you know's well as I do: the groom can't see his bride
on his wedding day, not until he sees her in church.

GEORGE:

Aw! — that's just a superstition. — Good morning, Mr. Webb.
   Enter Mr. Webb.

MR. WEBB:

Good morning, George.

GEORGE:

Mr. Webb, you don't believe in that superstition, do you?

MR. WEBB:

There's a lot of common sense in some superstitions, George.
   He sits at the table, facing right.

MRS. WEBB:

Millions have folla'd it, George, and you don't want to be the
first to fly in the face of custom.

GEORGE:

How is Emily?

MRS. WEBB:

She hasn't waked up yet. I haven't heard a sound out of her.

GEORGE:

Emily's *asleep*!!!

MRS. WEBB:

No wonder! We were up 'til all hours, sewing and packing. Now I'll tell you what I'll do; you set down here a minute with Mr. Webb and drink this cup of coffee; and I'll go upstairs and see she doesn't come down and surprise you. There's some bacon, too; but don't be long about it.

> *Exit Mrs. Webb.*
> *Embarrassed silence.*
> *Mr. Webb dunks doughnuts in his coffee.*
> *More silence.*

MR. WEBB:

> *Suddenly and loudly.*

Well, George, how are you?

GEORGE:

> *Startled, choking over his coffee.*

Oh, fine, I'm fine.

> *Pause.*

Mr. Webb, what sense could there be in a superstition like that?

MR. WEBB:

Well, you see, — on her wedding morning a girl's head's apt to be full of . . . clothes and one thing and another. Don't you think that's probably it?

GEORGE:

Ye-e-s. I never thought of that.

MR. WEBB:

A girl's apt to be a mite nervous on her wedding day.

> *Pause.*

GEORGE:

I wish a fellow could get married without all that marching up and down.

MR. WEBB:

Every man that's ever lived has felt that way about it, George;

but it hasn't been any use. It's the womenfolk who've built up weddings, my boy. For a while now the women have it all their own. A man looks pretty small at a wedding, George. All those good women standing shoulder to shoulder making sure that the knot's tied in a mighty public way.

GEORGE:

But . . . you *believe* in it, don't you, Mr. Webb?

MR. WEBB:
With alacrity.
Oh, yes; *oh, yes.* Don't you misunderstand me, my boy. Marriage is a wonderful thing, — wonderful thing. And don't you forget that, George.

GEORGE:

No, sir. — Mr. Webb, how old were you when you got married?

MR. WEBB:

Well, you see: I'd been to college and I'd taken a little time to get settled. But Mrs. Webb — she wasn't much older than what Emily is. Oh, age hasn't much to do with it, George, — not compared with . . . uh . . . other things.

GEORGE:

What were you going to say, Mr. Webb?

MR. WEBB:

Oh, I don't know. — Was I going to say something?
Pause.
George, I was thinking the other night of some advice my father gave me when I got married. Charles, he said, Charles, start out early showing who's boss, he said. Best thing to do is to give an order, even if it don't make sense; just so she'll learn to obey. And he said: if anything about your wife irritates you — her conversation, or anything — just get up and leave the house. That'll make it clear to her, he said. And, oh, yes! he said never, *never* let your wife know how much money you have, never.

GEORGE:

Well, Mr. Webb . . . I don't think I could . . . .

MR. WEBB:

So I took the opposite of my father's advice, and I've been happy ever since. And let that be a lesson to you, George, never to ask advice on personal matters. — George, are you going to raise chickens on your farm?

GEORGE:

What?

MR. WEBB:

Are you going to raise chickens on your farm?

GEORGE:

Uncle Luke's never been much interested, but I thought —

MR. WEBB:

A book came into my office the other day, George, on the Philo System of raising chickens. I want you to read it. I'm thinking of beginning in a small way in the back yard, and I'm going to put an incubator in the cellar —

Enter Mrs. Webb.

MRS. WEBB:

Charles, are you talking about that old incubator again? I thought you two'd be talking about things worth while.

MR. WEBB:

Bitingly.

Well, Myrtle, if you want to give the boy some good advice, I'll go upstairs and leave you alone with him.

MRS. WEBB:

Pulling George up.

George, Emily's got to come downstairs and eat her breakfast. She sends you her love, but she doesn't want to lay eyes on you. Good-bye.

GEORGE:

Good-bye.

George crosses the stage to his own home, bewildered and crestfallen. He slowly dodges a puddle and disappears into his house.

MR. WEBB:

Myrtle, I guess you don't know about that older superstition.

MRS. WEBB:

What do you mean, Charles?

MR. WEBB:

Since the cave men: no bridegroom should see his father-in-law on the day of the wedding, or near it. Now remember that.

> *Both leave the stage.*

STAGE MANAGER:

Thank you very much, Mr. and Mrs. Webb. — Now I have to interrupt again here. You see, we want to know how all this began — this wedding, this plan to spend a lifetime together. I'm awfully interested in how big things like that begin.

You know how it is: you're twenty-one or twenty-two and you make some decisions; then whisssh! you're seventy: you've been a lawyer for fifty years, and that white-haired lady at your side has eaten over fifty thousand meals with you.

How do such things begin?

George and Emily are going to show you now the conversation they had when they first knew that . . . that . . . as the saying goes . . . they were meant for one another.

But before they do it I want you to try and remember what it was like to have been very young.

And particularly the days when you were first in love; when you were like a person sleepwalking, and you didn't quite see the street you were in, and didn't quite hear everything that was said to you.

You're just a little bit crazy. Will you remember that, please? Now they'll be coming out of high school at three o'clock. George has just been elected President of the Junior Class, and as it's June, that means he'll be President of the Senior Class all next year. And Emily's just been elected Secretary and Treasurer.

I don't have to tell you how important that is.

> *He places a board across the backs of two chairs,*
> *which he takes from those at the Gibbs family's*

table. He brings two high stools from the wings and places them behind the board. Persons sitting on the stools will be facing the audience. This is the counter of Mr. Morgan's drugstore. The sounds of young people's voices are heard off left.

Yepp, — there they are coming down Main Street now.

Emily, carrying an armful of — imaginary — school-books, comes along Main Street from the left.

EMILY:

I can't, Louise. I've got to go home. Good-bye. Oh, Ernestine! Ernestine! Can you come over tonight and do Latin? Isn't that Cicero the worst thing — ! Tell your mother you *have* to. G'bye.

G'bye, Helen. G'bye, Fred.

George, also carrying books, catches up with her.

GEORGE;

Can I carry your books home for you, Emily?

EMILY:

Coolly.

Why . . . uh . . . Thank you. It isn't far.

She gives them to him.

GEORGE:

Excuse me a minute, Emily. — Say, Bob, if I'm a little late, start practice anyway. And give Herb some long high ones.

EMILY:

Good-bye, Lizzy.

GEORGE:

Good-bye, Lizzy. — I'm awfully glad you were elected, too, Emily.

EMILY:

Thank you.

They have been standing on Main Street, almost against the back wall. They take the first steps toward the audience when George stops and says:

GEORGE:

Emily, why are you mad at me?

EMILY:

I'm not mad at you.

GEORGE:

You've been treating me so funny lately.

EMILY:

Well, since you ask me, I might as well say it right out, George, —
>   *She catches sight of a teacher passing.*
Good-bye, Miss Corcoran.

GEORGE:

Good-bye, Miss Corcoran. — Wha — what is it?

EMILY:

>   *Not scoldingly; finding it difficult to say.*
I don't like the whole change that's come over you in the last year. I'm sorry if that hurts your feelings, but I've got to — tell the truth and shame the devil.

GEORGE:

A *change?* — Wha — what do you mean?

EMILY:

Well, up to a year ago I used to like you a lot. And I used to watch you as you did everything... because we'd been friends so long... and then you began spending all your time at *baseball* ... and you never stopped to speak to anybody any more. Not even to your own family you didn't ... and, George, it's a fact, you've got awful conceited and stuck-up, and all the girls say so. They may not say so to your face, but that's what they say about you behind your back, and it hurts me to hear them say it, but I've got to agree with them a little. I'm sorry if it hurts your feelings ... but I can't be sorry I said it.

GEORGE:

I ... I'm glad you said it, Emily. I never thought that such a thing was happening to me. I guess it's hard for a fella not to have faults creep into his character.

They take a step or two in silence, then stand still in misery.

EMILY:

I always expect a man to be perfect and I think he should be.

GEORGE:

Oh . . . I don't think it's possible to be perfect, Emily.

EMILY:

Well, my *father* is, and as far as I can see *your* father is. There's no reason on earth why you shouldn't be, too.

GEORGE:

Well, I feel it's the other way round. That men aren't naturally good; but girls are.

EMILY:

Well, you might as well know right now that I'm not perfect. It's not as easy for a girl to be perfect as a man, because we girls are more — more — nervous. — Now I'm sorry I said all that about you. I don't know what made me say it.

GEORGE:

Emily, —

EMILY:

Now I can see it's not the truth at all. And I suddenly feel that it isn't important, anyway.

GEORGE:

Emily . . . would you like an ice-cream soda, or something, before you go home?

EMILY:

Well, thank you. . . . I would.
> *They advance toward the audience and make an abrupt right turn, opening the door of Morgan's drug-store. Under strong emotion, Emily keeps her face down. George speaks to some passers-by.*

GEORGE:

Hello, Stew, — how are you? — Good afternoon, Mrs. Slocum.
> *The Stage Manager, wearing spectacles and assuming*

*the role of Mr. Morgan, enters abruptly from the right
and stands between the audience and the counter of
his soda fountain.*

STAGE MANAGER:

Hello, George. Hello, Emily. — What'll you have? — Why,
Emily Webb, — what you been crying about?

GEORGE:

He gropes for an explanation.
She . . . she just got an awful scare, Mr. Morgan. She almost
got run over by that hardware-store wagon. Everybody says
that Tom Huckins drives like a crazy man.

STAGE MANAGER:

Drawing a drink of water.
Well, now! You take a drink of water, Emily. You look all
shook up, I tell you, you've got to look both ways before you
cross Main Street these days. Gets worse every year. —
What'll you have?

EMILY:

I'll have a strawberry phosphate, thank you, Mr. Morgan.

GEORGE:

No, no, Emily. Have an ice-cream soda with me. Two
strawberry ice-cream sodas, Mr. Morgan.

STAGE MANAGER:

Working the faucets.
Two strawberry ice-cream sodas, yes sir. Yes, sir. There are a
hundred and twenty-five horses in Grover's Corners this
minute I'm talking to you. State Inspector was in here yester-
day. And now they're bringing in these auto-mo-biles, the
best thing to do is to just stay home. Why, I can remember
when a dog could go to sleep all day in the middle of Main
Street and nothing come along to disturb him.
He sets the imaginary glasses before them.
There they are. Enjoy 'em.
He sees a customer, right.
Yes, Mrs. Ellis. What can I do for you?
He goes out right.

EMILY:

They're so expensive.

GEORGE:

No, no, — don't you think of that. We're celebrating our election. And then do you know what else I'm celebrating?

EMILY:

N-no.

GEORGE:

I'm celebrating because I've got a friend who tells me all the things that ought to be told me.

EMILY:

George, *please* don't think of that. I don't know why I said it. It's not true. You're —

GEORGE:

No, Emily, you stick to it. I'm glad you spoke to me like you did. But you'll *see*: I'm going to change so quick — you bet I'm going to change. And, Emily, I want to ask you a favor.

EMILY:

What?

GEORGE:

Emily, if I go away to State Agriculture College next year, will you write me a letter once in a while?

EMILY:

I certainly will. I certainly will, George . . . .
> *Pause. They start sipping the sodas through the straws.*

It certainly seems like being away three years you'd get out of touch with things. Maybe letters from Grover's Corners wouldn't be so interesting after a while. Grover's Corners isn't a very important place when you think of all — New Hampshire; but I think it's a very nice town.

GEORGE:

The day wouldn't come when I wouldn't want to know everything that's happening here. I know *that's* true, Emily.

EMILY:

Well, I'll try to make my letters interesting.
  Pause.

GEORGE:

Y'know, Emily, whenever I meet a farmer, I ask him if he
thinks it's important to go to Agriculture School to be a good
farmer.

EMILY:

Why, George —

GEORGE:

Yeah, and some of them say that it's even a waste of time. You
can get all those things, anyway, out of the pamphlets the
government sends out. And Uncle Luke's getting old, — he's
about ready for me to start in taking over his farm tomorrow,
if I could.

EMILY:

My!

GEORGE:

And, like you say, being gone all that time . . . in other places
and meeting other people . . . Gosh, if anything like that can
happen, I don't want to go away. I guess new people aren't
any better than old ones. I'll bet they almost never are.
Emily . . . I feel that you're as good a friend as I've got. I
don't need to go and meet the people in other towns.

EMILY:

But, George, maybe it's very important for you to go and learn
all that about — cattle judging and soils and those things. . . .
Of course, I don't know.

GEORGE:

  After a pause, very seriously.
Emily, I'm going to make up my mind right now. I won't
go. I'll tell Pa about it tonight.

EMILY:

Why, George, I don't see why you have to decide right now.
It's a whole year away.

GEORGE:

Emily, I'm glad you spoke to me about that . . . that fault in my character. What you said was right; but there was *one* thing wrong in it, and that was when you said that for a year I wasn't noticing people, and . . . you, for instance. Why, you say you were watching me when I did everything . . . I was doing the same about you all the time. Why, sure, — I always thought about you as one of the chief people I thought about. I always made sure where you were sitting on the bleachers, and who you were with, and for three days now I've been trying to walk home with you; but something's always got in the way. Yesterday I was standing over against the wall waiting for you, and you walked home with *Miss Corcoran.*

EMILY:

George! . . . Life's awful funny! How could I have known that? Why, I thought —

GEORGE:

Listen, Emily, I'm going to tell you why I'm not going to Agriculture School. I think that once you've found a person that you're very fond of . . . I mean a person who's fond of you, too, and likes you enough to be interested in your character . . . Well, I think that's just as important as college is, and even more so. That's what I think.

EMILY:

I think it's awfully important, too.

GEORGE:

Emily.

EMILY:

Y-yes, George.

GEORGE:

Emily, if I do improve and make a big change . . . would you be . . . I mean: *could* you be . . . .

EMILY:

I . . . I am now; I always have been.

GEORGE:

> *Pause.*

So I guess this is an important talk we've been having.

EMILY:

Yes . . . yes.

GEORGE:

> *Takes a deep breath and straightens his back.*

Wait just a minute and I'll walk you home.

> *With mounting alarm he digs into his pockets for the money.*
> *The Stage Manager enters, right.*
> *George, deeply embarrassed, but direct, says to him:*

Mr. Morgan, I'll have to go home and get the money to pay you for this. It'll only take me a minute.

STAGE MANAGER:

> *Pretending to be affronted.*

What's that? George Gibbs, do you mean to tell me — !

GEORGE:

Yes, but I had reasons, Mr. Morgan. — Look, here's my gold watch to keep until I come back with the money.

STAGE MANAGER:

That's all right. Keep your watch. I'll trust you.

GEORGE:

I'll be back in five minutes.

STAGE MANAGER:

I'll trust you ten years, George, — not a day over. — Got all over your shock, Emily?

EMILY:

Yes, thank you, Mr. Morgan. It was nothing.

GEORGE:

> *Taking up the books from the counter.*

I'm ready.

> *They walk in grave silence across the stage and pass*

*through the trellis at the Webbs' back door and
disappear.*

*The Stage Manager watches them go out, then turns
to the audience, removing his spectacles.*

STAGE MANAGER:

Well, —

He claps his hands as a signal.

Now we're ready to get on with the wedding.

*He stands waiting while the set is prepared for the
next scene.*

*Stagehands remove the chairs, tables, and trellises
from the Gibbs and Webb houses.*

*They arrange the pews for the church in the center of
the stage. The congregation will sit facing the back
wall. The aisle of the church starts at the center of
the back wall and comes toward the audience.*

*A small platform is placed against the back wall on
which the Stage Manager will stand later, playing the
minister. The image of a stained-glass window is cast
from a lantern slide upon the back wall.*

*When all is ready, the Stage Manager strolls to the
center of the stage, down front, and, musingly,
addresses the audience.*

There are a lot of things to be said about a wedding; there are
a lot of thoughts that go on during a wedding.

We can't get them all into one wedding, naturally, and
especially not into a wedding at Grover's Corners, where
they're awfully plain and short.

In this wedding I play the minister. That gives me the right
to say a few more things about it.

For a while now, the play gets pretty serious.

Y'see, some churches say that marriage is a sacrament. I
don't quite know what that means, but I can guess. Like Mrs.
Gibbs said a few minutes ago: People were made to live two-
by-two.

This is a good wedding, but people are so put together that
even at a good wedding there's a lot of confusion way down
deep in people's minds and we thought that that ought to be
in our play, too.

The real hero of this scene isn't on the stage at all, and you know who that is. It's like what one of those European fellas said: every child born into the world is nature's attempt to make a perfect human being. Well, we've seen nature pushing and contriving for some time now. We all know that nature's interested in quantity; but I think she's interested in quality, too,— that's why I'm in the ministry.

And don't forget all the other witnesses at this wedding,— the ancestors. Millions of them. Most of them set out to live two-by-two, also. Millions of them.

Well, that's all my sermon. 'Twan't very long, anyway.

> *The organ starts playing Handel's "Largo."*
>
> *The congregation streams into the church and sits in silence.*
>
> *Church bells are heard.*
>
> *Mrs. Gibbs sits in the front row, the first seat on the aisle, the right section; next to her are Rebecca and Dr. Gibbs. Across the aisle Mrs. Webb, Wally, and Mr. Webb. A small choir takes its place, facing the audience under the stained-glass window.*
>
> *Mrs. Webb, on the way to her place, turns back and speaks to the audience.*

MRS. WEBB:

I don't know why on earth I should be crying. I suppose there's nothing to cry about. It came over me at breakfast this morning; there was Emily eating her breakfast as she's done for seventeen years and now she's going off to eat it in someone else's house. I suppose that's it.

And Emily! She suddenly said: I can't eat another mouthful, and she put her head down on the table and *she* cried.

> *She starts toward her seat in the church, but turns back and adds:*

Oh, I've got to say it: you know, there's something downright cruel about sending our girls out into marriage this way. I hope some of her girl friends have told her a thing or two. It's cruel, I know, but I couldn't bring myself to say anything. I went into it blind as a bat myself.

> *In half-amused exasperation.*

The whole world's wrong, that's what's the matter. There they come.

> *She hurries to her place in the pew.*
>
> *George starts to come down the right aisle of the theater, through the audience.*
>
> *Suddenly three members of his baseball team appear by the right proscenium pillar and start whistling and catcalling to him. They are dressed for the ball field.*

THE BASEBALL PLAYERS:

Eh, George, George! Hast — yaow! Look at him, fellas — he looks scared to death. Yaow! George, don't look so innocent, you old geezer. We know what you're thinking. Don't disgrace the team, big boy. Whoo-oo-oo.

STAGE MANAGER:

All right! All right! That'll do. That's enough of that.

> *Smiling, he pushes them off the stage. They lean back to shout a few more catcalls.*

There used to be an awful lot of that kind of thing at weddings in the old days,— Rome, and later. We're more civilized now, — so they say.

> *The choir starts singing "Love Divine, All Love Excelling —." George has reached the stage. He stares at the congregation a moment, then takes a few steps of withdrawal, toward the right proscenium pillar. His mother, from the front row, seems to have felt his confusion. She leaves her seat and comes down the aisle quickly to him.*

MRS. GIBBS:

George! George! What's the matter?

GEORGE:

Ma, I don't want to grow old. Why's everybody pushing me so?

MRS. GIBBS:

Why, George . . . you wanted it.

GEORGE:

No, Ma, listen to me —

MRS. GIBBS:

No, no, George,— you're a man now.

GEORGE:

Listen, Ma, — for the last time I ask you . . . All I want to do is
to be a fella —

MRS. GIBBS:

George! If anyone should hear you! Now stop. Why, I'm
ashamed of you!

GEORGE:

He comes to himself and looks over the scene.
What? Where's Emily?

MRS. GIBBS:

Relieved.
George! You gave me such a turn.

GEORGE:

Cheer up, Ma. I'm getting married.

MRS. GIBBS:

Let me catch my breath a minute.

GEORGE:

Comforting her.
Now, Ma, you save Thursday nights. Emily and I are coming
over to dinner every Thursday night . . . you'll see. Ma, what
are you crying for? Come on; we've got to get ready for this.
*Mrs. Gibbs, mastering her emotion, fixes his tie and
whispers to him.*
*In the meantime, Emily, in white and wearing her
wedding veil, has come through the audience and
mounted onto the stage. She too draws back, frightened, when she sees the congregation in the church.
The choir begins: "Blessed Be the Tie That Binds."*

EMILY:

I never felt so alone in my whole life. And George over there,
looking so . . .! I *hate* him. I wish I were dead. Papa! Papa!

MR. WEBB:

> *Leaves his seat in the pews and comes toward her anxiously.*

Emily! Emily! Now don't get upset. . . .

EMILY:

But, Papa, — I don't want to get married. . . .

MR. WEBB:

Sh — sh — Emily. Everything's all right.

EMILY:

Why can't I stay for a while just as I am? Let's go away, —

MR. WEBB:

No, no, Emily. Now stop and think a minute.

EMILY:

Don't you remember that you used to say, — all the time you used to say — all the time: that I was *your* girl! There must be lots of places we can go to. I'll work for you. I could keep house.

MR. WEBB:

Sh . . . You mustn't think of such things. You're just nervous, Emily.

> *He turns and calls:*

George! George! Will you come here a minute?

> *He leads her toward George.*

Why, you're marrying the best young fellow in the world. George is a fine fellow.

EMILY:

But Papa, —

> *Mrs. Gibbs returns unobtrusively to her seat.*
> *Mr. Webb has one arm around his daughter. He places his hand on George's shoulder.*

MR. WEBB:

I'm giving away my daughter, George. Do you think you can take care of her?

GEORGE:

Mr. Webb, I want to . . . I want to try. Emily, I'm going to do my best. I love you, Emily. I need you.

EMILY:

Well, if you love me, help me. All I want is someone to love me.

GEORGE:

I will, Emily. Emily, I'll try.

EMILY:

And I mean for *ever*. Do you hear? For ever and ever.
        They fall into each other's arms.
        The March from Lohengrin *is heard.*
        The Stage Manager, as clergyman, stands on the box,
        up center.

MR. WEBB:

Come, they're waiting for us. Now you know it'll be all right. Come, quick.
        George slips away and takes his place beside the Stage
        Manager-clergyman.
        Emily proceeds up the aisle on her father's arm.

STAGE MANAGER:

Do you, George, take this woman, Emily, to be your wedded wife, to have . . . .
        Mrs. Soames has been sitting in the last row of the
        congregation.
        She now turns to her neighbors and speaks in a shrill
        voice. Her chatter drowns out the rest of the clergy-
        man's words.

MRS. SOAMES:

Perfectly lovely wedding! Loveliest wedding I ever saw. Oh, I do love a good wedding, don't you? Doesn't she make a lovely bride?

GEORGE:

I do.

STAGE MANAGER:

Do you, Emily, take this man, George, to be your wedded husband, —

> *Again his further words are covered by those of Mrs. Soames.*

MRS. SOAMES:

Don't know *when* I've seen such a lovely wedding. But I always cry. Don't know why it is, but I always cry. I just like to see young people happy, don't you? Oh, I think it's lovely.

> *The ring.*
> *The kiss.*
> *The stage is suddenly arrested into silent tableau.*
> *The Stage Manager, his eyes on the distance, as though to himself:*

STAGE MANAGER:

I've married over two hundred couples in my day.
Do I believe in it?
I don't know.
M. . . . marries N. . . . millions of them.
The cottage, the go-cart, the Sunday-afternoon drives in the Ford, the first rheumatism, the grandchildren, the second rheumatism, the deathbed, the reading of the will, —

> *He now looks at the audience for the first time, with a warm smile that removes any sense of cynicism from the next line.*

Once in a thousand times it's interesting.
— Well, let's have Mendelssohn's "Wedding March"!

> *The organ picks up the March.*
> *The bride and groom come down the aisle, radiant, but trying to be very dignified.*

MRS. SOAMES:

Aren't they a lovely couple? Oh, I've never been to such a nice wedding. I'm sure they'll be happy. I always say: *happiness*, that's the great thing! The important thing is to be happy.

> *The bride and groom reach the steps leading into the audience. A bright light is thrown upon them. They descend into the auditorium and run up the aisle joyously.*

STAGE MANAGER:

That's all the Second Act, folks. Ten minutes' intermission.

CURTAIN

QUESTIONS

1. In his opening speech at the start of this act the Stage Manager calls Act One "Daily Life" and Act Two "Love and Marriage." He guesses that the audience will be able to figure out what the last act will be about. What do you think the final act of the play will be about?

2. Why is it humorous that in the drugstore scene Emily accuses George of being conceited? Was Emily ever conceited?

3. Just before the wedding, in what ways do Emily and George feel alike? What does the marriage mean to them? Why do they resist it?

4. During the wedding, Emily, wearing her white veil, actually walks down an aisle of the theater and mounts the stage. What does this do to the traditional barrier between actors and audience? Does the theater audience become part of the Grover's Corners congregation watching Emily's wedding?

ACT THREE

During the intermission the audience has seen the stage-hands arranging the stage. On the right-hand side, a little right of the center, ten or twelve ordinary chairs have been placed in three openly spaced rows facing the audience.

These are graves in the cemetery.

Toward the end of the intermission the actors enter and take their places. The front row contains: toward the center of the stage, an empty chair; then Mrs. Gibbs; Simon Stimson.

The second row contains, among others, Mrs. Soames. The third row has Wally Webb.

The dead do not turn their heads or their eyes to right or left, but they sit in a quiet without stiffness. When they speak their tone is matter-of-fact, without sentimentality and, above all, without lugubriousness.

The Stage Manager takes his accustomed place and waits for the house lights to go down.

STAGE MANAGER:

This time nine years have gone by, friends — summer, 1913.
Gradual changes in Grover's Corners. Horses are getting rarer.
Farmers coming into town in Fords.
Everybody locks their house doors now at night. Ain't been any burglars in town yet, but everybody's heard about 'em.
You'd be surprised, though — on the whole, things don't change much around here.
This is certainly an important part of Grover's Corners. It's on a hilltop — a windy hilltop — lots of sky, lots of clouds, — often lots of sun and moon and stars.
You come up here, on a fine afternoon and you can see range on range of hills — awful blue they are — up there by Lake Sunapee and Lake Winnipesaukee . . . and way up, if you've got a glass, you can see the White Mountains and Mt. Washington — where North Conway and Conway is. And, of course, our favorite mountain, Mt. Monadnock, 's right here — and all these towns that lie around it: Jaffrey, 'n East Jaffrey, 'n Peterborough, 'n Dublin; and
    Then pointing down in the audience.
there, quite a ways down, is Grover's Corners.
Yes, beautiful spot up here. Mountain laurel and li-lacks. I often wonder why people like to be buried in Woodlawn and Brooklyn when they might pass the same time up here in New Hampshire.
Over there —
    Pointing to stage left.
are the old stones, — 1670, 1680. Strong-minded people that come a long way to be independent. Summer people walk around there laughing at the funny words on the tombstones . . . it don't do any harm. And genealogists come up from Boston — get paid by city people for looking up their ancestors. They want to make sure they're Daughters of the American Revolution and of the *Mayflower*. . . . Well, I guess that don't do any harm, either. Wherever you come near the human race, there's layers and layers of nonsense. . . .

Over there are some Civil War veterans. Iron flags on their graves ... New Hampshire boys ... had a notion that the Union ought to be kept together, though they'd never seen more than fifty miles of it themselves. All they knew was the name, friends — the United States of America. The United States of America. And they went and died about it.

This here is the new part of the cemetery. Here's your friend Mrs. Gibbs. 'N let me see — Here's Mr. Stimson, organist at the Congregational Church. And Mrs. Soames who enjoyed the wedding so — you remember? Oh, and a lot of others. And Editor Webb's boy, Wallace, whose appendix burst while he was on a Boy Scout trip to Crawford Notch.

Yes, an awful lot of sorrow has sort of quieted down up here. People just wild with grief have brought their relatives up to this hill. We all know how it is ... and then time ... and sunny days ... and rainy days ... 'n snow. ... We're all glad they're in a beautiful place and we're coming up here ourselves when our fit's over.

Now there are some things we all know, but we don't take'm out and look at'm very often. We all know that *something* is eternal. And it ain't houses and it ain't names, and it ain't earth, and it ain't even the stars ... everybody knows in their bones that *something* is eternal, and that something has to do with human beings. All the greatest people ever lived have been telling us that for five thousand years, and yet you'd be surprised how people are always losing hold of it. There's something way down deep that's eternal about every human being.

　　Pause.

You know as well as I do that the dead don't stay interested in us living people for very long. Gradually, gradually, they lose hold of the earth ... and the ambitions they had ... and the pleasures they had ... and the things they suffered ... and the people they loved.

They get weaned away from earth — that's the way I put it, — weaned away.

And they stay here while the earth part of 'em burns away, burns out; and all that time they slowly get indifferent to what's goin' on in Grover's Corners.

They're waitin'. They're waitin' for something that they feel

is comin'. Something important, and great. Aren't they waitin'
for the eternal part in them to come out clear?
Some of the things they're going to say maybe'll hurt your
feelings — but that's the way it is: mother'n daughter ...
husband 'n wife ... enemy 'n enemy ... money 'n miser ...
all those terribly important things kind of grow pale around
here. And what's left when memory's gone, and your identity,
Mrs. Smith?

> *He looks at the audience a minute, then turns to the*
> *stage.*

Well! There are some *living* people. There's Joe Stoddard,
our undertaker, supervising a new-made grave. And here
comes a Grover's Corners boy, that left town to go out West.

> *Joe Stoddard has hovered about in the background.*
> *Sam Craig enters left, wiping his forehead from the*
> *exertion. He carries an umbrella and strolls front.*

SAM CRAIG:

Good afternoon, Joe Stoddard.

JOE STODDARD:

Good afternoon, good afternoon. Let me see now: do I know
you?

SAM CRAIG:

I'm Sam Craig.

JOE STODDARD:

Gracious sakes' alive! Of all people! I should'a knowed you'd
be back for the funeral. You've been away a long time, Sam.

SAM CRAIG:

Yes, I've been away over twelve years. I'm in business out in
Buffalo now, Joe. But I was in the East when I got news of my
cousin's death, so I thought I'd combine things a little and
come and see the old home. You look well.

JOE STODDARD:

Yes, yes, can't complain. Very sad, our journey today, Samuel.

SAM CRAIG:

Yes.

JOE STODDARD:

Yes, yes. I always say I hate to supervise when a young person is taken. They'll be here in a few minutes now. I had to come here early today — my son's supervisin' at the home.

SAM CRAIG:
           Reading stones.
Old Farmer McCarty, I used to do chores for him — after school. He had the lumbago.

JOE STODDARD:

Yes, we brought Farmer McCarty here a number of years ago now.

SAM CRAIG:
           Staring at Mrs. Gibbs' knees.
Why, this is my Aunt Julia . . . I'd forgotten that she'd . . . of course, of course.

JOE STODDARD:

Yes, Doc Gibbs lost his wife two-three years ago . . . about this time. And today's another pretty bad blow for him, too.

MRS. GIBBS:
           To Simon Stimson: in an even voice.
That's my sister Carey's boy, Sam . . . Sam Craig.

SIMON STIMSON:

I'm always uncomfortable when *they're* around.

MRS. GIBBS:

Simon.

SAM CRAIG:

Do they choose their own verses much, Joe?

JOE STODDARD:

No . . . not usual. Mostly the bereaved pick a verse.

SAM CRAIG:

Doesn't sound like Aunt Julia. There aren't many of those Hersey sisters left now. Let me see: where are . . . I wanted to look at my father's and mother's . . . .

JOE STODDARD:

Over there with the Craigs . . . Avenue F.

SAM CRAIG:

> *Reading Simon Stimson's epitaph.*

He was organist at church, wasn't he? — Hm, drank a lot, we used to say.

JOE STODDARD:

Nobody was supposed to know about it. He'd seen a peck of trouble.

> *Behind his hand.*

Took his own life, y' know?

SAM CRAIG:

Oh, did he?

JOE STODDARD:

Hung himself in the attic. They tried to hush it up, but of course it got around. He chose his own epy-taph. You can see it there. It ain't a verse exactly.

SAM CRAIG:

Why, it's just some notes of music — what is it?

JOE STODDARD:

Oh, I wouldn't know. It was wrote up in the Boston papers at the time.

SAM CRAIG:

Joe, what did she die of?

JOE STODDARD:

Who?

SAM CRAIG:

My cousin.

JOE STODDARD:

Oh, didn't you know? Had some trouble bringing a baby into the world. 'Twas her second, though. There's a little boy 'bout four years old.

SAM CRAIG:

> *Opening his umbrella.*

The grave's going to be over there?

JOE STODDARD:

Yes, there ain't much more room over here among the Gibbses, so they're opening up a whole new Gibbs section over by Avenue B. You'll excuse me now. I see they're comin'.

> *From left to center, at the back of the stage, comes a procession. Four men carry a casket, invisible to us. All the rest are under umbrellas. One can vaguely see: Dr. Gibbs, George, the Webbs, etc. They gather about a grave in the back center of the stage, a little to the left of center.*

MRS. SOAMES:

Who is it, Julia?

MRS. GIBBS:

> *Without raising her eyes.*

My daughter-in-law, Emily Webb.

MRS. SOAMES:

> *A little surprised, but no emotion.*

Well, I declare! The road up here must have been awful muddy. What did she die of, Julia?

MRS. GIBBS:

In childbirth.

MRS. SOAMES:

Childbirth.
    Almost with a laugh.
I'd forgotten all about that. My, wasn't life awful —
    With a sigh.
and wonderful.

SIMON STIMSON:
    With a sideways glance.
Wonderful, was it?

MRS. GIBBS:

Simon! Now, remember!

MRS. SOAMES:

I remember Emily's wedding. Wasn't it a lovely wedding! And I remember her reading the class poem at Graduation

The graveyard scene, from the
Jed Harris stage production, 1938.

Exercises. Emily was one of the brightest girls ever graduated from High School. I've heard Principal Wilkins say so time after time. I called on them at their new farm, just before I died. Perfectly beautiful farm.

A WOMAN FROM AMONG THE DEAD:

It's on the same road we lived on.

A MAN AMONG THE DEAD:

Yepp, right smart farm.

> *They subside. The group by the grave starts, singing "Blessed Be the Tie That Binds."*

A WOMAN AMONG THE DEAD:

I always liked that hymn. I was hopin' they'd sing a hymn.

> *Pause. Suddenly Emily appears from among the umbrellas. She is wearing a white dress. Her hair is down her back and tied by a white ribbon like a little girl. She comes slowly, gazing wonderingly at the dead, a little dazed.*
>
> *She stops halfway and smiles faintly. After looking at the mourners for a moment, she walks slowly to the vacant chair beside Mrs. Gibbs and sits down.*

EMILY:

> *To them all, quietly, smiling.*

Hello.

MRS. SOAMES:

Hello, Emily.

A MAN AMONG THE DEAD:

Hello, M's Gibbs.

EMILY:

> *Warmly.*

Hello, Mother Gibbs.

MRS. GIBBS:

Emily.

EMILY:

Hello.

With surprise.

It's raining.

Her eyes drift back to the funeral company.

MRS. GIBBS:

Yes . . . They'll be gone soon, dear. Just rest yourself.

EMILY:

It seems thousands and thousands of years since I .. . Papa remembered that that was my favorite hymn.

Oh, I wish I'd been here a long time. I don't like being new here. — How do you do, Mr. Stimson?

SIMON STIMSON:

How do you do, Emily.

Emily continues to look about her with a wondering smile; as though to shut out from her mind the thought of the funeral company she starts speaking to Mrs. Gibbs with a touch of nervousness.

EMILY:

Mother Gibbs, George and I have made that farm into just the best place you ever saw. We thought of you all the time. We wanted to show you the new barn and a great long ce-ment drinking fountain for the stock. We bought that out of the money you left us.

MRS. GIBBS:

I did?

EMILY:

Don't you remember, Mother Gibbs — the legacy you left us? Why, it was over three hundred and fifty dollars.

MRS. GIBBS:

Yes, yes, Emily.

EMILY:

Well, there's a patent device on the drinking fountain so that it never overflows, Mother Gibbs, and it never sinks below a certain mark they have there. It's fine.

Her voice trails off and her eyes return to the funeral group.

It won't be the same to George without me, but it's a lovely farm.

Suddenly she looks directly at Mrs. Gibbs.

Live people don't understand, do they?

MRS. GIBBS:

No, dear — not very much.

EMILY:

They're sort of shut up in little boxes, aren't they? I feel as though I knew them last a thousand years ago. . . . My boy is spending the day at Mrs. Carter's.

She sees Mr. Carter among the dead.

Oh, Mr. Carter, my little boy is spending the day at your house.

MR. CARTER:

Is he?

EMILY:

Yes, he loves it there. — Mother Gibbs, we have a Ford, too. Never gives any trouble. I don't drive, though. Mother Gibbs, when does this feeling go away? — Of being . . . one of *them?* How long does it . . . ?

MRS. GIBBS:

Sh! dear. Just wait and be patient.

EMILY:

With a sigh.

I know. — Look, they're finished. They're going.

MRS. GIBBS:

Sh —.

The umbrellas leave the stage. Dr. Gibbs has come over to his wife's grave and stands before it a moment. Emily looks up at his face. Mrs. Gibbs does not raise her eyes.

EMILY:

Look! Father Gibbs is bringing some of my flowers to you. He looks just like George, doesn't he? Oh, Mother Gibbs, I never realized before how troubled and how . . . how in the dark live persons are. Look at him. I loved him so. From morning till night, that's all they are — troubled.
> *Dr. Gibbs goes off.*

THE DEAD:

Little cooler than it was. — Yes, that rain's cooled it off a little. Those northeast winds always do the same thing, don't they? If it isn't a rain, it's a three-day blow. —
> *A patient calm falls on the stage. The Stage Manager appears at his proscenium pillar, smoking. Emily sits up abruptly with an idea.*

EMILY:

But, Mother Gibbs, one can go back; one can go back there again . . . into living. I feel it. I know it. Why just then for a moment I was thinking about . . . about the farm . . . and for a minute I *was* there, and my baby was on my lap as plain as day.

MRS. GIBBS:

Yes, of course you can.

EMILY:

I can go back there and live all those days over again . . . why not?

MRS. GIBBS:

All I can say is, Emily, don't.

EMILY:

> *She appeals urgently to the stage manager.*
But it's true, isn't it? I can go and live . . . back there . . . again.

STAGE MANAGER:

Yes, some have tried — but they soon come back here.

MRS. GIBBS:

Don't do it, Emily.

MRS. SOAMES:

Emily, don't. It's not what you think it'd be.

EMILY:

But I won't live over a sad day. I'll choose a happy one —
I'll choose the day I first knew that I loved George. Why
should that be painful?
> *They are silent. Her question turns to the Stage
> Manager.*

STAGE MANAGER:

You not only live it; but you watch yourself living it.

EMILY:

Yes?

STAGE MANAGER:

And as you watch it, you see the thing that they — down there
— never know. You see the future. You know what's going
to happen afterwards.

EMILY:

But is that — painful? Why?

MRS. GIBBS:

That's not the only reason why you shouldn't do it, Emily.
When you've been here longer, you'll see that our life here is
to forget all that, and think only of what's ahead, and be ready
for what's ahead. When you've been here longer you'll
understand.

EMILY:
> *Softly.*

But, Mother Gibbs, how can I *ever* forget that life? It's all I
know. It's all I had.

MRS. SOAMES:

Oh, Emily. It isn't wise. Really, it isn't.

EMILY:

But it's a thing I must know for myself. I'll choose a happy
day, anyway.

MRS. GIBBS:

No! — At least, choose an unimportant day. Choose the least important day in your life. It will be important enough.

EMILY:

> *To herself.*

Then it can't be since I was married; or since the baby was born.

> *To the Stage Manager, eagerly.*

I can choose a birthday at least, can't I? — I choose my twelfth birthday.

STAGE MANAGER:

All right. February 11th, 1899. A Tuesday. — Do you want any special time of day?

EMILY:

Oh, I want the whole day.

STAGE MANAGER:

We'll begin at dawn. You remember it had been snowing for several days; but it had stopped the night before, and they had begun clearing the roads. The sun's coming up.

EMILY:

> *With a cry; rising.*

There's Main Street . . . why, that's Mr. Morgan's drugstore before he changed it! . . . And there's the livery stable.

> *The stage at no time in this act has been very dark; but now the left half of the stage gradually becomes very bright — the brightness of a crisp winter morning. Emily walks toward Main Street.*

STAGE MANAGER:

Yes, it's 1899. This is fourteen years ago.

EMILY:

Oh, that's the town I knew as a little girl. And, *look*, there's the old white fence that used to be around our house. Oh, I'd forgotten that! Oh, I love it so! Are they inside?

STAGE MANAGER:

Yes, your mother'll be coming downstairs in a minute to make breakfast.

EMILY:
>   *Softly.*
> Will she?

STAGE MANAGER:
And you remember: your father had been away for several days; he came back on the early-morning train.

EMILY:
No . . . ?

STAGE MANAGER:
He'd been back to his college to make a speech — in western New York, at Clinton.

EMILY:
Look! There's Howie Newsome. There's our policeman. But he's *dead;* he *died.*
>   *The voices of Howie Newsome, Constable Warren, and Joe Crowell, Jr., are heard at the left of the stage. Emily listens in delight.*

HOWIE NEWSOME:
Whoa, Bessie! — Bessie! 'Morning, Bill.

CONSTABLE WARREN:
Morning, Howie.

HOWIE NEWSOME:
You're up early.

CONSTABLE WARREN:
Been rescuin' a party; darn near froze to death, down by Polish Town thar. Got drunk and lay out in the snowdrifts. Thought he was in bed when I shook'm.

EMILY:
Why, there's Joe Crowell. . . .

JOE CROWELL:
Good morning, Mr. Warren. 'Morning, Howie..
>   *Mrs. Webb has appeared in her kitchen, but Emily does not see her until she calls.*

MRS. WEBB:

Chil-*dren!* Wally! Emily! . . . Time to get up.

EMILY:

Mama, I'm here! Oh! how young Mama looks! I didn't know Mama was ever that young.

MRS. WEBB:

You can come and dress by the kitchen fire, if you like; but hurry.

> *Howie Newsome has entered along Main Street and brings the milk to Mrs. Webb's door.*

Good morning, Mr. Newsome. Whhhh — it's cold.

HOWIE NEWSOME:

Ten below by my barn, Mrs. Webb.

MRS. WEBB:

Think of it! Keep yourself wrapped up.

> *She takes her bottles in, shuddering.*

EMILY:

> *With an effort.*

Mama, I can't find my blue hair ribbon anywhere.

MRS. WEBB:

Just open your eyes, dear, that's all. I laid it out for you special — on the dresser, there. If it were a snake it would bite you.

EMILY:

Yes, yes. . . .

> *She puts her hand on her heart. Mr. Webb comes along Main Street, where he meets Constable Warren. Their movements and voices are increasingly lively in the sharp air.*

MR. WEBB:

Good morning, Bill.

CONSTABLE WARREN:

Good morning, Mr. Webb. You're up early.

MR. WEBB:

Yes, just been back to my old college in New York State. Been any trouble here?

CONSTABLE WARREN:

Well, I was called up this mornin' to rescue a Polish fella — darn near froze to death he was.

MR. WEBB:

We must get it in the paper.

CONSTABLE WARREN:

'Twan't much.

EMILY:

> *Whispers.*

Papa.

> *Mr. Webb shakes the snow off his feet and enters his house. Constable Warren goes off, right.*

MR. WEBB:

Good morning, Mother.

MRS. WEBB:

How did it go, Charles?

MR. WEBB:

Oh, fine, I guess. I told'm a few things. — Everything all right here?

MRS. WEBB:

Yes — can't think of anything that's happened, special. Been right cold. Howie Newsome says it's ten below over to his barn.

MR. WEBB:

Yes, well, it's colder than that at Hamilton College. Students' ears are falling off. It ain't Christian. — Paper have any mistakes in it?

MRS. WEBB:

None that I noticed. Coffee's ready when you want it.

> *He starts upstairs.*

Charles! Don't forget, it's Emily's birthday. Did you remember to get her something?

MR. WEBB:
> *Patting his pocket.*

Yes, I've got something here.
> *Calling up the stairs.*

Where's my girl? Where's my birthday girl?
> *He goes off left.*

MRS. WEBB:

Don't interrupt her now, Charles. You can see her at breakfast. She's slow enough as it is. Hurry up, children! It's seven
o'clock. Now, I don't want to call you again.

EMILY:
> *Softly, more in wonder than in grief.*

I can't bear it. They're so young and beautiful. Why did they
ever have to get old? Mama, I'm here. I'm grown up. I love
you all, everything. — I can't look at everything hard enough.
> *She looks questioningly at the Stage Manager, saying
> or suggesting: "Can I go in?" He nods briefly. She
> crosses to the inner door to the kitchen, left of her
> mother, and as though entering the room, says,
> suggesting the voice of a girl of twelve:*

Good morning, Mama.

MRS. WEBB:
> *Crossing to embrace and kiss her; in her characteristic
> matter-of-fact manner.*

Well, now, dear, a very happy birthday to my girl and many
happy returns. There are some surprises waiting for you on
the kitchen table.

EMILY:

Oh, Mama, you *shouldn't* have.
> *She throws an anguished glance at the Stage Manager.*

I can't — I can't.

MRS. WEBB:
> *Facing the audience, over her stove.*

But birthday or no birthday, I want you to eat your breakfast

good and slow. I want you to grow up and be a good strong
girl.

That in the blue paper is from your Aunt Carrie; and I reckon
you can guess who brought the post-card album. I found it on
the doorstep when I brought in the milk — George Gibbs . . .
must have come over in the cold pretty early . . . right nice of
him.

EMILY:

> *To herself.*

Oh, George! I'd forgotten that. . . .

MRS. WEBB:

Chew that bacon good and slow. It'll help keep you warm on
a cold day.

EMILY:

> *With mounting urgency.*

Oh, Mama, just look at me one minute as though you really
saw me. Mama, fourteen years have gone by. I'm dead.
You're a grandmother, Mama. I married George Gibbs,
Mama. Wally's dead, too. Mama, his appendix burst on a
camping trip to North Conway. We felt just terrible about it
— don't you remember? But, just for a moment now we're
all together. Mama, just for a moment we're happy. *Let's
look at one another.*

MRS. WEBB:

That in the yellow paper is something I found in the attic
among your grandmother's things. You're old enough to wear
it now, and I thought you'd like it.

EMILY:

And this is from you. Why, Mama, it's just lovely and it's just
what I wanted. It's beautiful!

> *She flings her arms around her mother's neck. Her
> mother goes on with her cooking, but is pleased.*

MRS. WEBB:

Well, I hoped you'd like it. Hunted all over. Your Aunt Norah
couldn't find one in Concord, so I had to send all the way to
Boston.

> *Laughing.*

Wally has something for you, too. He made it at manual-training class and he's very proud of it. Be sure you make a big fuss about it. — Your father has a surprise for you, too; don't know what it is myself. Sh — here he comes.

MR. WEBB:
> *Off stage.*
Where's my girl? Where's my birthday girl?

EMILY:
> *In a loud voice to the Stage Manager.*
I can't. I can't go on. It goes so fast. We don't have time to look at one another.
> *She breaks down sobbing.*
> *The lights dim on the left half of the stage. Mrs. Webb disappears.*
I didn't realize. So all that was going on and we never noticed. Take me back — up the hill — to my grave. But first: Wait! One more look. Good-bye, Good-bye, world. Good-bye, Grover's Corners . . . Mama and Papa. Good-bye to clocks ticking . . . and Mama's sunflowers. And food and coffee. And new-ironed dresses and hot baths . . . and sleeping and waking up. Oh, earth, you're too wonderful for anybody to realize you.
> *She looks toward the Stage Manager and asks abruptly, through her tears:*
Do any human beings ever realize life while they live it? — every, every minute?

STAGE MANAGER:
No.
> *Pause.*
The saints and poets, maybe — they do some.

EMILY:
I'm ready to go back.
> *She returns to her chair beside Mrs. Gibbs.*
> *Pause.*

MRS. GIBBS:
Were you happy?

EMILY:

No . . . I should have listened to you. That's all human beings are! Just blind people.

MRS. GIBBS:

Look, it's clearing up. The stars are coming out.

EMILY:

Oh, Mr. Stimson, I should have listened to them.

SIMON STIMSON:

With mounting violence; bitingly.

Yes, now you know. Now you know! That's what it was to be alive. To move about in a cloud of ignorance; to go up and down trampling on the feelings of those . . . of those about you. To spend and waste time as though you had a million years. To be always at the mercy of one self-centered passion, or another. Now you know — that's the happy existence you wanted to go back to. Ignorance and blindness.

MRS. GIBBS:

Spiritedly.

Simon Stimson, that ain't the whole truth and you know it. Emily, look at that star. I forget its name.

A MAN AMONG THE DEAD:

My boy Joel was a sailor, — knew 'em all. He'd set on the porch evenings and tell 'em all by name. Yes, sir, wonderful!

ANOTHER MAN AMONG THE DEAD:

A star's mighty good company.

A WOMAN AMONG THE DEAD:

Yes. Yes, 'tis.

SIMON STIMSON:

Here's one of *them* coming.

THE DEAD:

That's funny. 'Tain't no time for one of them to be here. — Goodness sakes.

EMILY:

Mother Gibbs, it's George.

MRS. GIBBS:

Sh, dear. Just rest yourself.

EMILY:

It's George.

> *George enters from the left, and slowly comes toward them.*

A MAN FROM AMONG THE DEAD:

And my boy, Joel, who knew the stars — he used to say it took millions of years for that speck o' light to git to the earth. Don't seem like a body could believe it, but that's what he used to say — millions of years.

> *George sinks to his knees, then falls full length at Emily's feet.*

A WOMAN AMONG THE DEAD:

Goodness! That ain't no way to behave!

MRS. SOAMES:

He ought to be home.

EMILY:

Mother Gibbs?

MRS. GIBBS:

Yes, Emily?

EMILY:

They don't understand, do they?

MRS. GIBBS:

No, dear. They don't understand.

> *The Stage Manager appears at the right, one hand on a dark curtain which he slowly draws across the scene. In the distance a clock is heard striking the hour very faintly.*

STAGE MANAGER:

Most everybody's asleep in Grover's Corners. There are a few lights on: Shorty Hawkins, down at the depot, has just watched the Albany train go by. And at the livery stable somebody's setting up late and talking. — Yes, it's clearing up. There are the stars — doing their old, old crisscross journeys in the sky. Scholars haven't settled the matter yet, but they seem to think there are no living beings up there. Just chalk . . . or fire. Only this one is straining away, straining away all the time to make something of itself. The strain's so bad that every sixteen hours everybody lies down and gets a rest.

  He winds his watch.

Hm. . . . Eleven o'clock in Grover's Corners. — You get a good rest, too. Good night.

CURTAIN

QUESTIONS

1. Why aren't we told immediately whose body it is that will be buried? What is the dramatic effect when we discover it is Emily's? How was Emily dressed the last time she was on stage? How is she dressed this time? Does this increase the shock still further? Would the shock have been as great if Dr. Gibbs — or Mr. Webb — had died? Why not?

2. How does Emily, being so new to the graveyard, differ from the others?

3. As Emily starts back to her twelfth birthday, she sees a policeman. "There's our policeman. But he's *dead*; he *died*." Why is the line ironic? What has Emily forgotten?

4. What do the dead realize about living that those who are alive neglect or forget or are unaware of?

AFTER THE CURTAIN

Romance or Reality?

Our Town is a play that attempts to find drama and consequence and miracle in the commonplace lives of ordinary people rather than in the exciting biographies of medical martyrs or grotesquely formed, poetic swordsmen. A student might ask, which of these approaches — realism or romance[1] — yields the better drama, the truer picture of life? The question can't be answered flatly, for there is no need to choose between romanticism and realism. They are both "true to life," for life is richly multi-layered: Cyrano, Stockmann, and the Stage Manager all speak to our condition as human beings. *Our Town* may, indeed, speak most clearly because it is both consciously American *and* universal — we all are born, love, and die. Yet Cyrano *and* Stockmann *and* the Stage Manager are parts of our multilayered personalities. To be fully human is to be a romantic, a martyr, a detached observer, a cynic, and a mystic all rolled up into one — though the emphasis may vary at different periods of our lives, according to our experiences. Which of these attitudes most nearly expresses your present outlook? (One clue to the answer may be found in the quality of your response to the plays in this book. Which speaks to you most personally? Can you explain why?)

Experimental Tragedy

Our Town ends tragically:[2] a young woman, Emily, is torn from life in childbirth, leaving husband and father bereft. All she has sought to accomplish, all her dreams, plans, and loves are nothing: she is dust. For all her schoolgirl pride and vanity, Emily has not deserved her death. It is disproportionate. As a result the reader or viewer senses both the fragility of human life and the unconcern of nature — which randomly gives or destroys life. Yet the purpose of tragic drama is not to depress or sadden its audience — to just "give them a good cry" — but through their emotional identification with the suffering of the play's main character, to strengthen the audience's awareness of what life can become even in the face and fact of death. In most tragedies the viewer is allowed to "pass through" the suffering of the hero's death to a point of calm reflection on its meaning. After Hamlet's fatal sword wound, for example, Horatio tries to sum up Hamlet's life

---

[1] **realism or romance:** For a discussion of these terms see pages 246–247 and the Glossary.

[2] See Glossary for **tragedy.**

and character. The viewer is in some sense instructed and reconciled by the final scene. "If this is the worst, then I too am ready to live with courage and to die in peace" is what a deeply moved audience may well feel on leaving *Oedipus* or *Hamlet*.

But in *Our Town*, aside from the few short comments of the Stage Manager — which may be an attempt to soothe the audience — there is no relief from the spectacle of George sprawled sobbing on the mound of Emily's grave. But if an audience leaves *Our Town* without the resigned calmness that classic tragedy creates, if instead it leaves the playhouse stunned at the unfairness of Emily's death, Wilder provides some relief for the sorrow. There is a partial redemption from time and death. Yet this relief must occur in the hearts and in the consciousness of the audience after the theater doors close. We ourselves must become more aware, and that awareness must occur, not on a stage — however stripped — but in ourselves. For man's flaw, his great sin against himself — as Wilder sees it — lies in his being unobservant of all the ordinary wonders and commonplace miracles that surround him every second he is on earth, and that cease the moment he dies.

A century earlier Thoreau said the same thing about everyday life when he wrote in *Walden*: ". . . reality is fabulous. If men would steadily observe realities only, and not allow themselves to be deluded, life, to compare it with such things as we know, would be like a fairy tale and the Arabian Nights Entertainment."

Play into Film

When a movie was made of *Our Town* in 1940, producer Sol Lesser wished to make the ending more acceptable for a mass audience. He wanted Emily to survive childbirth, merely dreaming the graveyard sequence. Lesser wrote Wilder for that permission:

> The first serious thing to decide is whether we should let Emily live or die. . . . I find myself bouncing from one side to the other, and I just hate myself because I can't make up my mind. . . . Doug Churchill . . . has counselled me to use the happy ending. . . . He concludes by saying: 'The picture

differs from the original play in . . . one respect: the ending — Emily lives. Those who are purists and who loved the play will be outraged, but to those countless others, like myself, who have . . . come to love Emily . . . it is a most satisfactory and logical conclusion. . . .

Wilder willingly agreed to the request for a changed ending:

> In the first place, I think Emily should live. I always thought so. In a movie you see the people so *close to* that a different relation is established. In the theater they are halfway abstractions in an allegory;[1] in the movie they are very concrete. So, insofar as the play is a generalized allegory, she dies — we die — they die; insofar as it's a concrete happening it's not important that she die; it's even disproportionately cruel that she die.
>
> Let her live. The idea will have been imparted anyway.

If it's possible for you to see the film on television or in the classroom, try to determine for yourself if the "idea" is as strong with the changed ending.

Wilder's "idea" — the theme that permeates the whole of *Our Town* — is expressed symbolically in the Stage Manager's opening address: "The morning star always gets wonderful bright the minute before it has to go." Emily reechoes this theme as she says good-bye to the big — and little — things of her life:

> Good-bye, Good-bye, world. Good-bye, Grover's Corners . . . Mama and Papa. Good-bye to clocks ticking . . . and Mama's sunflowers. And food and coffee. And new-ironed dresses and hot baths . . . and sleeping and waking up. Oh, earth, you're too wonderful for anybody to realize you.

That is, Thornton Wilder tells us in the simplest and most dramatic terms, there is no time but this present: it must be savoured, not deferred.

Writing, Reviewing, and Directing

1. Compare daily life in Grover's Corners with the way people live in your own town or city. How is your hometown like Grover's Corners? How does it differ? Be specific. What would the Stage Manager most likely point out in your town?

[1] See Glossary.

2. If you can see the film, decide for yourself how true it is that even with the happy ending, the idea has been imparted.

3. In his letters to Wilder, producer Sol Lesser describes two scenes that were heightened by imaginative camera work:

> In the Simon Stimson episodes, with the scenes played in moonlight, the photography will accentuate the black and white shadows. The little white New England houses, which look so lovely in other shots, will look naked and almost ghostly in relation to Simon Stimson, to whom they did not offer nice lovely homes but a cold world which ruined him.
>
> From the time the mourners under their umbrellas come into the graveyard, we never show the ground — every shot is just above the ground — never a coffin nor an open grave. It is all done by attitudes, poses, and movements and in long shots. The utter dejection of Dr. Gibbs — we have his clothes weighted down with lead weights so they sag — the composition of Dr. Gibbs at the tombstone is most artistic — and as Dr. Gibbs leaves the cemetery the cloud in the sky gradually lifts, revealing stars against the horizon — and as the cemetery itself darkens, a reflection from the star strikes a corner of the tombstone which is still wet from the recent rain, and the reflection (hilation) seems to give a star-like quality — and the scene gradually goes to complete darkness. We get a vast expanse of what seems to be sky and stars. When this dissolves to the dead people, this same reflection of hilation appears to touch the brows of the dead.
>
> — from "Our Town — from Stage to Screen,"

Theater Arts, December 4, 1939.

Imagine you are remaking the film. Take a short sequence from the play and describe, as Lesser did, how you would use the props, camera, actors, lights, and sets to make the play live on the screen.

4. Rupert Brooke, an English poet who died in World War I, made a list of those things he most loved in the world. His poem was called "The Great Lover" and part of it reads:

> These have I loved
>   White plates and cups, clean-gleaming
>   Ringed with blue lines . . .
>   Wet roofs, beneath the lamplight; the strong crust
>   Of friendly bread; and many-tasting food;
>   Rainbows, and the blue bitter smoke of wood. . . .

Now make a list of the things you most love on earth. In a short paper try to explain why you chose those things above all other possible choices in the world. Through your concrete use of language, let your reader see, taste, touch, smell, and feel those things in the world most precious to you.

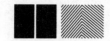

In White America

BEFORE THE CURTAIN

In White America is like no other play in this book. Although *Cyrano* was based on the life of an actual historical figure, and *An Enemy of the People* stemmed originally from the case of a Norwegian doctor who was driven from his town after exposing the unsanitary conditions in the kitchen of a public hospital, Rostand and Ibsen obviously created scene and language out of their own imaginations. In no sense is either play literally true. The same cannot be said about *In White America,* an example of a new kind of experimental theater called *documentary drama.* All the words spoken, all the events you are about to witness, actually happened. The central conflict of *In White America* is not between imagined characters or inside a person, but within a nation. The past speaks so strongly through the voices of living actors that we begin to understand what it has meant to be a Negro in America with our hearts as well as our heads. We begin to "know" through feeling as well as fact.

The author of *In White America,* Martin Duberman, is not a playwright, but a history professor who would dramatize history not only to make us understand the past, but to change the future. The history ranges from an early description of slave ships to the terrorizing of a fifteen-year-old girl who tried to integrate Little Rock High School in Arkansas. By using these incidents based on eyewitness reports, Duberman combines the emotional power of the spoken word with the startling truth of historical fact: this really happened; human beings *really* did such things. Through seeing this drama, Duberman hopes his audiences "would feel, not merely understand, the Negro's story. His experience might become our own, past reality might enter into present consciousness."

Some of this "docudrama" is conversation, dialogue between Negro and white. Try to hear in your mind the varying dialects, the pauses, the shifts in tone, the fear, contempt, hatred, and occasional tenderness. In the historical monologues, listen to the human voices through the words on these pages: the pride and outrage in the voice of John Brown, the shame in the voice of Reverend May in describing the destruction of Prudence Crandall's school for Negro girls, the growing hysteria in the voice of the lone teen-ager integrating Central High School as the mob becomes more abusive and threatening.

Folk music often accompanies these voices. As you read, try to hear and imagine the impact of overlaying John Brown's final words on earth with the singing of "John Brown's Body," or the reading from the Constitution accompanied by the rising musical chant of "Oh, freedom — Oh, freedom — Oh, freedom over me!" Hearing an excellent recording of this work — like that done by Columbia Records — will add a new dimension to your experience of this drama.

What you are about to read is not a happy document. It records torment, pain, brutality, and suffering. But to keep this anguish from remaining a series of random and meaningless crimes against the human spirit, it is necessary to first know it and feel it, so as never to inflict it. In this case drama — perhaps more than any other medium because of its direct and human impact — becomes a rehearsal for virtue. As such, theater returns to Ibsen's central social concern: the remaking of society through knowledge, honesty, courage, and justice.

In White America

MARTIN B. DUBERMAN

ACT ONE

(*On stage: 3 Negro and 3 white actors, 2 men and 1 woman in each case, and a guitarist*)

(WHITE MAN *comes forward, picks newspaper off table and reads aloud from it the current date.*)

WHITE MAN:
[January 12, 1964]
If God had intended for the races to mix, he would have mixed them himself. He put each color in a different place.

NEGRO MAN:
The American white man has a conscience, and the non-violent method appeals to that conscience.

WHITE WOMAN:
Negroes are demanding something that isn't so unreasonable — to get a cup of coffee at a lunch counter, to get a decent job.

NEGRO WOMAN:
What they really feels on the inside never changes. Eventually they'll wind up calling you a nigger.

WHITE MAN:
Negro impatience can be readily understood, but defiance breeds doubt, and riots breed hatred.

NEGRO MAN:
Sure I love my white brother, but I watch him!

441

NEGRO MAN:

To integrate with evil is to be destroyed with evil. We want
an area of this land we can call our own.

WHITE WOMAN:

My children won't be taking sides — unless we idiots tell
them there are sides to take.

NEGRO MAN:

After 400 years of barbaric treatment, the American Negro
is fed up with the unmitigated hypocrisy of the white man.

WHITE MAN (*reading again from newspaper*):

If they got guts enough to come down here, all they'll get
is a load of buckshot. The white people have shown remarkable restraint in not killing niggers wholesale.
[January 12, 1964]

> NEGRO ACTRESS (*sings*):
> *Oh, freedom, oh, freedom,*
> *Oh, freedom, over me!*
> *And before I'll be a slave,*
> *I'll be buried in my grave,*
> *And go home to my Lord*
> *And be free.*

NARRATOR:

(*Throughout the play the delivery of the narratives is alter-
nated among the actors.*)

*The story of the Negro in the United States begins with the
slave trade. A ship's doctor aboard a slave vessel in the mid-
eighteenth century described his impressions.*

SHIP'S DOCTOR:

The slave ships lie a mile below the town, in Bonny River,
off the coast of Guinea. Sometimes fifteen sail meet here
together. Scarce a day passes without some Negroes being
purchased and carried on board. . . .

The wretched Negroes are immediately fastened together, two and two, by handcuffs on their wrists and by irons riveted on their legs. They are then sent down between the decks and placed in a space partitioned off for that purpose. They are frequently stowed so close as to admit of no other position than lying on their sides. Nor will the height between decks allow them to stand.

The diet of the Negroes while on board consists chiefly of horsebeans boiled to the consistence of a pulp.

Upon the Negroes' refusing to take food, I have seen coals of fire, glowing hot, put on a shovel and placed so near their lips as to scorch and burn them. I have also been credibly informed that a certain captain in the slave trade poured melted lead on such of his Negroes as obstinately refused their food.

On board some ships the common sailors are allowed to have intercourse with such of the black women whose consent they can procure. The officers are permitted to indulge their passions among them at pleasure.

The hardships suffered by the Negroes during the passage are scarcely to be conceived. The exclusion of fresh air is the most intolerable. Whenever the sea is rough and the rain heavy it becomes necessary to shut every conveyance by which air is admitted. The Negroes' rooms very soon grow intolerably hot. The confined air produces fevers and fluxes which carry off great numbers of them. The floor of their rooms can be so covered with blood and mucus in consequence of the flux that it resembles a slaughterhouse. Last week by only continuing among them for about a quarter of an hour, I was so overcome with the heat, stench, and foul air that I nearly fainted; and it was only with assistance that I could get on deck . . . .

One evening while the ship lay in Bonny River, one of the Negroes forced his way through the network on the lar-

board side of the vessel, jumped overboard, and was de-
voured by the sharks. Circumstances of this kind are very
frequent.

Very few of the Negroes can bear the loss of their liberty
and the hardships they endure.

> NEGRO ACTRESS (*sings*):
> *And before I'll be a slave,*
> *I'll be buried in my grave,*
> *And go home to my Lord*
> *And be free.*

> QUAKER WOMAN (*reads aloud from parchment*):
> February 11, 1790. To the Senate and House of Representa-
> tives of the United States: The Address of the people called
> Quakers, in their annual assembly convened.

Firmly believing that unfeigned righteousness in public as
well as private stations is the only sure ground of hope for
the Divine blessing, we apprehend ourselves religiously
bound to request your serious Christian attention to the
gross national iniquity of trafficking in the persons of fellow-
men.

Many are the enormities abhorrent to common humanity,
and common honesty, which we judge it not needful to par-
ticularise to a body of men, chosen as eminently distinguished for wisdom as extensive information. But we find
it indispensably incumbent on us to attempt to excite your
attention to the affecting subject, that a sincere and impartial inquiry may take place, whether it be not in reality
within your power to exercise justice and mercy, which, if
adhered to, we cannot doubt, must produce the abolition of
the slave trade.

> FIRST CONGRESSMAN:
> Mr. President, this petition prays that we should take mea-
> sures for the abolition of the slave trade. This is desiring an
> unconstitutional act, because the Constitution secures that

trade to the States, independent of Congressional restrictions, for a term of twenty-one years. Therefore, it ought to be rejected as an attempt upon the virtue and patriotism of the House.

SECOND CONGRESSMAN:

I think it is incumbent upon every member of this House to sift the subject well and ascertain what can be done to restrain a practice so nefarious. The Constitution has authorized us to levy a tax upon the importation of such persons. I would willingly go to that extent; and if anything further can be devised to discountenance the trade, consistent with the terms of the Constitution, I shall cheerfully give it my assent and support.

FIRST CONGRESSMAN:

I fear that if Congress takes any measures indicative of an intention to interfere with the kind of property alluded to, it would sink in value very considerably and might be injurious to a great number of citizens, particularly in the Southern States.

SECOND CONGRESSMAN:

I think the gentleman carries his apprehensions too far. It appears to me that if the importation was crushed, the value of a slave would be increased instead of diminished.

FIRST CONGRESSMAN:

I differ much in opinion. If through the interference of the General Government the slave trade was abolished, it would evince to the people a disposition towards a total emancipation, and they would hold their property in jeopardy. The petitioners may as well come forward and solicit Congress to interdict the West India trade, because from thence we import rum, which has a debasing influence upon the consumer. But, sir, is the whole morality of the United States confined to the Quakers? Do they understand the rights of mankind, and the disposition of Providence, better than others? If they were to consult that Book, which claims our regard, they will find that slavery is not only allowed but commended. And if they fully examine the subject, they will find that slavery has been no novel doctrine since the days of Cain; but be these things as they may, I hope the House will order the petition to lie on the table, in order to prevent alarm to our Southern brethren.

NARRATOR:

The Quaker petition on the slave trade was tabled. Yet the whole question of the Negro's place in American life continued to disturb a few thoughtful men. Among them was Thomas Jefferson.

JEFFERSON:

The love of justice and the love of country plead equally the cause of these people, and it is a moral reproach to us that they should have pleaded it so long in vain. Yet the hour of emancipation is advancing. Nothing is more certainly written in the book of fate than that these people are to be free; nor is it less certain that the two races, equally free, cannot live in the same government. Nature, habit, opinion have drawn indelible lines of distinction between them.

(Coming forward)

The blacks are at least as brave, and more adventuresome. But this may perhaps proceed from a want of forethought, which prevents their seeing a danger till it be present. They are more ardent after their female; but love seems with them to be more an eager desire than a tender delicate mixture of sentiment and sensation. Their griefs are transient. Those numberless afflictions, which render it doubtful whether heaven has given life to us in mercy or in wrath, are less felt, and sooner forgotten with them. In general, their existence appears to participate more of sensation than reflection. It appears to me that in memory they are equal to the whites; in reason much inferior, as I think one could scarcely be found capable of tracing and comprehending the investigations of Euclid.[1] It will be right to make great allowances for the difference of condition, of education, of conversation, of the sphere in which they move. Yet we know that among the Romans, the condition of their slaves

[1] **Euclid** (yü′kləd) (c. 300 B.C.): Greek mathematician noted for his book on elementary geometry, *The Elements*.

was much more deplorable than that of the blacks on the continent of America. Notwithstanding, their slaves were often their rarest artists. They excelled too in science . . . . But they were of the race of whites.

To justify a general conclusion, requires many observations. I advance it, therefore, as a suspicion only, that the blacks, whether originally a distinct race, or made distinct by time and circumstances, are inferior to the whites in the endowments both of body and mind.

NEGRO ACTOR (*sings*):
My old missus promised me,
Hmm-mm-mm,
When she die, gonna set me free,
Hm-mm-mm.

Missus die nine years ago,
Hmm-mm-mm,
Here ah is in the same old row,
Hm-mm-mm.

NARRATOR:
White men rarely heard the slaves themselves talk about their condition. One of the few exceptions was a conversation recorded by a Northern journalist, Frederick Law Olmsted, with a house servant named William.

OLMSTED (*to audience*):
After leaving a plantation near New Orleans, I was driven about twenty miles in a buggy by one of the house servants. He was inclined to be talkative, and as he expressed great affection and respect for his owner, I felt at liberty to question him on some points upon which I had always previously avoided conversing with slaves. (*Crossing to where the slave, William, is seated*) He first said that he came from Virginia . . . .

WILLIAM:
I reckon there is no brack folks anywhere so well made as those who was born in Virginny. Is you from New Orleans, massa?

OLMSTED:

No, I live in the North.

WILLIAM:

Da's great many brack folks dah, massa?

OLMSTED:

No; very few.

WILLIAM:

Da's a great many in Virginny.

OLMSTED:

But I came from beyond Virginia — from New York.

WILLIAM:

If I was free, I would go to Virginny, and see my old mudder. I don't well know, exactly, how old I is; but I rec'lect, de day I was taken away, my ole mudder she tell me I was tirteen years old. I felt dreadful bad, but now I like it here. De people is almost all French. Is dere any French in New York?

OLMSTED:

Yes, but not as many as in Louisiana.

WILLIAM:

I s'pose dah is more of French people in Lusiana den dah is anywhar else in all de world — a'nt dah, massa?

OLMSTED:

Except in France.

WILLIAM:

Wa's dat, sar?

OLMSTED:

France is the country where all the Frenchmen came from, in the first place.

WILLIAM:

Wa's dat France, massa?

OLMSTED:

France is a country across the ocean, the big water, beyond
Virginia, where all the Frenchmen first came from; just as
the black people all came first from Africa, you know.

WILLIAM:

Is de brack folks better off to be here, massa?

OLMSTED:

I think so.

WILLIAM:

Why is it, then, massa, when de brack people is free, dey
wants to send 'em away out of dis country?

OLMSTED (*taken aback*):

Some people think Africa is a better place for you. (*Changing
the subject*) What would you do, if you were free?

WILLIAM:

If I was free, massa; *if I was free* . . . I would — Well, sar,
de fus thing I would do, if I was free, I would go to work
for a year, and get some money for myself, — den-den-den,
massa, dis is what I do — I buy me, fus place, a little house,
and little lot land, and den-no; den-den- I would go to old
Virginny and see my old mudder. Yes, sar, I would like to
do dat fus thing; den, when I com back, de fus thing I'd do,
I'd get me a wife; den, I'd take her to my house, and I would
live with her dar; and I would raise things in my garden,
and take 'em to New Orleans, and sell 'em dar, in the market.
Dat's de way I would live, if I was free.

OLMSTED:

Well, now, wouldn't you rather live on a plantation with a
kindly master like yours than to be free, William?

WILLIAM:

Oh! no, sir, I'd rather be free! Oh, yes, sir, I'd like it better
to be free; I would dat, master.

OLMSTED:

Why would you?

WILLIAM:

Why, you see, master, if I was free — if I was *free*, I'd have
all my time to myself. I'd rather work for myself. Yes. I'd
like dat better.

OLMSTED:

But then, you know, you'd have to take care of yourself, and
you'd get poor.

WILLIAM:

No, sir, I would not get poor, I would get rich; for you see,
master, then I'd work all the time for myself.

OLMSTED:

You don't suppose there would be much sugar raised, do you?

WILLIAM:

Why, yes, master, I do. Why not, sir? What would de brack
people do? Wouldn't dey hab to work for dar libben? and de
wite people own all de land — war dey goin' to work? Dey
hire demself right out again, and work harder dan dey do now
to get more wages — a heap harder. I tink so, sir. I would
do so, sir.

OLMSTED:

The black people talk among themselves about this, do they;
and they think so generally?

WILLIAM:

Oh! yes, sir; dey talk so; dat's wat dey tink.

OLMSTED:

Then they talk about being free a good deal, do they?

WILLIAM:

Yes, sir. Dey — (*suddenly on guard*) dat is, dey say dey wish it was so; dat's all dey talk, master — dat's all, sir.

(*The light fades.*)

NARRATOR:

Some of William's fellow slaves were interviewed many years later about their recollections of slavery.

MAN:

I sets and 'members the times in the world. I 'members now clear as yesterday things I forgot for a long time. I 'members 'bout the days of slavery, and I don't 'lieve they ever gwine have slaves no more on this earth. I think God done took that burden offen his black children, and I'm aiming to praise Him for it to His face in the days of glory.

WOMAN:

I's hear tell of them good slave days, but I ain't never seen no good times then. One time Aunt Cheyney was just out of bed with a suckling baby and she run away. Old Solomon gits the nigger hounds and takes her trail. They gits near her and she grabs a limb and tries to hist herself in a tree, but them dogs grap her and pull her down. The men hollers them onto her, and the dogs tore her naked and et the breasts plumb off her body. She got well and lived to be a old woman, but 'nother woman has to suck her baby, and she ain't got no sign of breasts no more.

MAN:

Sometimes I wishes that I could be back to the old place, 'cause we did have plenty to eat, and at hog-killing time us had more'n a plenty. Old Master kill eight or ten set-down hogs at one time . . . . What a set-down hog? It's a hog what done et so much corn he got so fat that he feets can't hold him up, and he just set on he hind quarters and grunts and eats, and eats and grunts, till they knock him in the head.

MAN:

Talking 'bout victuals, our eating was good. Can't say the same for all places. Some of the plantations half-starved

Remembering hard days, from the 1964
Touring Company's production.

their niggers till they wasn't fitting for work. They had to
slip about to other places to piece out their meals.

WOMAN:

I recollects once when I was trying to clean the house like
Ole Miss tell me, I finds a biscuit, and I's so hungry I et it,
'cause we never see such a thing as a biscuit...and she
comes in and say, "Where that biscuit?" I say, "Miss, I et
it 'cause I's so hungry." Then she grabs that broom and
start to beating me over the head with it and calling me
low-down nigger, and I guess I just clean lost my head 'cause
I knowed better than to fight her if I knowed anything 't all,
but I start to fight her, and the driver, he comes in and he
grabs me and starts beating me with that cat-o'-nine-tails,
and he beats me till I fall to the floor nearly dead. He cut
my back all to pieces, then they rubs salt in the cuts for more
punishment. Lord, Lord, honey! Them was awful days.

MAN:

The niggers didn't go to the church building; the preacher came and preached to them in their quarters. He'd just say, "Serve your masters. Don't steal your master's turkey. Don't steal your master's chickens. Don't steal your master's hogs. Don't steal your master's meat. Do whatsomever your master tells you to do." Same old thing all the time.

MAN:

My white folks didn't mind their niggers praying and singing hymns, but some places wouldn't 'low them to worship a-tall, and they had to put their heads in pots to sing or pray.

WOMAN:

Once Massa goes to Baton Rouge and brung back a yaller gal dressed in fine style. She was a seamster nigger. He builds her a house 'way from the quarters. This yaller gal breeds fast and gits a mess of white young-uns. She larnt them fine manners and combs out they hair.

Oncet two of them goes down the hill to the dollhouse, where the Missy's children am playing. They wants to go in the dollhouse and one of the Missy's boys say, "That's for white children." They say, "We ain't no niggers, 'cause we got the same daddy as you has, and he comes to see us near every day." They is fussing, and Missy is listening out her chamber window . . . .

When Massa come home his wife hardly say nothing to him, and he asks her what the matter, and she tells him, "Since you asks me, I'm studying in my mind 'bout them white young-uns of that yaller nigger wench from Baton Rouge." He say, "Now, honey, I fotches that gal just for you, 'cause she a fine seamster." She say, "It look kind of funny they got the same kind of hair and eyes as my children, and they got a nose look like yours." He say, "Honey, you just paying 'tention to talk of little children that ain't got no mind to what they say." She say, "Over in Mississippi I got a home and plenty with my daddy, and I got that in my mind."

Well, she didn't never leave, and Massa bought her a fine
new span of surrey hosses. But she don't never have no more
children, and she ain't so cordial with the Massa. That yaller
gal has more white young-uns, but they don't never go down
the hill no more.

MAN:

One thing what make it tough on the niggers was them times
when a man and he wife and their children had to be taken
'way from one another, sold off or taken 'way to some other
state. They was heaps of nigger families that I know what
was separated in the time of bondage that tried to find they
folkses what was gone. But the mostest of 'em never git
together again even after they sot free 'cause they don't
know where one or the other is.

MAN:

Slavery time was tough, boss. You just don't know how tough
it was. I can't 'splain to you just how bad all the niggers
want to get they freedom.

NEGRO ACTRESS (*sings*):
Right foot, left foot,
Along the road,
Follow the drinking gourd.

Up to the North,
Drop your load,
Follow the drinking gourd.

NARRATOR:
Slaves constantly tried to flee the plantation and head North
to freedom. Efforts by their masters to trace them led, in a
few rare cases, to an exchange of letters.

JOURDON ANDERSON:
To My Old Master, Colonel P. H. Anderson, Big Spring,
Tennessee.
Sir: I got your letter, and was glad to find that you had not
forgotten Jourdon, and that you wanted me to come back

and live with you again. Although you shot at me twice before I left you, I am glad you are still living.

I want to know particularly what the good chance is you propose to give me. I am doing tolerably well here. I get twenty-five dollars a month, with victuals and clothing; have a comfortable home for Mandy, — the folks call her Mrs. Anderson, — and the children — Milly, Jane, and Grundy — go to school and are learning well. The teacher says Grundy has a head for a preacher. They go to Sunday school, and Mandy and me attend church regularly. We are kindly treated.

Mandy says she would be afraid to go back without some proof that you were disposed to treat us justly and kindly; and we have concluded to test your sincerity by asking you to send us our wages for the time we served you. This will make us forget and forgive old scores, and rely on your justice and friendship in the future. I served you faithfully for thirty-two years, and Mandy for twenty years. At twenty-five dollars a month for me, and two dollars a week for Mandy, our earnings would amount to eleven thousand six hundred and eighty dollars. Add to this the interest for the time our wages have been kept back, and deduct what you paid for our clothing, and three doctor's visits to me, and pulling a tooth for Mandy, and the balance will show what we are in justice entitled to. Please send the money by Adam's Express, in care of V. Winters, Esq., Dayton, Ohio.

Say howdy to George Carter, and thank him for taking the pistol from you when you were shooting at me.

From your old servant,

Jourdon Anderson

MRS. SARAH LOGUE:

To Jarm: . . . I write you these lines to let you know the situation we are in, — partly in consequence of your running away and stealing Old Rock, our fine mare. Though we got the mare back, she never was worth much after you took her. If you will send me one thousand dollars, and pay for the old mare, I will give up all claim I have to you. In consequence of your running away, we had to sell Abe and Ann and twelve acres of land; and I want you to send me the money, that I may be able to redeem the land. If you do not comply with my request, I will sell you to someone else, and you may rest assured that the time is not far distant when things will be changed with you. A word to the wise is sufficient . . . . You know that we reared you as we reared our own children.

Yours, etc

Mrs. Sarah Logue

JARM:

Mrs. Sarah Logue: . . . had you a woman's heart, you never could have sold my only remaining brother and sister, because I put myself beyond your power to convert me into money.

You sold my brother and sister, Abe and Ann, and twelve acres of land . . . Now you ask me to send you $1000 to enable you to redeem the *land,* but not to redeem my poor brother and sister! You say that you shall sell me if I do not send you $1000, and in the same breath you say, "You know we raised you as we did our own children." Woman, did you raise your *own children* for the market? Did you raise them for the whipping post? Did you raise them to be driven off, bound to a coffle[2] in chains? Where are my poor bleeding brothers and sisters? Can you tell? Who was it that sent them off into sugar and cotton fields, to be kicked and cuffed, and whipped, and to groan and die . . . ?

Did you think to terrify me by presenting the alternative to give my money to you, or give my body to slavery? Then let me say to you, that I meet the proposition with scorn and contempt. I will not budge one hair's breadth. I will not breathe a shorter breath . . . I stand among free people.

NARRATOR:

Some Negroes reacted to slavery not by fleeing, but by rising in rebellion. In 1831, the slave Nat Turner, and his followers, turned on their masters in Southampton County, Virginia.

---

[2] **coffle:** prison cart built to transport slaves.

NAT TURNER:

I was thirty-five years of age the second of October last, and born the property of Benjamin Turner. In my childhood a circumstance occurred which made an indelible impression on my mind . . . . Being at play with other children, when three or four years old, I was telling them something, which my mother, overhearing, said had happened before I was born. I stuck to my story, however, and related some other things which went, in her opinion, to confirm it. Others being called on, were greatly astonished, and caused them to say, in my hearing, I surely would be a prophet . . . .

I studiously avoided mixing in society, and wrapped myself in mystery, devoting my time to fasting and prayer. I obtained influence over the minds of my fellow-servants — (not by the means of conjuring and such-like tricks — for to them I always spoke of such things with contempt), but by the communion of the Spirit . . . they believed and said my wisdom came from God.

About this time I had a vision — I saw white spirits and black spirits engaged in battle, and the sun was darkened — the thunder rolled in the heavens, and blood flowed in streams — and I heard a voice saying, "Such is your luck, such you are called to see; and let it come rough or smooth, you must surely hear it." I communicated the great work laid out for me to do. It was quickly agreed, neither age nor sex was to be spared.

It was my object to carry terror and devastation wherever we went. We killed Mrs. Waller and ten children. Then we started for Mr. William Williams . . . . Mrs. Williams fled, but she was pursued, overtaken, and after showing her the mangled body of her lifeless husband, she was told to get down and lay by his side, where she was shot dead. The white men pursued and fired on us several times. Five or six of my men were wounded, but none left on the field. . . . Finding myself defeated . . . I gave up all hope for the present . . . I was taken, a fortnight afterwards in a little hole I had dug out with my sword. I am here loaded with chains, and willing to suffer the fate that awaits me.

NEGRO ACTOR (*sings*):
For the old man is a-waitin'!
For to carry you to freedom
If you follow the drinking gourd.

NARRATOR:

In the North, although the Negroes were free, they were
segregated and despised. The Reverend Samuel J. May
described their treatment in Canterbury, Connecticut.

MAY:

In the summer or fall of 1832 I heard that Miss Prudence
Crandall, an excellent, well-educated Quaker, had been
induced by a number of ladies and gentlemen of Canterbury,
Connecticut to establish her boarding and day school there.

For a while the school answered the expectations of its
patrons, but early in the following year, trouble arose. Not far
from Canterbury there lived a colored man named Harris. He
had a daughter, Sarah, a bright girl about seventeen years of
age. She had passed, with good repute as a scholar, through
the school of the district and was hungering for more education. Sarah applied for admission into this new Canterbury
school and Miss Crandall admitted her.

The pupils, I believe, made no objection. But in a few days
the parents of some of them called and remonstrated. "They
would not have it said that their daughters went to school with
a nigger girl." Miss Crandall was assured that, if she did not
dismiss Sarah Harris, her white pupils would be withdrawn
from her.

She could not comply with such a demand . . . . Accordingly,
she gave notice that next term her school would be opened
for "young ladies and little misses of color." The whole
town was in a flame of indignation. Miss Crandall begged
me to come to her as soon as my engagements would permit.
When I arrived I was informed that a town meeting was to
be held. She requested that I might be heard as her attorney.

The Hon. Andrew T. Judson was undoubtedly the chief of Miss Crandall's persecutors. He was the great man of the town, much talked of by the Democrats as soon to be Governor, and a few years afterwards was appointed Judge of the United States District Court.

JUDSON:

Mr. May, we are not merely opposed to the establishment of this school in Canterbury; we mean there shall not be such a school set up anywhere in our State. The colored people never can rise from their menial condition in our country; they ought not to be permitted to rise here. They are an inferior race of beings and never can or ought to be recognized as the equals of the whites. Africa is the place for them.

MAY:

Mr. Judson, there never will be fewer colored people in this country than there are now. Of the vast majority of them this is the native land, as much as it is ours. The only question is whether we will recognize the rights which God gave them as men.

JUDSON:

That nigger school shall never be allowed in Canterbury, nor in any town of this State.

MAY (*to audience*):

Undismayed by such opposition, Miss Crandall received early in April fifteen or twenty colored young ladies from Philadelphia, New York, Providence, and Boston. At once all accommodations at the stores in Canterbury were denied her. She and her pupils were insulted whenever they appeared in the streets. The doors and doorsteps of her house were besmeared; her well was filled with filth. Finally the house was assaulted by a number of persons with heavy clubs and iron bars; five window sashes were demolished and ninety panes of glass dashed to pieces.

For the first time Miss Crandall seemed to quail, and her pupils had become afraid to remain another night under her roof. The front rooms of the houses were hardly tenantable; and it seemed foolish to repair them only to be destroyed again. After due consideration, therefore, it was determined that the school should be abandoned. The pupils were called together, and I was requested to announce to them our decision. Twenty harmless, well-behaved girls, whose only offence was that they had come together there to obtain useful knowledge, were to be told that they had better go away. The words almost blistered my lips. I felt ashamed of Canterbury, ashamed of Connecticut, ashamed of my country, ashamed of my color.

NARRATOR:
Many Northern Negroes were active in the anti-slavery struggle, and some took part in other reform movements as well. One of the most famous was the illiterate ex-slave Sojourner Truth, who in 1851 unexpectedly rose at a Woman's Rights Convention.

SOJOURNER TRUTH:
Wall, chilern, whar dar is so much racket dar must be somethin' out o' kilter. I tink dat 'twixt de black folks of de Souf and de womin at de Norf, all talkin' 'bout rights, de white men will be in a fix pretty soon. But what's all dis here talkin' 'bout?

Dat man ober dar say dat womin needs to be helped into carriages, and lifted ober ditches, and to hab de best place everywhar. Nobody eber helps me into carriages, or ober mud puddles, or gibs me any best place! And a'n't I a woman? Look at me! Look at my arm! I have ploughed, and planted, and gathered into barns and no man could head me! And a'n't I a woman? I have borne thirteen chilern, and seen 'em mos' sold off to slavery, and when I cried out with my mother's grief, none but Jesus heard me! And a'n't I a woman?

Den dey talks 'bout dis ting in de head; what dis dey call it? (*A voice whispering*): Intellect.

Dat's it, honey. What's dat got to do wid womin's rights? If my cup won't hold but a pint, and yourn holds a quart, wouldn't ye be mean not to let me have my little half-measure full?

Den dat little man in black dar, he say women can't have as much rights as men, 'cause Christ wan't a woman! Whar did your Christ come from? Whar did your Christ come from? From God and a woman! Man had nothin' to do wid Him!

If de fust woman God ever made was strong enough to turn de world upside down all alone, dese women togedder ought to be able to turn it back, and get it right side up again! And now dey is asking to do it, de men better let 'em.

CAST (*sings*):
God's gonna set this world on fire,
God's gonna set this world on fire
One of these days, hallelujah!
God's gonna set this world on fire,
Gonna set this world on fire one of these days.

NARRATOR:
In 1859, John Brown, who has alternately been called a saint and a madman, made an unsuccessful attempt at Harper's Ferry, Virginia, to free the slaves. Brought to trial and sentenced to death, John Brown addressed the court.

JOHN BROWN:
I have, may it please the Court, a few words to say.

In the first place, I deny everything but what I have all along admitted, — the design on my part to free the slaves. I never did intend murder or treason. Had I interfered in behalf of the rich, the powerful, the intelligent, the so-called great, it would have been all right; and every man in this court would have deemed it an act worthy of reward rather than punishment.

This court acknowledges, as I suppose, the validity of the law of God. I see a book kissed here which I suppose to be the Bible. That teaches me that all things whatsoever I would that men should do to me, I should do even so to them. It teaches me, further, to "remember them that are in bonds, as bound with them." I endeavored to act up to that instruction. I say, I am yet too young to understand that God is any respecter of persons. I believe that to have interfered as I have done — as I have always freely admitted I have done — in behalf of His despised poor, was not wrong, but right. Now, if it is deemed necessary that I should forfeit my life for the furtherance of the ends of justice, and mingle my blood further with the blood of millions in this slave country — I submit; so let it be done!

NARRATOR:
Just before John Brown was led from his cell to the gallows, he handed a guard this last message.

JOHN BROWN:
"I, John Brown, am now quite *certain* that the crimes of this *guilty land* will never be purged away but with *blood.* I had, as I now think vainly, flattered myself that without very much bloodshed it might be done."
(*Guitar chords of "John Brown's Body"*)

NARRATOR:
Civil war broke out in April 1861. Mary Boykin Chesnut, wife of the Senator from South Carolina, described in her diary the onset of war. April 8, 1861 . . . .

MRS. CHESNUT:
Talbot and Chew have come to say that hostilities are to begin. The men went off almost immediately, and I crept silently to my room where I sat down to a good cry . . . . Mrs. Wigfall came in and we had it out, on the subject of civil war. We solaced ourselves with dwelling on all its known horrors, and then we added some remarks about what we had a right to expect with Yankees in front and Negroes in the rear. "The slave owners must expect a servile insurrection, of course," said Mrs. Wigfall.

NARRATOR:

April 13, 1861 . . . .

MRS. CHESNUT:

Fort Sumter has been on fire . . . . Not by one word or look can
we detect any change in the demeanor of these Negro servants. Lawrence sits at our door, as sleepy and as respectful
and as profoundly indifferent. So are they all. They carry it
too far. You could not tell they even hear the awful noise that
is going on in the bay, though it is dinning in their ears night
and day. And people talk before them as if they were chairs
and tables, and they make no sign. Are they stolidly stupid, or
wiser than we are, silent and strong, biding their time.

NARRATOR:

August 1863, Portland, Alabama . . . .

MRS. CHESNUT:

Dick, the butler here, reminds me that when we were
children, I taught him to read as soon as I could read myself
. . . but he won't look at me now. He looks over my head; he
scents freedom in the air. He always was very ambitious.

He is the first Negro that I have felt a change in. They go
about in their black masks, not a ripple or an emotion showing; and yet on all other subjects except the War they are the
most excitable of all races. Now Dick might make a very
respectable Egyptian Sphynx, so inscrutably silent is he.
                    (*Guitar effect of drum rolls*)

NARRATOR:

*The first regiment of ex-slaves was mustered into the service
of the Union Army in 1862. It was under the command of a
white officer from Boston, Colonel Thomas Wentworth
Higginson.*

HIGGINSON:

November 24, 1862 . . . . Reporting to General Saxton, I had
the luck to encounter a company of my destined command,
marched in to be mustered into the United States service.

The first to whom I spoke had been wounded in a small expedition after lumber, in which he had been under fire.
(NEGRO SOLDIER *steps forward and stands at attention.*)

(*To* NEGRO SOLDIER): Did you think that more than you bargained for, my man?

NEGRO SOLDIER:
I been a-tinking, Mas'r, *dat's jess what I went for.*

HIGGINSON (*to audience*):
I thought this did well enough for my very first interchange of dialogue with my recruits.

(*Consulting his diary*)
December 5, 1862. This evening, after working themselves up to the highest pitch, a party suddenly rushed off, got a barrel, and mounted some man upon it, who brought out one of the few really impressive appeals for the American flag that I have ever heard . . . .

(*The lights dim on* HIGGINSON *and come up on
another* NEGRO SOLDIER.)
NEGRO SOLDIER:
Our mas'rs dey hab lib under de flag, dey got dere wealth under it, and ebryting, beautiful for dere chil'en. Under it dey hab grind us up, and put us in dere pocket for money. But de fus' minute dey tink dat ole flag mean freedom for we colored people, dey pull it right down, and run up de rag ob dere own. But we'll nebber desert de ole flag, boys, neber; we hab lib under it for *eighteen hundred sixty-two years*, and we'll die for it now.
(*Lights fade on the* SOLDIER *and come up on* HIGGINSON.)

HIGGINSON:
Their religious spirit grows more beautiful to me in living longer with them. Imbued from childhood with the habit of submission, they can endure everything. Their religion also gives them zeal, energy, daring. They could easily be made fanatics, if I chose; but I do not choose. Their whole mood is

essentially Mohammedan, perhaps, in its strength and its weakness. The white camps seem rough and secular, after this; and I hear our men talk about "a religious army," "a Gospel army," in their prayer meetings. They are certainly evangelizing the chaplain, who was rather a heretic at the beginning....

1st NEGRO SOLDIER (*praying*):
Let me lib dat when I die I shall *hab manners,* dat I shall know what to say when I see my Heabenly Lord.

2nd NEGRO SOLDIER (*praying*):
Let me lib wid de musket in one hand an' de Bible in de oder, — dat if I die at de muzzle ob de musket, I may know I hab de bressed Jesus in my hand, an' hab no fear.

3rd NEGRO SOLDIER (*praying*):
I hab lef' my wife in de land o' bondage; my little ones dey say eb'ry night, Whar is my fader? But when I die, when I shall stan' in de glory, den, O Lord, I shall see my wife an' my little chil'en once more.

HIGGINSON:
Expedition up the St. Mary's River: This morning, my surgeon sent me his report of killed and wounded: "One man killed instantly by a ball through the heart, and seven wounded, one of whom will die. Robert Sutton, with three wounds, — one of which, being on the skull, may cost him his life — would not report himself till compelled to do so by his officers."
(*He puts away the surgeon's report.*)

And one of those who were carried to the vessel — a man wounded through the lungs — asked only if I were safe, the contrary having been reported. An officer may be pardoned some enthusiasm for such men as these ....
(*He turns to another page in the diary.*)

January 1, 1863. Today we celebrated the issuance of President Lincoln's Proclamation of Emancipation. It was read by

Dr. W. H. Brisbane. Then the colors were presented to us by the Rev. Mr. French. All this was according to the programme. Then, the very moment the speaker had ceased, and just as I took and waved the flag. . . .

NEGRO SINGERS (*breaking in*):
My country, 'tis of thee,
Sweet land of liberty,
Of thee I sing!

(*The singing continues quietly under the rest of the speech.*)
HIGGINSON:
Firmly the quavering voices sang on, verse after verse; others of the colored people joined in; some whites on the platform began, but I motioned them to silence. I never saw anything so electric; it made all other words cheap; it seemed the choked voice of a race at last unloosed. Just think of it! — the first day they had ever had a country, the first flag they had ever seen which promised anything to their people! When they stopped, there was nothing to do for it but to speak, and I went on; but the life of the whole day was in those unknown people's song.

(*The singing swells.*)
SINGERS:
. . .*From every mountainside*
Let freedom ring!

QUESTIONS

1. The first act opens with people expressing racial attitudes in 1964, the time of the play's first production. Are these familiar attitudes? Have you ever heard anyone express similar feelings?

2. What were conditions on the ships that brought slaves from Africa to the New World?

3. How does the Quaker petitioner feel about slavery? Why does the First Congressman oppose discontinuing the slave trade? Why does the Second Congressman favor its restraint or abolition? Is it for humane reasons? What assumptions about slaves and slavery does each Con-

gressman share? Is there any moral difference in their positions? What is the assumption of the Quaker's position on slavery?

4. How did Jefferson feel about Negroes? Did he believe in integration? Does his attitude surprise you?

5. From the interview between Olmsted and William, describe how slaves felt about being enslaved. Why does William suddenly stop talking about freedom?

6. Does John Brown sound like a saint or a madman?

7. How were freed or escaped slaves treated in the North? Why did Prudence Crandall close her school?

8. According to Colonel Higginson, how did the Negro soldier differ from the whites? How did the Negro soldier view the Civil War?

ACT TWO

NEGRO ACTOR:

No more auction block for me,
No more, no more,
No more auction block for me,
Many thousand gone.

No more pint of salt for me,
No more, no more,
No more pint of salt for me,
Many thousand gone.

NEGRO MAN:

We was free. Just like that, we was free. Right off colored folks started on the move. They seemed to want to get closer to freedom, so they'd know what it was — like it was a place or a city . . . .

NEGRO WOMAN:

A heap of people say they going to name theirselves over. They name theirselves big names. Some of the names was Abraham, and some called theirselves Lincum. Any big name 'cepting their master's name.

NEGRO MAN:

The slaves don't know where to go. They's always 'pend on Old Marse to look after them. Three families went to get farms for theyselves, but the rest stay on for hands on the old place.

NEGRO WOMAN:

I remember someone asking — "You got to say 'Master'?" And somebody answered and said, "Naw." But they said it all the same. They said it for a long time.

NEGRO MAN:

They makes us git right off the place, just like you take a old hoss and turn it loose. That how us was. No money, no nothing.

NEGRO MAN:

What I likes best, to be slave or free? Well, it's this way. In slavery I owns nothing and never owns nothing. In freedom I's own the home and raise the family. All that cause me worriment, and in slavery I has no worriment, but I takes the freedom.

NARRATOR:

The whites reacted to the Negroes' freedom in a variety of ways. A Northern woman, Elizabeth Bothume, went South to teach the ex-slaves.

ELIZABETH BOTHUME:

On Oct. 25, 1864, I received the following communication: — "You are hereby appointed by the New England Freedman's Aid Society a teacher of freed people at Beaufort, South Carolina." I found my location was to be at Old Fort Plantation. A large number of colored refugees had been brought here and I was impatient to begin. Each hour showed me that at the North we had but a faint conception of the work to be done.

While the zeal of these people for learning never flags, they have no possible conception of time. Men, women, and children hurry to the schoolhouse at all hours and at most unseasonable times, expecting "to catch a lesson." Reproof is unheeded, or not understood; "Us had something *particular* to do," is the invariable excuse.

I must confess, the ignorance of some of the visitors in regard to the condition of the freed man is positively astounding. Some officers belonging to the "Tenth Army Corps" of Sherman's army visited the school. I was expecting them and had examined the children a little upon general subjects. Imagine my surprise, when they had sung and answered a few general questions, to have one of the visitors get up and ask, "Children, who is Jesus Christ?" For a moment the whole school seemed paralyzed. Then an older boy sprang up, and exclaimed, "Him's Massa Linkum" . . . .

Then General Howard made a short address, in which he gave them a motto, "To try hard." This all could understand. So when he asked what he should tell their friends at the North about them, they all answered, "Tell 'em we'se goin' to try hard."

At another school General Howard asked this question, and a little boy answered, "Massa, tell 'em we is rising."

NARRATOR:
The Negroes' freedom disrupted the pattern of Southern life, as a Georgia woman, Eliza Andrews, noted in her diary.

ELIZA ANDREWS:
Washington, Georgia. No power on earth can raise an inferior, savage race above their civilized masters and keep them there. No matter how high a prop they build under him, the Negro is obliged, sooner or later, to find his level. The higher above his natural capacity they force the Negro in their rash experiments, the greater must be his fall in the end, and the more bitter our sufferings in the meantime.

The town is becoming more crowded with "freedmen" every day, and their insolence increases with their numbers.

We have not even an errand boy now, for George, the only child left on the place, is going to school! . . . Everybody is doing housework. Father says this is what has made the Anglo-Saxon race great; they are not afraid of work. But it does seem to me a waste of time for people who are capable of doing something better to spend their time sweeping and dusting while scores of lazy Negroes that are fit for nothing else are lying around idle. Dr. Calhoun suggested that it would be a good idea to import some of those apes from Africa and teach them to take the place of the Negroes, but Henry said that just as soon as we had got them tamed, and taught them to be of some use, those crazy fanatics at the North would insist on coming down here to emancipate them and give them universal suffrage. A good many people seem to think that the Yankees are never going to be satisfied till they get the Negroes to voting. Father says it is the worst thing we have to fear now.

(*Guitar chords of "Dixie"*)

NARRATOR:

By 1866, the voting question was paramount. On February 7, Frederick Douglass, the chief spokesman for his race, and George T. Downing, another prominent Negro leader, brought the issue to Andrew Johnson, President of the United States.

GEORGE T. DOWNING:

We present ourselves to your Excellency in the name of the colored people of the United States. We are Americans, native born Americans. We are citizens. On this fact, and with confidence in the triumph of justice, we cherish the hope that we may be fully enfranchised.

PRESIDENT JOHNSON:

I do not like to be arraigned by some who can get up handsomely-rounded periods and deal in rhetoric. While I say I am a friend of the colored man, I do not want to adopt a policy that I believe will end in a contest between the races, in the extermination of one or the other. God forbid that I should be engaged in such a work!

FREDERICK DOUGLASS:
Mr. President, do you wish —

PRESIDENT JOHNSON:
I am not quite through yet . . . . The query comes up, whether these two races without time for passion and excitement to be appeased, and without time for the slightest improvement, are to be thrown together at the ballot box.

Will you say a majority of the people shall receive a state of things they are opposed to?

DOUGLASS:
That was said before the war.

JOHNSON:
I am now talking about a principle; not what somebody else said.

DOWNING:
Apply what you have said, Mr. President, to South Carolina, where a majority of the inhabitants are colored.

JOHNSON:
That doesn't change the principle at all. It is for the people to say who shall vote, and not for the Congress of the United States. It is a fundamental tenet in my creed that the will of the people must be obeyed. Is there anything wrong or unfair in that?

DOUGLASS (*smiling*):
A great deal that is wrong, Mr. President, with all respect.

JOHNSON:
It is the people of the States that must for themselves determine this thing.

God knows that anything I can do to elevate the races I will do, and to be able to do so is the sincere desire of my heart. (*Abruptly*) I am glad to have met you, and thank you for the compliments you have paid me.

DOUGLASS:

I have to return to you our thanks, Mr. President, for so kindly granting us this interview. We did not come here expecting to argue this question with your Excellency ... if you would grant us permission, of course we would endeavor to controvert some of the positions you have assumed.

JOHNSON:

I thought you expected me to indicate what my views were on the subjects touched upon by your statement.

DOWNING:

We are very happy, indeed, to have heard them.

DOUGLASS:

If the President will allow me, I would like to say one or two words in reply. You enfranchise your enemies and disfranchise your friends.

JOHNSON:

All I have done is to indicate what my views are, as I supposed you expected me to, from your address.

DOUGLASS:

But if your Excellency will be pleased to hear, I would like to say a word or two in regard to enfranchisement of the blacks as a means of *preventing* a conflict of races.

JOHNSON:

I repeat, I merely wanted to indicate my views, and not to enter into any general controversy. Your statement was a very frank one, and I thought it was due to you to meet it in the same spirit.

DOUGLASS:

Thank you, sir.

JOHNSON:

If you will all inculcate the idea that the colored people can live and advance to better advantage elsewhere than in the South, it would be better for them.

DOUGLASS:
But we cannot get away from the plantation.

JOHNSON:
What prevents you?

DOUGLASS:
The Negro is divested of all power. He is absolutely in the hands of those men.

JOHNSON:
If the master now controls him or his action, would he not control him in his vote?

DOUGLASS:
Let the Negro once understand that he has an organic right to vote, and he will raise up a party in the Southern States among the poor, who will rally with him.

JOHNSON:
I suggest emigration. If he cannot get employment in the South, he has it in his power to go where he can get it.

DOUGLASS (*to his fellow delegates*):
The President sends us to the people, and we go to the people.

JOHNSON:
Yes, sir; I have great faith in the people. I believe they will do what is right.

> (*Music — guitarist*)
> *I am a good old Rebel,*
> *And that's just what I am.*
> *And for this land of liberty,*
> *I do not give a damn.*
> *I'm glad I fought against it —*
> *I only wish we'd won,*
> *And I ain't askin pardon,*
> *For what I been or done.*

(As the lights fade on the scene, they come up on the figure
of a man wearing the hood of the Ku Klux Klan.)

NARRATOR:

In 1866, the Radical wing of the Republican party gained
control of Congress and gave the Negro the right to vote.
At once, the Ku Klux Klan rose to power in the South . . . .

THE HOODED FIGURE:

Before the immaculate Judge of Heaven and Earth, and upon
the Holy Evangelists of Almighty God, I do, of my own free
will and accord, subscribe to the sacredly binding obliga-
tion: We are on the side of justice, humanity, and constitutional
liberty, as bequeathed to us in its purity by our forefathers.
We oppose and reject the principles of the Radical party.

(Music — guitarist)
I hate the Freedmen's Bureau
And the uniform of blue,
I hate the Declaration of Independence, too.
I hate the Constitution
With all its fume and fuss,
And them thievin', lyin' Yankees,
Well, I hate 'em wuss and wuss.

NARRATOR:

Acts of violence by the Klan were investigated by the Federal
government in a series of hearings and trials.

PROSECUTOR:

What was the purpose of the Ku Klux Klan? What were the
raids for?

KLANSMAN:

To put down Radicalism, the raids were for.

PROSECUTOR:

In what way were they to put down Radicalism?

KLANSMAN:

It was to whip them and make them change their politics.

PROSECUTOR:

How many raids have you been on by order of the Chief?

KLANSMAN:

Two, sir.

PROSECUTOR:

Now, will you state to the jury what was done on those raids?

KLANSMAN:

Yes, sir. We were ordered to meet at Howl's Ferry, and went and whipped five colored men. Presley Holmes was the first they whipped, and then went on and whipped Jerry Thompson; went then and whipped Charley Good, James Leach, and Amos Lowell.

PROSECUTOR:

How many men were on these raids?

KLANSMAN:

I think there was twenty in number.

PROSECUTOR:

How were they armed and uniformed?

KLANSMAN:

They had red gowns, and had white covers over their horses. Some had pistols and some had guns.

PROSECUTOR:

What did they wear on their heads?

KLANSMAN:

Something over their heads came down. Some of them had horns on.

PROSECUTOR:

Disguises dropped down over their faces?

KLANSMAN:

Yes, sir.

PROSECUTOR:

What was the object in whipping those five men you have named?

KLANSMAN:

The object, in whipping Presley Holmes, was about some threats he had made about him going to be buried in Salem graveyard.

PROSECUTOR:

What was the first to occur?

KLANSMAN:

Well, sir, Webber — he was leading the Klan — ran into the yard and kicked down the door, and dragged him out, and led him off about two hundred yards, and whipped him.

PROSECUTOR:

How many lashes did they give him?

KLANSMAN:

I cannot tell you how many.

PROSECUTOR:

Did they whip him severely or not?

KLANSMAN:

His shirt was stuck to his back.

PROSECUTOR:

What occurred at the next place?

KLANSMAN:

They whipped Jerry Thompson at the next place; told him never to go to any more meetings; to stay at home and attend to his own business.

PROSECUTOR:

What was done at the next place?

KLANSMAN:

They went there and whipped Charley Good. They whipped him very severe; they beat him with a pole and kicked him down on the ground.

PROSECUTOR:

What did they tell him?

KLANSMAN:

To let Radicalism alone; if he didn't, his doom would be fatal.

(*The lights fade. They come up immediately on another examination. A Negro woman,* HANNAH TUTSON, *is being questioned.*)

LAWYER:

Are you the wife of Samuel Tutson?

MRS. TUTSON:

Yes, sir.

LAWYER:

Were you at home when he was whipped last spring?

MRS. TUTSON:

Yes, sir; I was at home.

LAWYER:

Tell us what took place then, what was done, and how it was done.

MRS. TUTSON:

That night, just as I got into bed, five men bulged right against the door, and it fell in the middle of the floor. George McRae ran right to me. As I saw him coming I took up the child — the baby — and held to him. I started to scream, and George McRae catched me by the throat and choked me. And he catched the little child by the foot and slinged it out of my arms. They got me out of doors. The old man was ahead of me, and I saw Dave Donley stamp on him. They carried me to a pine, and then they tied my hands there. They pulled off all my linen, tore it up so that I did not have a piece of rag on me as big as my hand. I said, "Men what are you going to do with me?" They said, "God damn you, we will show you; you are living on another man's premises." I said, "No; I am living on my own premises; I gave $150 for it and Captain Buddington and Mr. Mundy told me to stay here." They whipped me for awhile. Then George McRae would say, "Come here, True-Klux." Then the True-Klux would step off about as far as (*pointing to a member of the committee*) that gentleman and whisper; when they came back they would whip me again. Every time they would go off, George McRae would make me squat down by the pine, and he would get his knees between my legs and say, "Old lady, if you don't let me have to do with you, I will kill you." I said, "No"; they whipped me. There were four men whipping me at once.

LAWYER:

How many lashes did they give you in all?

MRS. TUTSON:

I cannot tell you, for they whipped me from the crown of my head to the soles of my feet. I was just raw. After I got away from them that night I ran to my house. My house was torn down. I went in and felt where my bed was. I could not feel my little children and I could not see them.

LAWYER:

Did you find your children?

MRS. TUTSON:

I did next day at 12 o'clock.

LAWYER:

Where were they?

MRS. TUTSON:

They went out into the field.

LAWYER:

Did the baby get hurt — the one you had in your arms when they jerked it away?

MRS. TUTSON:

Yes, sir; in one of its hips. When it began to walk one of its hips was very bad, and every time you would stand it up it would scream. But I rubbed it and rubbed it, and it looks like he is outgrowing it now.

(Music — Guitarist)
You've got to cross that lonesome valley,
You've got to cross it by yourself.
There ain't nobody can do it for you,
You've got to cross it all alone.

NARRATOR:

The Federal investigations were not followed by effective Federal action. From 1878 to 1915 over 3000 Negroes were lynched in the South — a necessary protection, it was said, against Negro rapists. Yet most lynchings were either for no offense or for such causes as "Insult," "Bad Reputation," "Running Quarrentine," "Frightening Children by Shooting at Rabbits," or "Mistaken Identity."

On January 21, 1907, United States Senator Ben Tillman, of South Carolina, gave his views on the subject from the Senate floor.

SENATOR TILLMAN:

Mr. President, a word about lynching and my attitude toward it. A great deal has been said in the newspapers, North, and South, about my responsibility in connection with this matter.

I have justified it for one crime, and one only. As governor of South Carolina I proclaimed that, although I had taken the oath of office to support law and enforce it, I would lead a mob to lynch any man who had ravished a woman.

Mr. President . . . . When stern and sad-faced white men put to death a creature in human form who has deflowered a white woman, they have avenged the greatest wrong, the blackest crime in all the category of crimes.

The Senator from Wisconsin prates about the law. Look at our environment in the South, surrounded, and in a very large number of counties outnumbered, by the Negroes — engulfed, as it were, in a black flood of semi-barbarians. For forty years these Negroes have been taught the damnable heresy of equality with the white man. Their minds are those of children, while they have the passions and strength of men.

Let us carry the Senator from Wisconsin to the backwoods in South Carolina, put him on a farm miles from a town or railroad, and environed with Negroes. We will suppose he has a fair young daughter just budding into womanhood; and recollect this, the white women of the South are in a state of siege . . . .

The Senator's daughter undertakes to visit a neighbor or is left home alone for a brief while. Some lurking demon who has watched for the opportunity seizes her; she is choked or beaten into insensibility and ravished, her body prostituted, her purity destroyed, her chastity taken from her, and a memory branded on her brain as with a red-hot iron to haunt her night and day as long as she lives.

In other words, a death in life. This young girl thus blighted and brutalized drags herself to her father and tells him what has happened. Is there a man here with red blood in his veins who doubts what impulses the father would feel? Is it any wonder that the whole countryside rises as one man and with set, stern faces, seek the brute who has wrought this infamy? And shall such a creature, because he has the semblance of a man, appeal to the law? Shall men coldbloodedly stand up and demand for him the right to have a fair trial and be punished in the regular course of justice? So far as I am concerned he has put himself outside the pale of the law, human and divine. He has sinned against the Holy Ghost. He has invaded the holy of holies. He has struck civilization a blow, the most deadly and cruel that the imagination can conceive. It is idle to reason about it; it is idle to preach about it. Our brains reel under the staggering blow and hot blood surges to the heart. Civilization peels off us, any and all of us who are men, and we revert to the original savage type whose impulses under such circumstances has always been to "kill! kill! kill!"

NARRATOR:
The Negro's intimidation was reflected in the views of Mr. Booker T. Washington, the most prominent Negro at the turn of the century, when he addressed a predominantly white audience at Atlanta.

WASHINGTON:
The Negroes' greatest danger is, that in the great leap from slavery to freedom we may overlook the fact that the masses of us are to live by the production of our hands. It is at the bottom of life we must begin, and not the top. You can be sure in the future, as you have been in the past, that you and your families will be surrounded by the most patient, faithful, law-abiding, and unresentful people that the world has seen.

In all things that are purely social we can be as separate as the fingers, yet one as the hand in all things essential to mutual progress.

The wisest among my race understand that the agitation of questions of social equality is the extremist folly. It is important and right that all privileges of the law be ours, but it is vastly more important that we be prepared for the exercise of those privileges. The opportunity to earn a dollar in a factory just now is worth infinitely more than the opportunity to spend a dollar in an opera house.

NARRATOR:
W. E. B. DuBois, later one of the founders of the N.A.A.C.P., was not satisfied with Mr. Washington's leadership.

DUBOIS:

One hesitates to criticize a life which, beginning with so little, has done so much. And yet the time is come when one may speak in all sincerity and utter courtesy of the mistakes and shortcomings of Mr. Booker T. Washington. Mr. Washington represents in Negro thought the old attitude of adjustment and submission. He practically accepts the alleged inferiority of the Negro races and withdraws many of the high demands of Negroes as men and American citizens. Mr. Washington asks that black people concentrate all their energies on industrial education, the accumulation of wealth and the conciliation of the South.

We do not expect that the free right to vote, to enjoy civic rights, and to be educated, will come in a moment; we do not expect to see the bias and prejudices of years disappear at the blast of a trumpet; but we are absolutely certain that the way for a people to gain their reasonable rights is not by voluntarily throwing them away and insisting that they do not want them; that the way for a people to gain respect is not by continually belittling and ridiculing themselves; that, on the contrary, Negroes must insist continually, in season and out of season, that voting is necessary to modern manhood, that color discrimination is barbarism, and that black boys need education as well as white boys.

NARRATOR:

The segregation of Federal employees became widespread for the first time during Woodrow Wilson's administration. To protest this policy, a delegation of Negro leaders, led by Monroe Trotter, called upon President Wilson in November 1914.

MONROE TROTTER:

Mr. President, one year ago we came before you and presented a national petition, signed by colored Americans in thirty-eight states, protesting against the segregation of employees of the National Government as instituted under your administration. We came to you, Mr. President, a year after to renew the protest and appeal.

PRESIDENT WILSON:

After our last visit, I and my cabinet officers investigated as promised, and my cabinet officers told me the segregation was caused by friction between colored and white clerks, and not done to injure or humiliate the colored clerks, but to avoid friction. Members of the cabinet have assured me that the colored clerks would have comfortable conditions, though separated. The white people of the country, as well as I, wish to see the colored people progress, admire the progress they have already made, and want to see them continue along independent lines. There is, however, a great prejudice against colored people, and we must deal with it as practical men. Segregation is not humiliating but a benefit, and ought to be so regarded by you gentlemen. If your organization goes out and tells the colored people of the country that it is a humiliation, they will so regard it.

TROTTER (*angrily*):

Mr. President, it is not in accord with known facts to claim that segregation was started because of race friction of the white and colored clerks, for the simple reason that for fifty years white and colored clerks have been working together in peace and harmony and friendliness, doing so even through two Democratic administrations. Soon after your inauguration began segregation was drastically introduced.

WILSON:

If this organization is ever to have another hearing before me it must have another spokesman. Your manner offends me.

TROTTER:

In what way?

WILSON:

Your tone, with its background of passion.

TROTTER:

But I have no passion in me, Mr. President, you are entirely mistaken; you misinterpret my earnestness for passion. We cannot control the minds of the colored people and would

not if we could on the segregation question. Two years ago
you were regarded as a second Abraham Lincoln.

WILSON:
I want no personal reference.

TROTTER:
Sir, if you will allow me to continue, you will see my intent.

WILSON:
I am the one to do the interrupting, Mr. Trotter.

TROTTER:
We colored leaders are denounced in the colored churches
as traitors to our race.

WILSON:
What do you mean by traitors?

TROTTER:
Because we supported the Democratic ticket in 1912.[3]

WILSON:
Gentlemen, the interview is at an end.

NARRATOR:
During World War I the French, at the request of the Amer-
ican authorities, issued a directive concerning Negro Amer-
ican Troops.

FRENCH OFFICER:
To the French Military Mission stationed with the American
Army. August 7, 1918. Secret information concerning the
Black American Troops.

It is important for French officers who have been called
upon to exercise command over black American troops, or
to live in close contact with them, to recognize that Ameri-

[3] **Because we ... 1912:** Since Lincoln was a Republican, that party was
traditionally regarded then by Negroes as the Freedom Party.

can opinion is unanimous on the "color question," and does not admit of any discussion.

The French public has become accustomed to treating the Negro with familiarity and indulgence.

These are matters of grievous concern to the Americans. They consider them an affront to their national policy. It is of the utmost importance that every effort be made to avoid profoundly estranging American opinion.

We must not eat with the blacks, must not shake hands or seek to talk or meet with them outside of the requirements of military service. Americans become greatly incensed at any public expression of intimacy between white women with black men.

Military authority cannot intervene directly in this question, but it can through the civil authorities exercise some influence on the population.

[Signed] Linard
(Guitar — "Mademoiselle from Armentières")

NARRATOR:
After World War I, Negro resentment became more vocal. Marcus Garvey's movement of Black Nationalism, a forerunner of today's Black Muslims, attracted hundreds of thousands of followers.

MARCUS GARVEY:
We are too large and great in numbers not to be a great people, a great race, and a great nation. We are the descendants of a suffering people. We are the descendants of a people determined to suffer no longer. The time has now come when we must seek our place in the sun. If Europe is for the Europeans, then Africa shall be for the black peoples of the world. We are not asking all the Negroes of the United States to leave for Africa. The majority of us may remain here, but we must send our scientists, our mechanics, and our artisans, and let them build railroads, let them build

the great educational and other institutions necessary, and when they are constructed, the time will come for the command to be given, "Come Home!"

The hour has come for the Negro to take his own initiative. No more fear, no more cringing, no more sycophantic begging and pleading. Destiny leads us to liberty, to freedom; that freedom that Victoria of England never gave; that liberty that Lincoln never meant; that freedom, that liberty, that will see us men among men, that will make us a great and powerful people.

NEGRO ACTRESS (*sings*):
I'm on my way
To Canaan's land,
I'm on my way
To Canaan's land.

I'm on my way
To Canaan's land,
I'm on my way,
Good Lord, I'm on my way.

NARRATOR:
Out of the difficult years of the Depression emerged the colorful personality of Father Divine. His blend of religion, charity, and personal drama brought him thousands of Negro and white followers.

MISS BEAUTIFUL LOVE:
Peace, my dearest Father:
I thank You for allowing me to write as it is my deepest desire to try to please You more each minute. I thank You for Your world at large and Your beautiful, sweet Peace that You have given to all of the children.

I thank you to report some cases of retribution, Father.

There is one whose name is Yaddy, who used dirty words. He stated You were a little bigger sport than he was. His wife has given birth to a baby who has never closed its mouth. I saw the baby when it was about 9 months old and its mouth hung open very wide.

There is one whose name is Mr. James Barr, who also thinks he is cursing you. He and his truck fell 20 feet below the level . . . . He was sent to the hospital . . . now he is going blind.

Father, I will try to please you each day. I will try to make you as happy as the rambling piano keys on Easter Sunday morning, or a happy angel when she does a holy dance.

Very truly yours,
Miss Beautiful Love

FATHER DIVINE:

My dear Miss Love:
You can see in every instance that those who tried to measure ME with the measure of a man received the reward meted out to finite man.

In the case of the man, who you say, classed ME with himself, the man who you say, thought he could curse ME suffered retribution and is going blind. Things don't just happen, but they happen Just! What he intended for me came to him heaped up, pressed down, and running over.

Thus, retribution rolls on, striking here and there at those who think they can criticize and slander ME, but none can reach ME. Hence, it does not pay to defy MY Name, for this leaves ME, as I AM ever Well, Healthy, Joyful, Peaceful, Lively, Loving, Successful, Prosperous, and Happy in Spirit, Body, and Mind and in every organ, muscle, sinew, joint, limb, vein and bone and even in every ATOM, fiber, and cell of MY BODILY FORM.

Respectfully and Sincere, I AM
REV. M. J. DIVINE, MsD., D.D.
(Better known as FATHER DIVINE)

(Guitar — reprise of "I'm on My Way")

NARRATOR:

As the rest of the nation began to recover from the Depression, Negroes continued to be economically exploited.

LABORER:

I was born in Elbert County, Georgia. I never went to school a day in my life. When I reached twenty-one, I signed a contract — that is, I made my mark — to work on a farm for one year. My white employer was to give me $3.50 a week and furnish me a little house on the plantation. All the people called him Senator. At the end of the first year, the Senator suggested that I sign up a contract for ten years; then, he said, we wouldn't have to fix up papers every year. I asked my wife about it; she consented; and so I made a ten-year contract.

It was then made plain to us that in the contracts, we had agreed to be locked up in a stockade at any time the Senator saw fit. And if we got mad and ran away, we could be run down by bloodhounds, and the Senator might administer any punishment he thought proper. What could we do about it? We shut our mouths and went to work.

But at the close of the ten-year period, to a man, we all wanted to quit. We refused to sign new contracts — even for one year. But two or three years before, the Senator had started a large store, which was called the commissary. All of us laborers were forced to buy our supplies — food, clothing and so on — from that store. We were charged all sorts of high prices.

Well, at the close of the tenth year, when we meant to leave, the Senator said to some of us with a smile — and I never will forget that smile — I can see it now . . . .

(*Lights up on two white men, the* SENATOR *and his* STORE-KEEPER. *The* STOREKEEPER *is holding an account book.*)

SENATOR:

Boys, I'm sorry you're going to leave me. I hope you will do well in your new places — so well that you will be able to pay the little balances which most of you owe me.

(*He turns to the* STOREKEEPER, *who steps forward and reads from the account book.*)

STOREKEEPER:
Frank Raines: One hundred and seventy-three dollars. Joe Simpson: One hundred and forty-six dollars. Cato Brown: One hundred and ninety-eight dollars . . . .

(*The lights fade on the two white men.*)

LABORER:
According to the books there was no man who owed less than $100. I owed $165, according to the bookkeeper. No one of us would have dared to dispute a white man's word. We were told we might go, if we signed acknowledgments. We would have signed anything, just to get away. So we stepped up and made our marks. The next morning it was explained to us that in the papers we had signed we had not only made acknowledgments of our debt, but had also agreed to work for our employer until the debts were paid by hard labor. And from that day forward we were treated just like convicts. Really we had made ourselves slaves, or peons, as the laws called us.

The working day on a peon farm begins with sunrise and ends when the sun goes down. Hot or cold, sun or rain, this is the rule. It was a hard school that peon camp was. A favorite way of whipping a man was to strap him down to a log and spank him fifty or sixty times on his bare feet with a piece of plank. I could tell more, but I've said enough . . . .

But I didn't tell you how I got out. When I had served for nearly three years — and you remember I owed them only $165 — one of the bosses came up to me and said that my time was up. He was the one who was said to be living with my wife. He took me in a buggy into South Carolina, set me down and told me to "git." I been here in the Birmingham district since and I reckon I'll die either in a coal mine or an iron furnace. It don't make much difference which. Either is better than a Georgia peon camp.

(*Guitar — a few bars of "Sometimes I Feel like a Motherless Child"*)

NARRATOR:

When the Second World War began, segregation was still the official policy of the United States armed forces. It remained so throughout the war. Persistent rumors of conflict between Negro and white troops reached Walter White, Secretary of the N.A.A.C.P., who went overseas to investigate. Among the places he visited was Guam.

WALTER WHITE:

There were no Negro combat troops in Guam, only service units. Negro resentment at this would probably never have been translated into action had not a long series of unchecked and unpunished insults and attacks been made upon these Negroes. Stones, empty beer bottles, and other missiles were thrown from trucks into the Negro camp accompanied by such epithets as "niggers," "night-fighters" and "black sons-of-bitches." Twice hand grenades were hurled into the Negro camp. Small gangs of Marines began to run Negroes out of Agana, the largest town on Guam.

On the afternoon of Christmas Day, 1944, two intoxicated Marines shot and killed a Negro sailor. Neither of them was even arrested . . . .

Around nightfall, a jeep with a machine gun mounted on it drove past firing into the Negro camp. By this time the camp was in a state of almost hysterical apprehension. Negroes climbed aboard two trucks and set out for Agana. A road block was thrown up and all of the Negro men — forty-four in number — were arrested . . . .

Among the crimes charged against them were unlawful assemblage, rioting, theft of government property, and attempted murder. The recommendations of the Board of Inquiry, despite the evidence, resulted in courts-martial and the sentencing of all forty-four men to prison terms. Happily these were later reversed when we appealed the convictions. But we had to take the cases all the way to the Secretary of the Navy and the White House to achieve this.

It was this pattern which was responsible for the cynical re-mark I heard so often from Negro troops — "We know that our battle for democracy will begin when we reach San Francisco on our way home!"

NARRATOR:
There was no major breakthrough until 1954, when the Su-preme Court declared segregation in public schools uncon-stitutional. Southern resistance to the court's decision came to a head three years later at Little Rock, Arkansas, when a fifteen-year-old girl tried to go to school at Central High.

GIRL:
The night before I was so excited I couldn't sleep. The next morning I was about the first one up. While I was pressing my black and white dress — I had made it to wear on the first day of school — my little brother turned on the TV set. They started telling about a large crowd gathered at the school. The man on TV said he wondered if we were going to show up that morning. Mother called from the kitchen, where she was fixing breakfast, "Turn that TV off!" She was so upset and worried. I wanted to comfort her, so I said, "Mother, don't worry!"

Dad was walking back and forth, from room to room, with a sad expression. He was chewing on his pipe and he had a cigar in his hand, but he didn't light either one. It would have been funny, only he was so nervous.

Before I left home Mother called us into the living room. She said we should have a word of prayer. Then I caught the bus and got off a block from the school. I saw a large crowd of people standing across the street from the soldiers guarding Central. As I walked on, the crowd suddenly got very quiet. For a moment all I could hear was the shuffling of their feet. Then someone shouted, "Here she comes, get ready!" The crowd moved in closer and then began to follow me, calling me names. I still wasn't afraid. Just a little bit nervous. Then my knees started to shake all of a sudden and I wondered whether I could make it to the center entrance a block away. It was the longest block I ever walked in my whole life.

Even so, I still wasn't too scared because all the time I kept thinking that the guards would protect me.

When I got right in front of the school, I went up to a guard. He just looked straight ahead and didn't move to let me pass him. I stood looking at the school — it looked so big! Just then the guards let some white students go through.

The crowd was quiet. I guess they were waiting to see what was going to happen. When I was able to steady my knees, I walked up to the guard who had let the white students in. He too didn't move. When I tried to squeeze past him, he raised his bayonet and then the other guards closed in and they raised their bayonets.

They glared at me with a mean look and I was very frightened and didn't know what to do. I turned around and the crowd came toward me.

They moved closer and closer. Somebody started yelling, "Lynch her!" "Lynch her!"

I tried to see a friendly face somewhere in the mob — someone who maybe would help. I looked into the face of an old woman and it seemed a kind face, but when I looked at her again, she spat on me.

They came closer, shouting, "No nigger bitch is going to get in our school. Get out of here!" Then I looked down the block and saw a bench at the bus stop. I thought, "If I can only get there, I will be safe." I don't know why the bench seemed a safe place to me, but I started walking toward it. I tried to close my mind to what they were shouting, and kept saying to myself, "If I can only make it to the bench, I will be safe."

When I finally got there, I don't think I could have gone another step. I sat down and the mob crowded up and began shouting all over again. Someone hollered, "Drag her over to this tree! Let's take care of the nigger." Just then a white man sat down beside me, put his arm around me, and patted my shoulder.

(During last part of speech, white actor sits beside her on bench.)

WHITE MAN:
She just sat there, her head down. Tears were streaming down her cheeks. I don't know what made me put my arm around her, saying, "Don't let them see you cry." Maybe she reminded me of my 15-year-old daughter.

Just then the city bus came and she got on. She must have been in a state of shock. She never uttered a word.

GIRL:
I can't remember much about the bus ride, but the next thing I remember I was standing in front of the School for the Blind, where Mother works. I ran upstairs and I kept running until I reached Mother's classroom.

Mother was standing at the window with her head bowed, but she must have sensed I was there because she turned around. She looked as if she had been crying, and I wanted to tell her I was all right. But I couldn't speak. She put her arms around me and I cried.

WHITE ACTOR *(sings)*:
They say down in Hines County
No neutrals can be met,
You'll be a Freedom Rider,
Or a thug for Ross Barnett.[4]

(WHOLE CAST, *looking at each other, not the audience, quietly sings four lines of "Which Side Are You On"*)

NARRATOR:
After 1957, the Negro protest exploded — bus boycotts, sit-ins, Freedom Rides, drives for voter registration, job protests.

NEGRO MAN:
After 400 years of barbaric treatment, the American Negro is fed up with the unmitigated hypocrisy of the white man.

[4] *Ross Barnett:* governor of Mississippi, 1960–1964.

WHITE MAN:

The Negroes are demanding something that isn't so unreasonable.

NEGRO MAN:

To have a cup of coffee at a lunch counter.

WHITE MAN:

To get a decent job.

NEGRO WOMAN:

The Negro American has been waiting upon voluntary action since 1876.

WHITE MAN:

If the thirteen colonies had waited for voluntary action this land today would be part of the British Commonwealth.

WHITE WOMAN:

The demonstrations will go on for the same reason the thirteen colonies took up arms against George III.

NEGRO MAN:

For like the colonies we have beseeched.

NEGRO WOMAN:

We have implored.

NEGRO MAN:

We have supplicated.

NEGRO MAN:

We have entreated.

NEGRO WOMAN:

We are writing our declaration of independence in shoe leather instead of ink.

WHITE MAN:

We're through with tokenism and gradualism and see-how-far-you've-comeism.

WHITE MAN:

We're through with we've-done-more-for-your-people-than-anyone-elseism.

NEGRO WOMAN:

We can't wait any longer.

NEGRO MAN:

Now is the time.

WHITE ACTOR (*stepping forward, reads from document*):
We the people of the United States, in Order to form a more perfect Union . . . .

WHITE ACTOR (*cont'd*):	NEGRO ACTRESS (*sings under "We the people . . .," slowly building in volume*):
. . . establish Justice, insure domestic Tranquility, provide for the common defense, promote the general Welfare, and secure the Blessings of Liberty to ourselves and our Posterity, do ordain and establish this Constitution for the United States of America	*Oh, freedom* — *Oh, freedom* — *Oh, freedom over me!* *And before I'll be a slave,* *I'll be buried in my grave,*

WHOLE CAST:
. . . And go home to my Lord
And be free!

ALTERNATE ENDING

The decision to make "Little Rock" the last major scene came about only after considerable experimentation. At various times later selections from Martin Luther King, James Baldwin, Malcolm X, and President Kennedy were added on, but I finally decided not to develop the post-1957 story fully; it was difficult to "top" the Little Rock scene dramatically, and, at any rate, I felt events since then were sufficiently familiar.

For the actual close of the play, I originally used a speech of Lincoln's instead of the Preamble to the Constitution. But this did not "play" as well as it read, and so the Preamble was substituted. As this is a reading version of the script, however, I thought it would be well to include the "Lincoln ending." Perhaps some future production might again wish to experiment with it as an alternate.

This speech would follow *"Now* is the time," and would be read instead of "We the people . . ." and without the singing of "Oh freedom . . . ."

NEGRO ACTOR:

Fellow-citizens, *we* cannot escape history. We will be remembered in spite of ourselves. No personal significance, or insignificance, can spare one or another of us. The fiery trial through which we pass will light us down, in honor or dishonor, to the latest generation. We shall nobly save, or meanly lose, the last best hope of earth. The way is plain, peaceful, generous, just — a way which, if followed, the world will forever applaud, and God must forever bless. (*He closes book*)

Abraham Lincoln's second annual message to Congress. December 1, 1862.

Good night.

QUESTIONS

1. Contrast the slaves' attitude towards freedom with the attitude in Act One toward slavery. How do they differ?

2. In the interview on Negro voting rights, President Andrew Johnson says: "It is a fundamental tenet in my creed that the will of the people must be obeyed." What is ironic about his statement? Is the irony intended or unintended? Who are the people whose will is to be followed? Who is excluded? Why does Douglass say: "You enfranchise your enemies and disfranchise your friends"?

3. Are there any differences between conditions for the Negro at the peon farm and conditions under slavery?

4. In what ways do the attitudes of Booker T. Washington conflict with those of W. E. B. DuBois on the position of the Negro in American society?

5. Which ending do you prefer? Why?

AFTER THE CURTAIN

Art is by and large a process of selection, choosing from an almost limitless range of possibilities the right word or gesture or character to make the point the artist is striving for. While creating *In White America,* Duberman faced an immense number of documents, letters, journals, and reminiscences to choose from. To have presented them all on stage would have resulted in a theatrical experience lasting weeks and — worse — one without a point of view, a theme. By cutting and selecting, Duberman created a two-act documentary drama with a coherent theme and a controlling irony. Employing a chronological, past to present, frame in Act One, Duberman explores Negro-white relationships up to Lincoln's Emancipation Proclamation. Until this event, the life of freed Northern Negroes as well as enslaved Southern ones had usually been limited, blocked, wretched. What is the tone and feel at the end of the first act? Is it elated or depressed? What does this tone lead you to expect in the second act, when freedom has become the law of the land?

Describe the prevailing tone of the second act, especially after the initial reactions of the slaves to their sudden freedom. Are they allowed to vote? Can they assert themselves as free men? What does the Ku Klux Klan see as its social responsibility? Had white attitudes in the North and the South shifted significantly after the Civil War? What does Senator Tillman's speech about lynching reveal of common Southern attitudes? What does President Wilson's conversation and the World War I directive to French troops reveal about official, government attitudes? What is the essential similarity about white attitudes towards blacks that unifies Act One and Act Two?

The second act presents the irony of a century passing while white racial attitudes remain basically frozen in a pre-Civil War position, with segregation maintained and Negroes being owned and exploited — as in the Georgia peon camp — just as they were a century earlier. Despite a few gestures, the passage of a century had changed little.

A second theme that runs through *In White America* is psychological rather than chronological: the self-deception of the white man in respect to Negroes and slavery led to a greater debasement of the white than the black. What effect, for example, do you suppose it had on the character of the congressmen who regarded slaves merely as a kind of property that would lose value if the slave trade were suppressed? On the American President who regarded segregation as a benefit rather than a humiliation? On the grown men and women who bullied a fifteen-year-old child on her way to a public school? In each case, the whites saw the blacks as somehow less than human, fit to be exploited, abused, or ignored because of the genetic accident of skin pigmentation. By their treatment of Negroes, these white Americans revealed that it was they themselves — not the Negroes — who behaved in a fashion that was less than human. The "Negro problem," it seems, really was — and is — largely a white problem.

Did you find documentary drama as exciting as conventional drama? What are its advantages? Its limitations? Do you think *In White America* can be effective, as the author hoped, in creating a new America? Explain.

Writing and Dramatic Readings

1. Duberman offers an alternate ending because the second ending did not "play" as well. Can you sense why the first ending "plays" better? Experiment with the endings: enact both before the class. Was Duberman's judgment right?

2. Edith Oliver writes in *The New Yorker*: ". . . *In White America* isn't really a play . . . but I don't see how anything could have made the story of the American Negro more theatrical or moving. . . ." Do you agree with her that *In White America* is not a play? What *is* a play?

3. Read a copy of *Ebony* magazine. How is it similar to *Life* magazine? How does it differ? Study the ads. Are they the same as in *Life*? Are there any products advertised in it that aren't touted in *Life*? Write a paper describing the typical Negro reader as near as you can tell from studying *Ebony*. Base your estimate on ads, subject matter of articles, editorials, and vocabulary level in the magazine.

4. Write a paper describing your feelings about Negro-white relationships in your school and community. Try to get down what you really feel rather than how you are supposed to feel.

5. (a) Read William Styron's *Confessions of Nat Turner*. Review it for the class.

(b) Read or listen to the record of *John Brown's Body*, by Stephen Vincent Benét. Select for comparison with *In White America* passages describing slave life, the experience of Civil War soldiers, the character of Abraham Lincoln. Give comparative readings in class.

GLOSSARY OF LITERARY TERMS

action: in the narrowest sense, a physical movement by an actor. In the broadest sense, the sum of events making up a play. Further, the term may refer either to outward acts or to the inner drama of thought and feeling.

allegory: the use of characters representing moral qualities or general concepts to convey a truth or generalization about life.

antagonist: the chief opponent of the hero, or protagonist, of a drama.

anticlimax: an event which is trivial or ridiculous in comparison with preceding events.

aside: a remark made by a character to the audience. By convention, it is not supposed to be heard by other characters on stage.

box-set stage: a conventional three-walled stage with the fourth "wall" formed by the proscenium arch.

character: one of the persons of a drama. A *static character* is one who does not change or develop during the course of a play. In contrast, the *dynamic character* grows and changes.

climax: in the general sense, the moment of highest interest and tension in a play. Sometimes, however, the term is used to denote a crucial turning point in the action (as is the term *crisis*).

comedy: a light, amusing play with a happy ending.

conflict: the struggle between opposing forces upon which drama depends. The conflict may be between the main character and an external force — nature, society, circumstances, another character — or between opposing ideas which the characters are made to represent. Much great drama relies upon an internal or psychological conflict within a character.

denouement: the resolution of the dramatic complications of a plot; the outcome of a play or story.

dialogue: the speeches exchanged between two or more characters in a play.

docudrama: a recent form of social drama which draws heavily on social or historical documents for lines which are spoken by a chorus of actors. All incidents depicted represent actual historical events.

dramatic foil: a character who serves as a contrast to another character.

epigram: a brief, cleverly expressed, often witty saying.

exposition: the presentation, through dialogue, of background information necessary to an understanding of the action.

expressionism: a style of drama in which inner or psychological events are symbolized by non-realistic stage effects or devices such as distorted scenery or tilted stages.

farce: a type of comedy in which foolish, and usually low, characters are placed in ridiculous situations. Probability is often sacrificed to the effects of broad humor, and the action is rapid and slapstick.

foreshadowing: indication of coming events by symbolic suggestion.

irony: *verbal irony* occurs when the intended meaning of words differs from their apparent meaning. *Dramatic irony* refers to a contrast between the true situation and the situation as it is apprehended by the characters in a drama.

melodrama: a type of play in which the emphasis is on suspenseful action. A melodrama usually pictures a struggle between good and evil characters in which virtue triumphs and villainy is punished.

pantomime: a play without words. The meanings are expressed entirely through the movements and facial expressions of the actors.

plot: the sequence of events in a play, and their relation to each other.

problem play: a social drama which focusses attention on a sociological problem.

properties (props): the objects used by the actors during the course of a play.

protagonist: the hero of a dramatic conflict, or the chief character of a play.

realism: in the theater, a production style in which the real or outside world is represented on stage, often with the use of everyday props. It may deal with the lower class or sordid problems.

rising action: the increasing complications by which the action of a play is brought to its climax.

romanticism: a literary attitude stressing the triumph of human will and ideals, often leading to improbable but heroic events.

satire: the censure, through literature or other arts, of human failings or social vices by exposing them to ridicule or scorn.

scene: a division of an act in a play, presenting action or dialogue in one place.

set: the scenery and furniture which occupies the stage during a particular act or scene of a play.

soliloquy: a speech made by an actor alone on the stage, as if he had no hearers, giving the impression of a succession of unspoken thoughts.

stage business: actions, often invented by the actors, for the purpose of clarifying a situation, delineating character, or creating atmosphere.

stage left (stage right, stage front, stage rear): All directions are given from the actor's vantage point as he faces the audience. Stage right is actor's right. Upstage is the part of the stage farthest from the audience, downstage is nearest.

structure: the arrangement of details and scenes that make up a dramatic work. Plays often move first through rising action to the climax, then through falling action to the conclusion.

symbol: something that stands for something larger, less definable, as a flag symbolizes a nation.

tempo: the pace at which action occurs on stage.

theater: the elements or aspects of a play that emerge during its performance and that result from acting, lighting, sound effects — that is, from production. Distinguished from *drama*, the play considered as literature.

theme: a general idea or truth implied by the action of a play or other work of literature. More than one theme may be expressed by a given play.

tragedy: a serious play whose action involves defeat or death for the main character, either because of some defect in his own nature or because of external forces beyond his control. The suffering of a tragic hero arouses us to pity; identification with him moves us to fear or awe; his nobility of character excites us to admiration.